COLLINS PHOTOGUIDE TO

WILD FLOWERS

of Britain
and Northern Europe

COLLINS PHOTOGUIDE TO

WILD FLOWERS

of Britain and Northern Europe

Oleg Polunin

Prepared for publication by John Akeroyd
Line drawings by Rosemary Wise

Collins, Grafton Street, London

Dedicated to John Akeroyd in appreciation for
all his hard work and devotion in bringing my
husband's final work to fruition.

Lorna Polunin
Godalming
October 1986

William Collins Sons & Co Ltd
London · Glasgow · Sydney · Auckland
Toronto · Johannesburg

Editor: Amanda Kent
Index: Lorna Polunin
Design: Caroline Hill

Cover photographs: (*front*) Hans Reinhard,
courtesy of Bruce Coleman Limited;
(*back*) Oleg Polunin

Typesetting: Ace Filmsetting Ltd., Frome, Somerset
Reproduction: Gilchrist Brothers Ltd., Leeds

ISBN 0 00 219709 X
Printed and bound by William Collins Sons & Co. Ltd., Glasgow

CONTENTS

PREFACE

Oleg Polunin died on 2 July 1985, having been ill for some months. Despite much weariness, he continued to work on the manuscript of this book until the day before he died. At his death the text descriptions were complete and he had gathered together a 'short-list' of colour transparencies from which the plates were to be selected. He had also outlined the general principles, with some examples, regarding the material that he visualized for the line drawings. His introduction explains the layout and content of the book and the choice of species for the text. My job has been that of editor, checking information on ecology, name changes, new data on geographical distribution and other small points. Like any science, traditional field botany is dynamic and must take account of new discoveries. It is remarkable, for example, how many of the botanically well-explored territories covered by this volume have had several new species added to their floras during the last ten or fifteen years.

Oleg was a kindly, generous man, who gave freely of his botanical knowledge, built up over many years of travel and plant-hunting in the British Isles, Europe and beyond. He was always eager to help the most inexpert novice on the subject. He had often said that he would like to write *A First 100 Flowers of Europe*: perhaps the present book is that – but a little bigger! Reading the text for the first time, I was astonished at the array of species included, for he had said that it was to be a book for the beginner. Familiar and much-loved wayside flowers rub shoulders with obscure 'botanist's' plants: for this reason I have made almost no changes to the species selected by Oleg. This range of material, presented to a wider public, demonstrates why Oleg was respected by the professional botanists who study Europe's flora, and at the same time so much appreciated by his large, non-professional readership, to whom he made available the results of modern floristic research.

John Akeroyd
Reading
September 1986

INTRODUCTION

Photographs of flowers taken in the field are, to the novice and layman, the most direct way of getting to know the commoner flowering plants of the countryside. Coloured drawings may show more details, but it is not always easy to match these with the living plants.

Often, similar looking species may differ by small botanical characters, not infrequently requiring a hand-lens for confirmation. In this case not only are they described in the text, but drawings to show such distinctive characters have been added, so that they can be compared directly with the living plant. It is hoped that, by this combination of colour photographs, detailed drawings and concise descriptions, many of the 1750 or more species growing in our selected area will be quickly identified. However, in order not to make this field guide too large, it has been decided to exclude all trees and shrubs over 1 m tall (which explains why familiar wayside plants such as Dog-rose *Rosa canina*, and Traveller's Joy *Clematis vitalba*, have been omitted), and also the grasses, sedges, rushes and similar species, which require considerable perseverance and experience to identify. At the same time, a number of alien species have been included where they have become well-established locally, or in some cases over large areas, and are self propagated. Much of our flora may have migrated from other regions at some time in the past, notably the arable weeds.

The area covered by this field guide includes the whole of Scandinavia (Norway (N), Sweden (S), and Finland (SF)), Iceland (IS), Great Britain (GB), Ireland (IRL), Denmark (DK), West Germany (D), Holland (NL), Belgium (B), and France (F) southwards to the Loire and eastwards to the Swiss border. The great majority of flowering plants found in this area are included (excluding those already mentioned), though some, such as, for example the high mountain plants, which extend just over the border into our area, may be excluded. The abbreviations of each country, as shown above, are in accordance with widely accepted international usage.

The families, genera and species are arranged in the order used in the international, authoritative botanical work, *Flora Europaea*, Vols 1–5, and the Latin names of the plants also follow this work. Older Latin names, often superseded by more recent research, are not included, neither are the authorities for the Latin names. A few recent name changes are indicated by the presence of the older name in brackets.

The English names are taken from the second edition (1986) of *English Names of Wild Flowers* (by J. G. Dony, S. L. Jury & F. H. Perring), a recommended list by the Botanical Society of the British Isles; also from *Flowers of Europe*, a Field Guide by Oleg Polunin; *Wild Flowers of Britain and Northern Europe* by Fitter, Fitter & Blamey; and *Alpine Flowers of Britain and Europe* by C. Grey-Wilson.

The description of each species concentrates on its distinctive and essential distinguishing characters. In general it seemed advisable to commence the description of a plant by any distinctive features, or to give a brief summary of its outstanding characters. Thereafter follows the details of the leaves, branching, inflorescence, flower structure, and, finally, the fruit. Size of plant, flowers, leaves and fruit are usually given to augment the photographs. In cases where two or more species are similar in most characters, only the differentiating characteristics and structures are listed, and in some cases drawn, to help the user to distinguish these differences. (We are grateful to the curators of the herbaria at Oxford and Reading Universities for providing the specimens on which the drawings are based.) Cross-headings are used in larger genera containing many species to group species together which have similar, readily distinguishable characters, and to distinguish them from other species with different characters, such as flower-colour, leaf-shape, fruit, etc. In large genera such as the Buttercups *Ranunculus*, this system of cross-headings does help to make identification easier, particularly when photographs are used.

The species are all numbered, which facilitates cross-reference between descriptions, and between descriptions and photographs.

Oleg Polunin
Godalming
June 1985

The following abbreviations have been used in the species descriptions:

Int. introduced
Nat. naturalized
† Species is now extinct here.

Abbreviations of areas covered are explained opposite, in the Introduction.
A number in **bold** at the end of a species description denotes the page number where a colour photograph may be found of that species.

WILLOW FAMILY

Salicaceae

Shrubs (or trees) with separate male and female plants. Leaves alternate, simple. Flowers grouped in catkins that are pollinated by insects; Fruit a 2-valved capsule. Seeds small, each with tuft of silky hairs that aid dispersal by wind. The smaller Willow *Salix* species are dwarf, often creeping, shrubs of heaths, sand-dunes, tundra and mountains.

SALIX
STEMS CREEPING UNDERGROUND; MOUNTAIN AND ARCTIC PLANTS

1 Dwarf Willow *Salix herbacea*
Dwarf shrub with creeping underground stems, and short aerial stems with bright green, shining, rounded, or kidney-shaped, toothed leaves with prominent veins on both sides. Catkins erect, rounded, 0.5–1,5cm, 2- to 12-flowered; scales more or less ovate, 6–20mm, yellowish-green and usually hairless. Capsule ovoid-conical, hairless, often reddish. Jun–Jul. Open stony ground on mountains. GB, SF, F, D, IRL, IS, N, S.

2 *Salix polaris*
Differs from **1** in having broadly elliptic leaves with entire or shallowly wavy margins near the base (leaves toothed in **1**). Leaves dark green, shiny above, paler beneath. Ovary woolly-haired. Catkins with c. 15 flowers, bracts purplish-black, hairy. Jul. Arctic Europe, southwards to 60° north. SF, N, S.

SALIX
STEMS CREEPING; PLANTS OF LOWLAND BOGS, SWAMPS, OR ON SAND

3 Creeping Willow *Salix repens*
Shrub with creeping stems and ascending branches 10–150cm, silky-hairy twigs and variable leaves with adpressed silvery hairs when young. Catkins appearing before leaves, cylindrical, to 2.5cm long. Male catkins slender, ovoid to oblong; female globular to oblong; scales hairy. Leaves oval to lanceolate, blunt or acute, entire or finely toothed. Apr–May. Damp and wet heaths, sand-dunes. Throughout area covered, except IS.

4 *Salix rosmarinifolia*
Like **3** but leaves linear with 10–12 pairs of lateral veins (4–6 pairs of veins in **3**). Catkins globular. Capsule hairy (hairless in **3**). Apr–May. Bogs and swamps. DK, D, SF, S.

5 *Salix arenaria*
Like **3** but previous year's twigs thick, dark, hairy, and

Leafy shoots of Willow

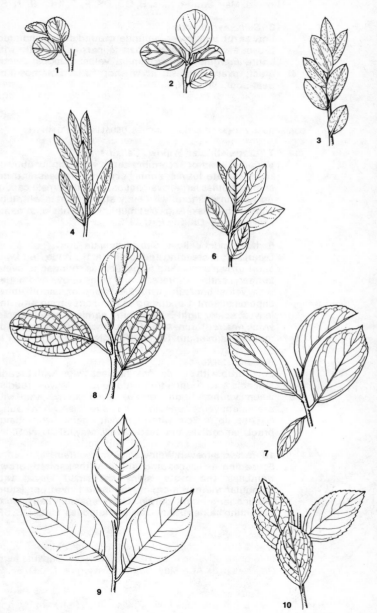

stipules present. Leaves obovate, densely covered with silky hairs on both sides; lateral veins 5–8 pairs. Catkins ovoid. May. Sand-dunes. B, GB, DK, F, D, IRL, NL, N, S.

6 *Salix myrtilloides*
Low shrub with creeping underground stems and erect brown twigs, leaves rounded to narrowly elliptic with entire margins and prominent veins. Catkins c. 2cm erect; ovary hairless, style short. Jun. Swamps and peat-bogs. SF, D, N, S.

SALIX
LOW SHRUBS WITH ASCENDING BRANCHES, USUALLY LESS THAN 1M.

7 Large-stipuled Willow *Salix hastata*
Variable, erect or ascending shrub with elliptic, obovate to lanceolate leaves, soon becoming hairless and not shiny. Stipules large, oval, not persistent. Female catkins up to 6cm or more, with leafy stems; bracts with long white hairs. May–Aug. Wet meadows, banks of streams, rocky places. DK, SF, F, D, N, S.

8 Net-leaved Willow *Salix reticulata*
Dwarf shrub, creeping and rooting at the nodes, and with short brown ascending twigs. Leaves rounded to ovate, leathery, entire, impressed with veins above and netted with veins beneath, with 2–5 pairs of lateral veins; stipules absent. Catkins up to 2cm, appearing after the leaves; scales light brown, hairy within. Capsule ovoid, woolly-haired. Jun–Aug. Damp rocks and screes; on mountains in south. GB, SF, F, D, N, S. **232**

9 *Salix starkeana*
Low shrub with slender pale hairless twigs, with broadly lanceolate to rounded-obovate toothed leaves, reddish when young, bright green, often shiny, and with prominent veins beneath; stipules reddish when young. Catkins up to 3cm with stalk, with dense white hairs; bracts lanceolate, greenish-yellow. May. SF, D, N, S.

10 Whortle-leaved Willow *Salix myrsinites*
Spreading or ascending shrub with knotted brown branches and ovate, shiny net-veined leaves with glandular toothed margins, the dead leaves persisting. Catkins large, dark purple. Ovary sparsely hairy, soon becoming hairless. May–Jun. Rock-ledges, cliffs. GB, SF, N, S.

10

BIRCH FAMILY

Betulaceae

Shrubs (or trees) with male and female flowers on the same plant. Leaves alternate, simple. Male flowers in drooping catkins; female flowers in erect catkins; wind-pollinated. Fruit a winged nutlet, falling with catkin-scale.

11 Dwarf Birch *Betula nana*
Spreading shrub with hairless twigs, and rounded deeply toothed leaves up to 15mm, which are downy when young. Fruiting catkins erect, up to 10mm; scales with 3 equal erect lobes. Jun–Jul. Moors, bogs, tundra. GB, SF, F, D, IS, N, S. **187**

HEMP FAMILY

Cannabaceae

Herbs, with separate male and female plants. Leaves lobed. Flowers green, wind-pollinated. Nutlets enclosed in persistent perianth.

12 Hop *Humulus lupulus*
Climbing herbaceous perennial up to 6m, with opposite broadly heart-shaped, 3- to 5-lobed, coarsely toothed leaves. Male flowers c. 5mm across, in branched clusters; female flowers in globular axillary clusters up to 2cm across. Fruiting structure cone-like, with enlarged pale green ovate bracts concealing the nutlets. Jul–Aug. Hedges and bushy places. Throughout area covered, (but probably introduced in the north), except IS. **187**

13 Hemp *Cannabis sativa*
Erect aromatic-smelling annual up to 2.5m; palmate leaves with 3–9 narrow lanceolate toothed lobes. Flowers green, the male in branched clusters with pendulous stamens, the female flowers in a spike. Fruiting structure globular. Jun–Jul. Hedges, waste places. Int B, F, D, GB. **194**

NETTLE FAMILY

Urticaceae

Herbs with separate male and female plants. Leaves simple. Flowers green, in pendent axillary clusters, wind-pollinated. Nettles *Urtica* are densely armed with stinging hairs, and occur in places where the soil is rich in nitrogen and phosphorus.

14 Common Nettle *Urtica dioica*
Perennial with 4-angled stems up to 1.5m, with usually ovate, coarsely toothed leaves, heart-shaped at base, covered with stinging hairs. Stipules 4 at each node of stem. Flowers green, in axillary spreading or drooping clusters usually longer than the subtending leaf-stalk. Plants one-sexed; female flowers with 4 hairy unequal segments. Fruit a nutlet, enclosed in 2 large segments. Jun–Sep. Woods, banks, fens, waste places, often by farms. Throughout area covered. **187**

15 Small Nettle *Urtica urens*
Annual with 4-angled stems up to 60cm, with ovate deeply toothed light green leaves with heart-shaped or wedge-shaped base, lower leaves long-stalked. Flowers green, in clusters up to c. 1.5cm, with several female and few male flowers. Segments of female flowers with margins fringed with hairs. Jun–Sep. Cultivated ground, waste places. Throughout area covered. **187**

16 Roman Nettle *Urtica pilulifera*
Readily distinguished by its long-stalked, globular, female flower clusters. Annual up to 1m, with ovate toothed or entire leaves, with leaf-stalk almost as long as blade. Male flowers in spike-like clusters; female flowers with inflated segments. Apr–Jun. Waysides and cultivated ground. F; int B, D. **187**

17 Pellitory-of-the-wall *Parietaria diffusa*
Perennial with several spreading or ascending much-branched stems, up to 40cm. Leaves ovate, long-pointed, up to 5cm. Flowers green, with yellow stamens, in axillary clusters, 2–2·5mm across, usually one-sexed. Male flowers with blunt lobes and longer stamens; female flowers with lanceolate acute hairy lobes. Nutlets ovoid, shiny black. Jun–Oct. Shady rocks, walls, hedgebanks. GB, F, D, IRL, NL; int B.

18 *Parietaria officinalis*
Like **17**, but erect perennial more than 30cm. Leaves larger, 3–12cm, and bracts completely fused (fused at base only in **17**). May–Oct. Shady walls, rocks, waste places. F, D; int B, DK, NL. **236**

17

SANDALWOOD FAMILY

Santalaceae

Perennial herbs, often woody at the base, with usually slender stems and narrow, more or less linear leaves. Perianth small, 4- to 5-lobed, greenish-yellow or greenish-white. Fruit a green nutlet, crowned by the persistent perianth. Bastard Toadflaxes *Thesium* are parasitic on the roots of other grassland herbs.

19 Alpine Bastard Toadflax *Thesium alpinum*
Perennial with simple erect or ascending stems up to 20cm, with numerous linear to linear-oblong leaves. Flowers tiny, greenish-yellow, in a lax inflorescence. Flowers tubular with 4 spreading lobes. Fruit a tiny rounded nutlet, with perianth lobes 2–3 times longer. Jun–Jul. Meadows on hills and mountains. F, D, S.

20 Pyrenean Bastard Toadflax *Thesium pyrenaicum*
Like **19** but differing in having 5-lobed perianth, which is about as long as the nutlet. Inflorescence usually not one-sided (usually one-sided in **19**). Jun–Jul. Acid grasslands. B, F, D.

21 Bastard Toadflax *Thesium humifusum*
Slender perennial with spreading or erect branches, up to 20cm, with terminal branched inflorescence.Leaves linear. Flowers greenish-white, 3–4mm, with 5 triangular lobes. Fruit ovoid, ribbed. Jun–Aug. Calcareous grasslands. B, GB, F, NL.

22 *Thesium ebracteatum*
Distinguished by having only 1 bract below each flower. Stems erect or ascending up to 15cm, with linear-oblong leaves. Bract about 3 times as long as flower or fruit. Perianth broadly bell-shaped, 5-lobed. Nutlet elliptic. May–Jul. Dry grasslands. DK, D.

23 Flax-leaved Bastard Toadflax *Thesium linophyllon*
Distinguished by its nutlet which is longitudinally veined, and its much shorter persistent perianth. Stems robust, rigid, with branched inflorescence. Jul–Aug. Dry grasslands, rocks, sand-dunes. F, D.

MISTLETOE FAMILY

Loranthaceae

Parasitic shrubs. Fruit a viscid berry, dispersed by birds. The European mistletoes represent a fragment of a large tropical family.

24 Mistletoe *Viscum album*
Yellowish-grey, much-branched parasitic perennial, growing on the branches of trees, up to 1m. Leaves opposite, leathery, oblong to narrowly obovate. Flowers greenish, in stalkless axillary clusters. Fruit a globular berry, usually white but sometimes yellowish. Feb–May. Parasitic on scattered trees or on the margin of woods. Throughout area covered, except SF, IRL, IS. **194**

BIRTHWORT FAMILY

Aristolochiaceae

Rhizomatous herbs, with often large leaves. Perianth forming a tube, usually 3-merous. Other floral parts in multiples of 6. Fruit containing many seeds.

25 Asarabacca *Asarum europaeum*
Creeping herbaceous plant forming patches, with hairy stems up to 10cm, and roundish, kidney-shaped, dark green leaves with long leaf-stalks. Flowers solitary, brownish-red, bell-shaped with 3 lobes, up to 1·5cm long, borne in axils of leaves. Mar–May. Damp woods. B, GB, F, D, N, S; int. DK, NL.

26 Birthwort *Aristolochia clematitis*
Erect unbranched strong-smelling perennial, with many stems 30–70cm. Leaves ovate, with heart-shaped base. Flowers pale yellow, clustered in leaf axils; corolla with a globular base and curved tube with a long terminal oblong to ovate limb. Fruit ovoid to pear-shaped. Jun–Sep. Naturalized in waste places, often near old buildings. B, GB, F, D, NL. **206**

25

Polygonaceae

Annual or perennial herbs. Leaves simple. Stipules present, united in a sheath (ochrea). Perianth-segments 3–6, sepal-like and green, or petal-like and pink, red or white. Fruit a 3-faced or flattened nut enclosed by persistent perianth. Plants of rather open habitats such as cultivated ground, waysides, stream and lake margins.

27 Iceland Purslane *Koenigia islandica*
Dwarf annual up to 5cm, with reddish stems, and small, broadly elliptic rather fleshy leaves up to 5mm. Flowers pale green, in terminal and axillary clusters, with 3 rounded sepal-like lobes c. 1mm. Anthers reddish. Jun–Aug. Open stony ground in the most northern parts of area covered. GB, SF, IS, N, S.

27

POLYGONUM
PERENNIALS. FLOWERS IN A LAX SPIKE, SHEATHING STIPULES WHITE, SILVERY AND PAPERY

28 Sea Knotgrass *Polygonum maritimum*
Perennial with a woody rootstock and spreading branches up to 50cm. Leaves blue-green, narrowly elliptic, 5–25mm long; sheathing stipules reddish-brown at base and silvery above, with conspicuous veins. Flowers pink or white, in axils of leaves. Nuts glossy. Jul–Sep. Coastal sands and shingle. GB, F, IRL, NL. **236**

29 Ray's Knotgrass *Polygonum oxyspermum*
Annual or perennial with spreading stems up to 1m. Leaves broadly to narrowly elliptic, but variable; sheathing stipules much shorter than internodes (longer in **28**), with simple veins. Flowers white, or segments with red or pink margins. Nuts glossy. Jul–Sep. Coastal sands and shingle. GB, DK, SF, F, D, IRL, N, S.

POLYGONUM
PERENNIALS. FLOWERS USUALLY IN A DENSE SPIKE, SHEATHING STIPULES BROWN, USUALLY OPAQUE

30 Amphibious Bistort *Polygonum amphibium*
Perennial with two growth forms: in water, with broad floating hairless leaves and submerged stems; and in damp places, with erect stems and narrow, spreading hairy leaves. Leaves obovate to lanceolate pointed; sheathing stipules without hairs. Flower spikes terminal, stalked, up to 2·5cm; flowers deep pink. Jun–Sep. Ponds, ditches, slow rivers. Throughout area covered. **236**

31 Himalayan Knotweed *Polygonum polystachyum*
Stout erect perennial up to 120cm, with oblong-lanceolate fine pointed leaves, usually with red veins; sheathing stipules thick, brown. Flowers white, 4mm across, in lax leafy branched clusters; stamens 6–8. Jul–Oct. Naturalized in waste places, often by rivers. Native of Himalaya; int B, GB, DK, F, D, IRL, NL.

32 Common Bistort *Polygonum bistorta*
Erect perennial up to 45cm, with ovate or oblong blunt basal leaves, and few triangular stem-leaves, with sheathing bases; sheathing stipules brown, obliquely cut-off and more or less divided into narrow segments. Flowers pink, 4–5mm across, in a dense, broad cylindrical, solitary terminal spike. May–Jun. Damp meadows, roadsides. B, GB, F, D, NL; int DK, IRL, N, S.

33 Alpine Bistort *Polygonum viviparum*
Differs from **32** in having a more slender flower spike, and the lower part of the spike bearing purple bulbils. Basal leaves lanceolate, tapering to the base (basal leaves with cut-off or shallow heart-shaped base in **32**), and leaf-stalk not winged. Flowers white, few. Jun–Aug. Mountain grassland, wet rocks. GB, F, D, IRL, SF, IS, N, S. **161**

32

POLYGONUM
ANNUALS. SHEATHING STIPULES WHITE, SILVERY AND PAPERY

34 Common Knotgrass *Polygonum aviculare*
Hairless annual, with robust erect or spreading stems up to 2m. Leaves lanceolate to ovate-lanceolate, varying in size; sheathing stipules c.5mm. Flowers pink, white or greenish, c. 3mm across, solitary or in clusters in axils of upper leaves. Stamens 8. Nuts dull, enclosed in perianth. Jun–Oct. Waste places, roadsides, cultivated land. Throughout area covered.

35 Northern Knotgrass *Polygonum boreale*
Differs from **34** in having broader obovate to spoon-shaped leaves, and leaf-stalks projecting from the sheathing stipules. Flowers have broad perianth segments with bright pink margins. Nuts 4mm (3mm in **34**). Jul–Aug. Waste ground, roadsides in more northern part of area covered. GB, SF, IS, N, S.

34

36 Cornfield Knotgrass *Polygonum rurivagum*
Like **35** but a smaller, slender, flexuous annual, usually erect, rarely more than 30cm. Leaves linear to linear-lanceolate 1·5–3·5cm on main stem, much smaller on branches; sheathing stipules longer, up to 1cm, brownish below. Flowers few; perianth segments usually reddish, scarcely overlapping. Jul–Oct. Weed of arable fields. B, GB, DK, F, D, NL, N, S.

37

37 Equal-leaved Knotgrass *Polygonum arenastrum*
A spreading mat-forming branched annual. Leaves elliptic to lanceolate, up to 2cm; sheathing stipules silvery-transparent. Flowers in axillary clusters in axils of leafy bracts. Perianth-tube at least half as long as perianth lobes. Nuts dull, slightly longer than perianth. Jun–Oct. Roadsides, waste ground, especially trampled places. Throughout area covered.

38 *Polygonum bellardii* (=*P. patulum*)
Annual with usually erect, much-branched stem, up to 1m. Leaves narrowly lanceolate to oblong-elliptic. Flowers in lax or moderately dense spikes, lower flowers having leafy bracts, the upper with papery bracts. Flowers greenish, 3–4mm long, widely spaced on slender branches. Nuts glossy, enclosed in perianth. Jun–Sep. Calcareous arable fields, waste ground. F.

POLYGONUM
ANNUALS. SHEATHING STIPULES. BROWN, USUALLY OPAQUE, ENTIRE OR CILIATE. FLOWERS USUALLY IN DENSE SPIKES

39 Water-pepper *Polygonum hydropiper*
Nearly hairless acrid-tasting annual with erect stems up to 80cm. Leaves lanceolate, pointed; sheathing stipules fringed with short hairs. Flowers pinkish to greenish-white, in numerous lax slender nodding spikes; perianth covered with shiny glandular dots. Nuts dark brown or black, not shiny. Jul–Sep. Damp places. Throughout area covered, except IS. **236**

40 Tasteless Water-pepper *Polygonum mite*
Like **39** but not acrid, sheathing stipules conspicuously and coarsely fringed, and leaves abruptly narrowed at base. Flowers pink, rarely white, in nearly erect spikes; perianth without glandular dots. Nuts shiny. Jul–Sep. Ditches, margins of ponds, rivers. B, GB, F, D, IRL, NL.

41 Small Water-pepper *Polygonum minus*
Slender, hairless, spreading or ascending annual up to 40cm, with narrow lanceolate leaves less than 8mm wide, to 7·5cm long. Sheathing stipules with conspicuous hairy margins. Flowers deep pink, up to 2mm across, rarely white, in slender erect spikes which are interrupted below. Nuts glossy black. Aug–Sep. Damp places, margins of ponds. Throughout area covered, except IS.

42 *Polygonum foliosum*
Like **41** but sheathing stipules without cilia, or cilia short. Leaves linear. Inflorescence sparser and more leafy. Perianth and nuts 1·5–2mm. Jul. Damp places. SF, N, S.

43 Pale Persicaria
Polygonum lapathifolium (=*P. nodosum*)
Distinguished by its dense stout spikes of dull pink or

41

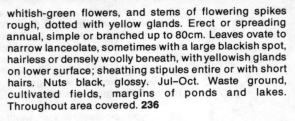

whitish-green flowers, and stems of flowering spikes rough, dotted with yellow glands. Erect or spreading annual, simple or branched up to 80cm. Leaves ovate to narrow lanceolate, sometimes with a large blackish spot, hairless or densely woolly beneath, with yellowish glands on lower surface; sheathing stipules entire or with short hairs. Nuts black, glossy. Jul–Oct. Waste ground, cultivated fields, margins of ponds and lakes. Throughout area covered. 236

44 Redshank *Polygonum persicaria*
Similar to **43**, with a dense stout cylindrical spike of bright or pale pink flowers. Differs in having stems of flowering spikes smooth without glands (flower stems glandular in **43**). Annual to 80cm; leaves lanceolate, shortly ciliate. Nuts black, glossy. Jul–Oct. Weed of cultivation, margins of ponds and lakes. Throughout area covered. 236

45 Black Bindweed
Fallopia (=*Bilderdykia*) *convolvulus*
Twining or spreading annual up to 1m, with broad arrow-shaped stalked leaves. Flowers greenish-white, 2mm across in narrow spike-like stalked axillary clusters. Perianth segments usually 5, the outer larger, keeled or winged. Nuts finely glandular, dull black, to 5mm. Jul–Oct. Waste places, cultivated ground. Throughout area covered, except IS.

46 Copse Bindweed
Fallopia (=*Bilderdykia*) *dumetorum*
Like **45** but taller and with longer fruiting stalks 5–8mm (fruiting stalks 1–3mm in **45**). Outer perianth segments with broad wings in fruit. Nuts smooth and glossy, smaller, 2·5–3mm. Jul–Oct. Hedges, woods. B, GB, DK, SF, F, D, NL, N, S.

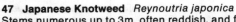

47 Japanese Knotweed *Reynoutria japonica*
Stems numerous up to 3m, often reddish, and forming a dense thicket. Leaves ovate-triangular, pointed, up to 12cm. Flowers white, in axillary branched clusters up to 12cm long. Aug–Sep. Waste places. Native of Japan. Int. B, GB, DK, S, SF, F, D, IRL, NL, N.

48 Giant Knotweed *Reynoutria sachalinensis*
Like **47**, but stems stouter and leaves narrower, less pointed, and up to 30cm. Flowers greenish, in branched clusters. Aug–Sep. Native of E. Asia. Int B, GB, DK, S, SF, F, IRL, NL.

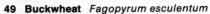

49 Buckwheat *Fagopyrum esculentum*
Hollow-stemmed annual 15–60cm, tinged red at maturity. Leaves arrow-shaped to heart-shaped, the lower stalked, upper stalkless. Flowers greenish-white

tipped pink, 3–4mm, in terminal and axillary clusters. Nuts dark brown, angled, smooth. Jul–Aug. Waste places, field verges. Native of E.C. Asia. Naturalized or persistently casual throughout area covered, except IRL, IS. **237**

50 Green Buckwheat *Fagopyrum tataricum*
Differs from **49** in having smaller, usually green flowers c. 2mm across and nutlets irregularly rough, with toothed angles. Jul–Sep. Waste places, weed of cultivated areas. Native of Asia. Int B, DK, SF, F, NL, N, S.

50

51 Mountain Sorrel *Oxyria digyna*
Hairless perennial with stems up to 30cm, and distinctive rounded/kidney-shaped, long-stalked leaves. Flowers tiny, reddish, 3mm, in branched lax leafless clusters. Perianth-segments 4, the inner enlarging in fruit but without a swelling. Fruit broadly winged. Jul–Aug. Damp rocks, streamsides on mountains. GB, D, IRL, IS, N, S.

RUMEX
LEAVES SPEAR-SHAPED OR ARROW-SHAPED AND TASTING OF ACID

52 Sheep's Sorrel *Rumex acetosella*
Small usually erect perennial, branching from the middle or above, with whorls of greenish flowers. Leaves lanceolate to arrow-shaped, with spreading basal lobes. Inflorescence leafless or nearly so. Perianth segments 6. Nut shining dark brown. Apr–Sep. Sandy heaths, acid soils. Throughout area covered. **232**

53 Narrow-leaved Sorrel *Rumex tenuifolius*
Like **52** but spreading or ascending, branched below the middle. Leaves linear with narrow basal lobes. Jun–Jul. Dry sandy heaths. Throughout area covered.

54 French Sorrel *Rumex scutatus*
A shrubby-looking, much branched perennial, up to 50cm, with leaves about as long as wide, blunt and with diverging basal lobes. Flowers in a very lax cluster; fruiting perianth segments heart-shaped, without swellings 4·4–6mm. Nuts yellowish-grey. May–Aug. Calcareous rocks and screes, old walls. B, F, NL, D; int GB, N, S.

55 Common Sorrel *Rumex acetosa*
Erect, usually nearly hairless perennial up to 130cm, with oblong-lanceolate leaves with downward-directed basal lobes; upper leaves clasping stem. Flowers greenish-brown, in lax leafless branched inflorescence. Outer perianth segments reflexed after flowering; fruiting segments 3–5mm, rounded, heart-shaped. Nuts shiny, blackish. May–Jul. Grassland, especially meadows. Throughout area covered; int IS. **237**

56 *Rumex thyrsiflorus*
Differs from **55** in having branches of inflorescence repeatedly branched, with dense clusters of flowers and smaller fruiting segments. Basal leaves 3–4 times as long as wide, stem leaves progressively narrower above. Nuts dark brown. Flowering 2–6 weeks later than **55**. Jul–Aug. Dry open habitats, grassland. DK, SF, D, NL, S. Int F, N.

RUMEX
BASAL LEAVES HEART-SHAPED WITH ROUNDED OR WEDGE-SHAPED BASE.
INNER FRUITING PERIANTH WITHOUT SWELLINGS AT BASE

57 Scottish Dock *Rumex aquaticus*
Large stout perennial up to 2m, with erect branches and narrow inflorescences. Leaves broadly oval with heart-shaped base, to 50cm. Flowers green in dense rounded whorls, flower-stalks very slender. Fruiting segments rounded, net-veined. Nuts shiny, brown. Jul–Sep. Wet places, lakes, streamsides. GB, DK, SF, F, D, N, S.

58 Northern Dock *Rumex longifolius*
Stout perennial up to 120cm, with broadly lanceolate leaves up to 80cm. Inflorescence dense, spindle-shaped. Flowers with slender stalks c. $1\frac{1}{2}$ times as long as perianth segments (up to $2\frac{1}{2}$ times as long in **57**). Fruiting segments 6mm, kidney-shaped, entire without swellings. Jun–Jul. Ditches, riversides, damp grasslands. GB, DK, SF, IS, N, S.

RUMEX
AT LEAST ONE INNER PERIANTH-SEGMENT WITH CORKY SWELLING AND
SEGMENTS WITH ENTIRE MARGIN OR SHORT TEETH (see also **65**)

59 Water Dock *Rumex hydrolapathum*
Stout erect perennial up to 2m, with large lanceolate to ovate leaves. Inflorescence much-branched; flowers green, in crowded whorls. Inner perianth segments ovate and pointed in fruit, each with an elongate swelling and margin with few short teeth. Jun–Sep. Marshes, rivers, streams, pond verges. Throughout area covered, except IS.

60 Curled Dock *Rumex crispus*
Erect much-branched perennial up to 1·5m. Leaves narrowly lanceolate, usually with wavy margins. Flowers green, in whorls, the lower whorls widely spaced. Perianth segments of fruit heart-shaped, entire, with three (rarely one) swellings. Jun–Aug. Waste ground, fields, sea-shores, estuarine mud. Throughout area covered; int IS. **232**

61 Clustered Dock *Rumex conglomeratus*

Slender perennial up to 80cm, with lanceolate leaves with undulate margins. Flowers reddish, in widely spaced whorls in a large spreading branched inflorescence. Perianth segments of fruit oblong-ovate entire, all with ovoid swellings. Jun–Aug. Riversides, waste places. Throughout area covered, except IS, SF, N. **232**

62 Wood Dock *Rumex sanguineus*

Differs from **61** in having only one perianth segment with an orbicular swelling, and flower-stalks longer than segments (flower-stalks about as long as segments in **61**). Only the lower whorls of flowers subtended by leaves (usually all whorls subtended by leaves in **61**). Slender erect perennial up to c. 1m. Jun–Aug. Shady places. B, GB, DK, F, D, IRL, NL, N, S. **187**

63 Shore Dock *Rumex rupestris*

Like **61** but branches of inflorescence upright. Leaves blue-green with oblong blade much longer than leaf-stalk. Perianth segments of fruit all with large swellings. Jun–Jul. Cliffs, damp places in sand-dunes. GB, F.

RUMEX

SEGMENTS OF FRUITING PERIANTH WITH CONSPICUOUS TEETH

64

64 Fiddle Dock *Rumex pulcher*

Perennial up to 60cm, with small fleshy oblong or fiddle-shaped basal leaves, twice as long as wide with heart-shaped base; upper leaves lanceolate, constricted in the middle and with undulate margins and heart-shaped base. Flowers in distant whorls subtended by leaves on wide-spreading branches. Perianth segments of fruit strongly net-veined, with 4 long teeth on each margin. Jun–Aug. Waste places, grasslands by the sea. GB, F; int DK, S.

65 Broad-leaved Dock *Rumex obtusifolius*

Perennial up to 120cm, with large basal leaves twice as long as wide and with leaf-stalks slightly longer than blade. Flowers in lax distant whorls, in erect branched inflorescence. Flower-stalks slender (thick in **64**) some at least twice as long as fruiting perianth segments. Segments with several long marginal teeth; one segment with basal swelling. Jun–Aug. Waste ground, shady places, cultivated land. Throughout area covered; int SF, IS. **232**

Ssp. *sylvestris* has all segments with swellings and entire or short-toothed margins. Ssp. *transiens* is intermediate in form.

66 Marsh Dock *Rumex palustris*

Erect annual or biennial up to 60cm, with many curved

23

ascending branches with dense whorls of brownish-yellow flowers. Basal leaves lanceolate pointed, margins undulate. Whorls of flowers all subtended by linear-lanceolate leaves. Fruiting perianth segments with swellings, and 2–3 stiff teeth on each margin as long as the width of the segment. Jul–Aug. Damp ground, marshes, meadows. B, GB, DK, F, D, NL, N, S.

67 Golden Dock *Rumex maritimus*
Erect annual up to 50cm, that becomes golden-yellow in fruit. Basal leaves narrowly elliptic. Flowers in densely mostly closely-spaced whorls, in a branched up-curved inflorescence. Fruiting perianth segments ovate-triangular, with swellings, and 2 long hair-like teeth on each margin longer than the width of the segment. Jun–Sep. Coastal marshes, wet places. Throughout area covered, except IS; int SF.

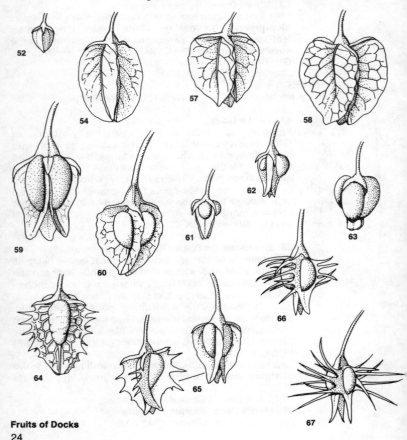

Fruits of Docks

GOOSEFOOT FAMILY

Chenopodiaceae

Annual or perennial herbs (or small shrubs). Flowers small, inconspicuous, green, often in clusters. Perianth segments 3–5, persistent and sometimes fleshy in fruit. Stamens 5; stigmas 2. Fruit a tiny achene. Typically plants of saline or nitrogen-rich habitats; many are weeds of cultivated ground.

68 Polycnemum *Polycnemum majus*
Short spreading or erect hairless annual up to 30cm, with many narrow spine-tipped leaves. Flowers tiny, greenish, solitary, ranged up stem in axils of longer bracts; bracteoles 2. Perianth segments 5; stamens usually 3. Jun–Sep. Dry places, bare ground. B, F, D.

69 Sea Beet *Beta vulgaris* ssp. *maritima*
A spreading hairless, often red-tinged, stout perennial with thick woody ribbed stems up to 80cm. Lower leaves ovate, leathery, with winged leaf-stalks. Flowers green, 3–4mm across, in clusters, the lower clusters in the axils of narrow elliptic leaves. Perianth segments 5, thickening in fruit. Jul–Sep. Sea-shores. B, GB, DK, F, D, IRL, NL, S. **Beet** ssp. *vulgaris* is up to 2m; root swollen; leaves larger. Widely cultivated, and often persists as a casual near fields. **188**

68

CHENOPODIUM
DISTINGUISHED IN FRUIT; FRUIT IS SURROUNDED BY 2–5 PERSISTENT PERIANTH SEGMENTS

70 Good King Henry *Chenopodium bonus-henricus*
Robust perennial 20–80cm, erect or ascending, distinguished by triangular spear-shaped or arrow-shaped leaves with basal lobes. Flowers green, 2mm across, in a narrow terminal spike leafless above. Perianth 5-lobed, not covering black seed. May–Jun. Waste ground, roadsides. Throughout area covered, except IS. **232**

71 Strawberry-blite *Chenopodium capitatum*
Distinguished by its fleshy red strawberry-like fruit. Erect annual up to 1m, with narrow triangular, toothed or entire leaves, the upper leaves spear-shaped to lanceolate. Flowers in many globular stalkless clusters up to 1cm across. Jun–Sep. Cultivated ground, waste places. Origin unknown; int GB, DK, F, D.

72 Oak-leaved Goosefoot *Chenopodium glaucum*
Spreading or erect much branched annual up to 40cm or

more. Leaves elliptic to narrowly lanceolate, usually wavy-margined, green above, densely mealy blue-green beneath. Flowers green, in narrow lax terminal and lateral clusters; perianth 2–5-lobed, the lobes keeled. Jun–Sep. Bare places on rich soils. Throughout area covered, except IRL, IS.

73 Red Goosefoot *Chenopodium rubrum*
Like **72**, hairless spreading or erect but usually reddish annual up to 1m, with shining rhomboidal leaves, the lower coarsely and sharply toothed, upper entire. Flowers green, in dense short, simple or branched terminal and axillary clusters. Perianth 2- to 4-lobed, not or scarcely keeled. Jul–Oct. Waste land, cultivated ground, often near sea. Throughout area covered, except IS. **188**

74 Small Red Goosefoot *Chenopodium botryodes*
Like **73**, but stems more spreading or prostrate. Leaves broadly triangular, entire or slightly toothed, rather thick. Flower clusters usually distant; perianth with bag-like lobes encircling the fruit and fused almost to their apices, ribbed or keeled when young. Jul–Sep. Salt-marshes, ditches by the sea. S, GB, DK, F, D, IRL.

75 Maple-leaved Goosefoot *Chenopodium hybridum*
Distinguished by its triangular-rhomboid pointed leaves with few large conspicuous pointed teeth. Erect annual up to 1m. Inflorescence lax, with spreading leafless branches. Perianth segments not or obscurely keeled. Seeds black, not enclosed by perianth. Jul–Sep. Waste places, cultivated ground. Throughout area covered, except IRL, IS; int SF.

76 Many-seeded Goosefoot
Chenopodium polyspermum

Erect or spreading hairless annual up to 1m, with ovate-elliptic entire leaves, or rarely with a single tooth on each side just above the base; stem 4-angled. Inflorescence long, lax tapering, with many axillary clusters. Perianth segments 5, not keeled. Jul–Sep. Fields, river-banks, vineyards. Throughout area covered, except IS.

77 Stinking Goosefoot *Chenopodium vulvaria*
Mealy, much branched spreading annual up to 35cm, smelling strongly of bad fish. Leaves rhomboid to obovate, margins entire or with a single tooth-like angle on one or both sides; blade very mealy beneath. Flowers grey-green, in terminal and axillary clusters. Perianth segments ovate, not keeled, covering ripe fruit. Jul–Sep. Salt-marshes, fields, waste places. Throughout area covered, except IRL, IS, N.

78 Upright Goosefoot *Chenopodium urbicum*
Erect nearly hairless annual up to 1m, with lower leaves

Goosefoot leaves

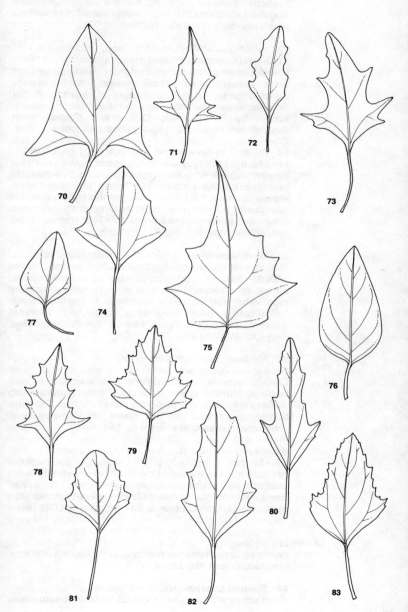

triangular and narrowed to the leaf-stalk, with usually long hooked teeth. Flowers green, in crowded ascending branches. Perianth segments 5, not keeled. Seeds black. Aug–Sep. Cultivated ground, waste places. Throughout area covered, except IRL, NL, IS.

79 Nettle-leaved Goosefoot *Chenopodium murale*
Stout erect much-branched mealy annual up to 90cm. Lower leaves rhomboid or triangular, with coarse blunt teeth towards apex, upper leaves linear-lanceolate. Flowers green, in dense clusters in much branched inflorescence. Perianth segments 5, bluntly keeled above. Seeds black. Jul–Oct. Waste places, fields, sand-dunes. Throughout area covered, except IRL, IS, N.

80 Fig-leaved Goosefoot *Chenopodium ficifolium*
Like **79**, but distinguished by the lower leaves which are lanceolate with long basal lobes directed forwards, the mid-lobe oblong and slightly lobed to entire, upper leaves slightly lobed or entire. Inflorescence much branched, with slender branches; perianth segments green with white margin, keeled. Jul–Sep. Waste ground, rich arable soils. B, GB, DK, SF, NL, N, S.

81 Grey Goosefoot *Chenopodium opulifolium*
Rather robust, erect, much-branched annual, up to 150cm, usually grey-mealy. Leaves rhombic-ovate, almost as broad as long, with prominent lobe on each side, otherwise entire or with several marginal teeth. Inflorescence very grey-mealy, branched. Perianth green, 5-lobed, the lobes keeled. Seeds not pitted. Aug–Oct. Waste places. B, GB, DK, F, D, S.

82 Fat Hen *Chenopodium album*
Grey-green mealy annual up to 1m, with reddish stem. Leaves variable, from rhombic to lanceolate, usually toothed. Flowers green, in dense clusters forming long leafless spikes, or in broader branched clusters. Perianth segments 5, keeled. Jul–Oct. Waste places, arable land. Throughout area covered; int IS. **188**

83 Green Goosefoot *Chenopodium suecicum*
Like **82**, but plant usually bright blue-green, and stem not red. Leaves ovate-rhombic with sharp ascending teeth (sometimes 3-lobed), upper leaves oval to linear. Seed-coat with more numerous and deeper furrows than in **82**. Jul–Oct. Waste places. DK, SF, N, S. Int GB, IRL.

ATRIPLEX
DISTINGUISHED BY ITS FRUIT WHICH IS ENCLOSED BETWEEN 2 MORE OR LESS VERTICAL ADPRESSED BRACTEOLES

84 Frosted Orache *Atriplex laciniata*
A branched white or silvery annual, with spreading stems

GOOSEFOOT FAMILY

up to 30cm, and with ovate to rhomboid wavy-margined, thick, very mealy leaves. Flowers green, in small axillary clusters. Bracteoles of fruit broadly rhombic, rounded or toothed on the lateral angles, and becoming hard in the lower half. Aug–Sep. Coastal sands and shingle. B, GB, DK, F, D, IRL, NL, N, S.

85 *Atriplex rosea*
Differs from **84**: bracteoles irregularly toothed in upper part, and large appendages on back. Erect or ascending much-branched annual, up to 1m. Leaves white, ovate-rhombic or triangular, with toothed margins. Flower clusters mostly axillary; bracteoles 12mm. Aug–Sep. Saline and nitrogen-rich soils. F, D. Int B, NL.

86 Spear-leaved Orache
Atriplex prostrata (=*A. hastata*)

Annual up to 1m, usually erect, branched but variable; stem often reddish. Leaves arrow-shaped, with cut-off base at right angles to the leaf-stalk, uppermost leaves lanceolate with base tapering to short leaf-stalk. Flowers in clusters, in slender, branched, almost leafless inflorescence. Bracteoles in fruit 3–12mm, ovate-pointed, with or without swellings. Jul–Sep. Roadsides, cultivated ground, waste places, seashores. Throughout area covered, except IS.

86

87 Babington's Orache *Atriplex glabriuscula*
Distinguished from **86** by its thick inflated bracteoles. A spreading often reddish annual, to 50cm. Leaves arrow-shaped with 2 pointed basal lobes. Jul–Sep. Coastal sands and shingle. Throughout area covered, except SF.

88 Long-stalked Orache *Atriplex longipes*
Differs from **87**: some bracteoles distinctly stalked. Spreading or erect annual, with arrow-shaped leaves. Jun–Jul. Tall salt-marsh vegetation. GB, DK, SF, S. Int N.

89 Common Orache *Atriplex patula*

Much-branched annual up to 150cm, with stem strongly ridged. Lower leaves broadly arrow-shaped with wedge-shaped base, upper leaves lanceolate to linear. Flowers in axillary clusters or in long spike-like clusters. Bracteoles broadly rhombic, entire or toothed, smooth or with swelling on back. Jul–Oct. Cultivated ground, waste places. Throughout area covered.

90 Grass-leaved Orache *Atriplex littoralis*
Distinguished by its narrow linear-oblong entire or toothed leaves, the upper stalkless. Inflorescence spike-like, nearly leafless. Annual, much branched, up to 1m. Bracteoles of fruit triangular-ovate, conspicuously covered with small swellings. Jul–Aug. Sea shores, salt-marshes. Throughout area covered, except IS.

90

91 Sea Purslane *Halimione portulacoides*
Small silvery-hairy shrub, 20–80cm. Leaves opposite, thick, fleshy, oblong to obovate, entire. Flowers very small, in dense clusters in a terminal branched inflorescence. Fruit stalkless, with 3-lobed bracteoles fused almost to the apex. Jul–Oct. Salt-marshes, coastal cliffs. B, GB, DK, F, D, IRL, NL. **194**

92 Stalked Orache *Halimione pedunculata*
Small silvery-mealy branched annual, 10–50cm, with alternate oblong-elliptic entire leaves. Fruit stalked, with bracteoles 3-lobed, the middle lobe very small. Jul–Sep. Saline soils, saltmarshes. B, DK, F, †BR, D, NL, S.

93 Hairy Seablight *Bassia hirsuta*
Spreading or ascending, usually hairy, greyish annual, up to 60cm, with linear rounded fleshy leaves to 1·5cm. Flowers greenish, with 5 hairy perianth segments, enlarging in fruit and with a conical or hooked spine on the back. Aug–Sep. Coastal sands, saline soils inland. DK, D.

94 *Kochia laniflora*
Erect annual up to 80cm, with slender thread-like soft leaves. Flowers green, with 5 ovate perianth segments. Fruiting perianth enlarged 4–5mm, with ovate segments with a transverse wing on back. Aug–Oct. Dry sandy places. F, D.

95 Summer Cypress *Kochia scoparia*
Differs from **94** in having flat, narrowly lanceolate, 3-veined leaves. Fruiting perianth very shortly winged. Erect annual up to 150cm. Aug–Oct. Dry places; also cultivated for ornamental foliage. Temperate Asia. Int DK, F, D, NL.

96 *Corispermum leptopterum*
Usually hairless annual, branched from the base, up to 60cm, with linear-lanceolate flat leaves. Flowers greenish, in a branched, usually dense inflorescence. Perianth segment 1. Lower bracts covering fruit; achenes winged. Jul–Sep. Sandy places. F; int B, D, NL.

97 Perennial Glasswort *Arthrocnemum perenne*
Small shrub forming mats, up to 1m across, woody below and with succulent stems above, with opposite scale-like leaves. Inflorescence spike-like, jointed, with 2 three-flowered clusters embedded in the pair of bracts arising from the node above. Perianth segments usually 4; stamens 2. Aug–Sep. Salt-marshes. GB, F, IRL.

98 Glasswort *Salicornia europaea*
Fleshy annual with jointed stems 5–30cm, simple or much-branched, later turning red or purple. Terminal spike with 3–12 fertile segments, each with 3 flowers

embedded in a bract of each segment, the central flower larger than the laterals. Aug–Sep. Salt-marshes. Throughout area covered, except IS.

Other closely related species occur in area, but are difficult to distinguish; they include *Salicornia ramosissima, S. pusilla, S. nitens, S. fragilis* and *S. dolichostachya.* **273**

99 Annual Sea-blite *Suaeda maritima*

Small erect or spreading, blue-green or reddish, variable annual up to 50cm, with linear, fleshy rounded acute leaves up to 5cm. Flowers greenish or reddish, 2·5mm across, in dense axillary clusters; bracteoles 2, minute. Perianth segments 5, fleshy; stamens 5, stigmas 2. Fruit a one-seeded nutlet. Jul–Sep. Salt-marshes, muddy shores. Throughout area covered, except IS. **188**

100 Shrubby Sea-blite *Suaeda vera*

Small densely-branched shrub up to 120cm with fleshy, blue-green, narrow cylindrical leaves, to 18mm. Flowers usually reddish, 3mm across, in small axillary clusters; stigmas 3. Fleshy perianth green, not inflated. May–Oct. Coastal rocks, sands and shingle. GB, F. **194**

101 Prickly Saltwort *Salsola kali*

Erect or spreading prickly annual up to 1m, with linear/awl-shaped fleshy pointed leaves to 4cm. Flowers solitary in axils of spiny bracteoles; perianth segments ovate, winged. Fruit top-shaped, enclosed in persistent thickened perianth. Jul–Sep. Coastal sands. Throughout area covered, except IS. **188**

AMARANTH FAMILY

Amaranthaceae

Annual herbs. Flowers inconspicuous, small, green, grouped in often dense inflorescences. Perianth segments 3–5. Fruit membranous. Weeds of dry waste and cultivated ground, introduced in N. Europe mostly from the Americas.

102 Green Amaranth *Amaranthus hybridus*
Erect annual up to 1m, with rhombic-ovate leaves. Inflorescence a long, dense, often branched spike-like cluster, leafless above. Perianth-segments green, narrowly ovate-acute. Fruit splitting transversely. Jul–Oct. Waste places, sandy soils. Tropical and sub-tropical America. Int DK, F, D, NL.

103 Common Amaranth *Amaranthus retroflexus*
Differs from **102** in having spoon-shaped perianth segments, blunt with a short spine. Stem woolly-hairy above. Jul–Sep. Cultivated ground, waste places. N. America. Int B, GB, DK, F, D, NL, S.

104 White Amaranth *Amaranthus albus*
Distinguished by having usually 3 perianth segments (perianth segments usually 5 in **102** and **103**). Erect or spreading much-branched annual up to 50cm. Leaves oblong or spoon-shaped, with undulate margins. Inflorescence of short axillary clusters. Perianth-segments narrowly elliptic. Jul–Sep. Cultivated ground, waste places. North America. Casual in GB, DK, F, D, NL.

102

MEZEMBRYANTHEMUM FAMILY

Aizoaceae

Fleshy, usually trailing, dwarf shrubs. Flowers large and conspicuous, with numerous, brightly coloured petals. Introduced on coasts; mostly from South Africa.

105 Hottentot-fig *Carpobrotus edulis*
Trailing branched perennial forming dense mats with very distinctive fleshy leaves which are triangular in section. Flowers large 7–9cm across, yellow, pink or magenta with numerous linear, pointed petals and numerous yellow stamens. Fruit fleshy, indehiscent. May–Jul. Cliffs, sand-dunes, walls by sea. Native of South Africa. Int GB, F, IRL.

105

PURSLANE FAMILY

Portulacaceae

Annual herbs, with rather fleshy leaves. Flowers in terminal clusters. Fruit a globose capsule, containing few seeds.

106 Blinks *Montia fontana*
Spreading annual or perennial which has a tufted growth form on land and weak branching stems in water. Leaves narrowly spoon-shaped, up to 2cm. Flowers white, tiny, with 5 spreading petals in the axils of leaves and terminal. May–Aug. Damp ground, mud, in water. Throughout area covered.

107 Spring Beauty *Claytonia* (=*Montia*) *perfoliata*
A fleshy annual with several erect stems, 10–30cm, each bearing white flowers subtended by a distinctive cup-shaped pair of fused leaves. Basal leaves in a rosette, elliptic-rhomboid, fleshy. Flowers c. 5mm across, in short branched clusters. Apr–Jul. Cultivated ground on sandy soils. Native of N. America. Int B, GB, DK, F, D, NL. **161**

106

108 Pink Purslane *Claytonia* (=*Montia*) *sibirica*
Like **107** but flowers larger up to 2cm across, and usually pink, rarely white, with 2-lobed petals. Stem leaves ovate, the upper not fused together at their bases. May–Aug. Shady places on sandy soils. Native of W. North America; int D, GB. **237**

PINK FAMILY

Caryophyllaceae

Annual, biennial or perennial herbs, occasionally woody at the base. Leaves simple. Stipules sometimes present. Petals usually 5, free, white or pink (or rarely purple). Fruit usually a capsule, with many seeds. A large, widespread family in N-W. Europe, especially in the mountains; often on calcareous soils.

ARENARIA
PERENNIALS

110

109 English Arctic Sandwort *Arenaria norvegica*
A dwarf tufted hairless perennial or annual with many spreading leafy stems up to 7cm, with terminal white flowers. Leaves oblanceolate, slightly fleshy, hairy below. Flowers 8mm across, usually 1–2 in cluster; petals longer than sepals; anthers white. Capsule about equalling sepals. Jun–Jul. Stony screes, rocks, river shingle. GB, IRL, IS, N, S.

110 Fringed Sandwort *Arenaria ciliata*
Differs from **109** in having leaves not fleshy, distinctly 1-veined and with hairy leaf-margins. Low spreading perennial, with elliptic to spoon-shaped leaves. Flowers white, up to 16mm across, in terminal clusters of 1–7. Jun–Jul. Open places on alkaline soils, limestone cliffs. SF, F, D, IRL, N.

111 *Arenaria humifusa*
Small, mat-forming perennial with very slender stems up to 3cm, with usually solitary white flowers; petals only slightly longer than sepals and with pale purple anthers. Leaves elliptic to narrowly ovoid, nearly hairless. Sepals usually hairless, with narrow papery margins. Jul. Moist alkaline soils. N, S.

ARENARIA
ANNUALS OR BIENNIALS (see also **109**)

112 Thyme-leaved Sandwort *Arenaria serpyllifolia*
Low spreading or tufted greyish-hairy annual, with tiny white flowers in a lax terminal cluster, and with white petals half as long as sepals. Leaves ovate, stalkless, fringed with hairs on margin. Flowers up to 8mm across, with spreading ovate-lanceolate sepals, the inner with papery margins; petals blunt. Capsule flask-shaped, swollen at base. May–Aug. Bare ground, arable fields, chalk downs, coastal sands and shingle. Throughout area covered, except IS.

112

PINK FAMILY

113 Slender Sandwort *Arenaria leptoclados*
Differs from **112** in having smaller flowers up to 5mm across, with lanceolate sepals, and capsule with straight sides, (swollen at base in **112**). A slender, more diffusely spreading plant. May–Aug. Bare ground, walls, open ground. Throughout area covered, except SF, IS.

114 Three-nerved Sandwort *Moehringia trinervia*
Slender much-branched annual up to 40cm, with ovate, distinctly 3-veined, ciliate leaves. Flowers white, 6mm across, long-stalked, in axils of upper leaves. Petals 5, ovate, to ⅔ as long as lanceolate pointed sepals which are 3-veined, with wide papery margins. Fruit rounded. May–Jul. Woods and shady places on rich soils. Throughout area covered, except IS.

115 *Moehringia muscosa*
Differs from **114** in having 4 petals, longer than the 1-veined sepals, and flowers in terminal clusters of usually 3–6. Stamens 8. Jun–Aug. Woods, damp rocks in mountains. F, D.

116 *Moehringia lateriflora*
Erect perennial with broadly elliptic blunt upper leaves. Flowers axillary, petals 5, twice as long as sepals. Jul. Woods. SF, N, S.

MINUARTA
ANNUALS OR BIENNIALS

117 *Minuartia viscosa*
Usually a glandular-hairy annual, with slender erect branched stems. Leaves linear awl-shaped. Flowers white, 6mm across, in lax clusters; petals and capsules shorter than lanceolate sepals. Jul–Aug. Dry sandy places. DK, F, D, S.

118 Fine-leaved Sandwort *Minuartia hybrida*
Differs from **117** in having fruiting capsules 1–1½ times as long as sepals (capsule shorter than sepals in **117**). A more robust annual, with erect stems up to 12cm or more, usually glandular-hairy. Flowers 5mm across; petals white, slightly shorter than sepals. May–Jun. Dry sandy places. B, GB, F, D, NL. Int DK, IRL.

MINUARTIA
PERENNIALS

119 Spring Sandwort *Minuartia verna*
Lax spreading perennial, usually with glandular-hairy ascending flowering shoots up to 15cm. Leaves linear-lanceolate, strongly 3-veined, up to 2cm. Flowers white, 8–12mm across with petals mostly longer than

35

sepals, which are usually glandular-hairy. Anthers red. Capsule conical, 3-toothed. Variable species. May–Sep. Dry stony places, screes, rocks. B, GB, F, D, IRL. **161**

120 Mountain Sandwort *Minuartia rubella*
Small tufted perennial, like **119**, but leaves linear, 4–8mm. Petals white, ovate, blunt (acute in **119**), shorter than sepals; anthers red. Capsule with 3–4 teeth. Jul. Hills on basic soils. GB, SF, IS, N, S.

121 Teesdale Sandwort *Minuartia stricta*
Small slender hairless perennial with lax tufts of rosettes with small thread-like leaves. Leaves linear acute, up to 1·5cm. Flowers white, c. 6mm across in much-branched clusters; petals slightly shorter than the broadly lanceolate acute hairless sepals. May–Jun. Rocky and stony places, sandy fields. GB, SF, IS, N, S.

120

122 Mossy Cyphel *Minuartia sedoides*
Small mat-forming perennial, with densely overlapping, fleshy, linear-lanceolate 3-veined leaves with rough margins. Flowers scarcely longer than tuft of leaves; petals absent, sepals yellow-green, linear blunt 5mm. Capsule 1½–2 times as long as sepals. Jun–Aug. Rocks, stony ground and moraines in the mountains. GB, F, D.

123 *Minuartia biflora*

122

Slender tufted perennial, with flowering stems up to 10cm. Leaves linear, blunt, 1-veined. Flowers white or sometimes pale lilac, solitary or up to 3; petals as long or up to 1½ times as long as sepals which are obovate-oblong, 3-veined. Jul. Damp open places in mountains. SF, IS, N, S.

124 Sea Sandwort *Honkenya peploides*
Fleshy leafy spreading perennial, with stems rooting at the nodes and sometimes forming extensive patches, with ovate pointed leaves up to 2cm. Flowers greenish-white, 6–10mm across, solitary, axillary; petals equalling sepals in male flowers, shorter in female flowers. Capsule globular, twice as long as sepals. May–Aug. Coastal sands and shingle. Throughout area covered. **194**

STELLARIA

LOWER LEAVES DISTINCTLY STALKED: LEAVES NEVER LINEAR-LANCEOLATE

125 Wood Stitchwort *Stellaria nemorum*
Straggling weak hairy-stemmed perennial up to 65cm, with ovate heart-shaped, entire leaves, the lower long-stalked, the upper stalkless. Flowers white, up to 12mm across, in lax clusters. Petals deeply bi-lobed, twice as long as ovate blunt sepals which have

conspicuous narrow papery margins. Stamens 10. May–Jun. Damp woods, usually in hills. B, GB, DK, SF, F, D, NL, N, S. **161**

126 Common Chickweed *Stellaria media*
Very variable branched straggling annual, with ovate acute leaves, the lower stalked. Flowers white, numerous in branched clusters. Petals deeply bi-lobed, not longer than the ovate-lanceolate sepals. Stamens 3–8, with violet-red anthers. Feb–Dec. Waste places, weed of cultivation. Throughout area covered. **161**

127 Greater Chickweed *Stellaria neglecta*
Like **126** but with white petals as long or longer than sepals, and stamens usually 10. Annual to perennial with weak branching stems up to 90cm. Sepals 5–6·5mm. Apr–Jul. Damp shady places, hedgerows, wood margins, streamsides. B, GB, DK, D, IRL, NL, S. **161**

128 Lesser Chickweed *Stellaria pallida*
Yellowish annual; stems slender, spreading up to 30cm with usually 1 line of hairs. Distinguished from **126** by its petals which are absent or minute and sepals usually less than 3mm; stamens usually 1–3. Mar–Jun. Sandy fields, sand-dunes. B, GB, DK, F, D, IRL, NL, S.

129 Bog Stitchwort *Stellaria alsine*
Small slender straggling perennial up to 40cm, with 4-angled smooth stems. Leaves elliptic to broadly lanceolate, up to 1·5cm, somewhat blue-green, stalkless; leaves stalked on overwintering shoots. Flowers white, c. 6mm across, petals deeply lobed, shorter than sepals. Stamens 10. May–Jun. Bogs, wet places. Throughout area covered, except IS.

130 Greater Stitchwort *Stellaria holostea*
Perennial up to 60cm, with weak, sharply 4-angled stems, and lanceolate pointed stalkless leaves 3–8cm. Flowers white, 1·5–3cm across, with deeply lobed petals up to twice as long as sepals. Capsule globular. Apr–Jun. Hedgerows, shady places. Throughout area covered, except IS. **162**

129

131 Marsh Stitchwort *Stellaria palustris*
Hairless creeping perennial with erect branched flowering stems up to 60cm; stem smooth 4-angled, leaves linear-lanceolate often blue-green. Flowers white, usually 2–9 in lax cluster, up to 1·3cm across; petals deeply lobed, up to twice as long as sepals which are lanceolate, 3-veined, with broad papery margins. Capsule ovoid. May–Jul. Marshes, fens. Throughout area covered, except IS, IRL.

132 Lesser Stitchwort *Stellaria graminea*
Perennial with weak ascending usually much branched

stems up to 90cm; stems 4-angled. Leaves linear to broadly lanceolate, hairless, to 5cm. Flowers white in a lax cluster of 10–60; petals shorter or longer than sepals. Bracts papery, usually ciliate. Capsule ovoid-elliptic. May–Aug. Heaths, grassy places, woodland margins. Throughout area covered. **162**

133 *Stellaria crassipes*
Creeping or tufted perennial with rounded stems, up to 10cm. Leaves ovate, thick and rigid, 3–15mm. Flowers white, usually solitary, on short stout stalks; petals longer than sepals which are 3–4mm. Aug. N, S.

134 *Stellaria longifolia*
Creeping perennial with ascending 4-angled stems up to 25cm. Leaves linear to linear-lanceolate, to 4cm. Inflorescence with many white flowers; petals equalling sepals which are 2–4mm. Bracts papery often with green midrib. Jul–Aug. SF, D, N, S.

135 *Stellaria calycantha*
Shortly creeping or tufted perennial, with 4-angled stems up to 45cm. Leaves ovate to linear-lanceolate, usually pale yellowish-green, with hairy margins. Flowers white, few or solitary; petals shorter than sepals or absent. Bracts leafy. Jul–Aug. SF, IS, N, S.

136 *Stellaria crassifolia*
Distinguished from **135** by its leaves and bracts having hairless margins, and leaves usually less than 1·5cm and somewhat fleshy. Petals white, longer than sepals. Jul. DK, SF, D, IS, N, S.

137 *Stellaria humifusa*
Differs from **136** in having smaller leaves 2–8mm, and sepals to 6mm, equalling ripe capsule (sepals shorter than ripe capsule in **136**). Jul. Coasts. SF, IS, N.

138 Umbellate Chickweed *Holosteum umbellatum*
Distinguished by its umbel-like terminal clusters of small white or pale pink flowers. Erect annual 5–20cm, glandular-hairy, blue-green towards base. Basal leaves oblanceolate stalked, the upper elliptic stalkless. Flowers 9–12mm across. Petals irregularly toothed, about twice as long as sepals. Flower-stalks varied in length, deflexed in fruit. Mar–May. Light sandy soils, disturbed ground, walls. B, †GB, DK, F, D, NL, S.

CERASTIUM
STYLES 3, 4 OR 6; TEETH OF CAPSULE 6, 8 OR 12

139 Starwort Mouse-ear *Cerastium cerastoides*
Loosely matted perennial, hairless except for a line of

hairs down stem, with flowering stems 5–15cm, spreading or ascending. Leaves linear-oblong, somewhat fleshy, 6–20mm, usually curving to one side. Flowers 9–12mm on slender glandular-hairy stems; petals white, deeply bilobed, longer than sepals. Styles usually 3. May–Aug. In mountains and arctic regions. GB, SF, F, D, IS, N, S.

140 Sea Mouse-ear *Cerastium diffusum*
Glandular-hairy annual up to 30cm, with lower leaves oblanceolate to spoon-shaped, grey-green; upper leaves ovate to elliptic, hairy. Petals white, 2-lobed, shorter than the ovate to lanceolate sepals which are 4–9mm, with glandular hairs and papery margin above. Mar–Jul. Dry places near sea. B, GB, DK, F, D, IRL, NL, N, S.

139

CERASTIUM
STYLES 5; TEETH OF CAPSULE 10. PERENNIALS WITH SHORT NON-FLOWERING BRANCHES IN AXILS OF LEAVES

141 Alpine Mouse-ear *Cerastium alpinum*
Tufted perennial up to 20cm, with ovate to broadly oblanceolate leaves, often with long soft hairs, but very variable. Flowers 18–23mm across, with white petals about twice as long as sepals. Bracts with white papery margins. Jun–Aug. Mountain rock-ledges and grasslands. GB, SF, F, D, IS, N, S. **162**

142 Arctic Mouse-ear *Cerastium arcticum*
Distinguished from **141** by its bracts which are green and leaf-like without papery margins. Spreading much-branched loosely tufted perennial, with flowering stems up to 15cm. Leaves narrower than **141**, covered with soft white hairs. Flowers 18–25mm across; petals white, shallowly lobed, more than twice as long as papery-margined sepals. Jun–Aug. Rocks in mountains. GB, SF, IS, N, S.

143 Field Mouse-ear *Cerastium arvense*
Spreading much-branched hairy perennial, with flowering stems up to 30cm. Leaves linear-lanceolate, softly hairy. Flowers white, 15–17mm across, in lax clusters. Petals 2-lobed, twice as long as sepals which are glandular-hairy with papery margin and acute papery apex. Very variable species. Apr–Aug. Sandy heaths, dry grassland. B, GB, DK, F, D, IRL, NL, S. Int SF, N. **162**

144 Common Mouse-ear *Cerastium fontanum*
Spreading to erect perennial up to 60cm, with short basal non-flowering shoots. Leaves lanceolate; upper bracts with papery margins. Petals shorter or scarcely longer than sepals. Capsule curved. Very variable species. Apr–Nov. Grasslands, bare ground. Throughout area covered.

144

145 Little Mouse-ear *Cerastium semidecandrum*
Spreading or erect, usually glandular-hairy annual up to
20cm, with oblong-lanceolate, stalked basal leaves and
broader upper leaves. Bracts papery in upper $\frac{1}{3}$ or more.
Flowers 5–6mm across, in small dense clusters. Petals
white, slightly notched, shorter than lanceolate
papery-margined sepals. Capsule nearly straight, as long
or little longer than sepals. Apr–May. Dry open ground,
sand-dunes. Throughout area covered, except IS.

146 Sticky Mouse-ear *Cerastium glomeratum*
White flowers in compact clusters, which remain
compact in fruit. Slender, more or less erect rather
yellowish glandular-hairy annual up to 30cm. Basal
leaves oblanceolate, hairy, stem leaves broader. Flowers
4–5mm across, with narrow deeply notched petals as
long as the hairy sepals, on flower-stalks shorter than
sepals. Bracts leafy, hairy. Capsule curved, twice as long
as sepals. Apr–Oct. Fields, waste ground, walls,
sand-dunes. Throughout area covered, except SF. 162

147 Grey Mouse-ear *Cerastium brachypetalum*
Shaggy-haired, greyish annual up to 40cm, with
lanceolate broadly stalked lower leaves and stalkless
upper leaves. Flowers in a lax cluster with green leafy
bracts. Petals white, about $\frac{1}{2}$ as long as sepals, 2-lobed to
$\frac{1}{3}$ their length and hairy-margined at base. Capsule little
longer than sepals. Apr–Jun. Fields, lawns. Throughout
area covered, except SF, IS.

147

148 Dwarf Mouse-ear *Cerastium pumilum*
Differs from **147** in having bracts with a papery apex and
upper part of margin. Glandular-hairy annual with
ascending slender stems up to 14cm, stems often reddish below. Lower leaves oblanceolate stalked, upper
ovate to oblong blunt, hairy. Petals white or purplish-
tinged, bi-lobed, equalling or slightly longer than the
papery-margined sepals. Apr–May. Grasslands on limestone. Throughout area covered, except N. 162

149 Upright Chickweed *Moenchia erecta*
Small erect greyish annual 3–8cm, with linear-
lanceolate, blue-green leaves up to 1cm. Flowers white,
c. 8mm across, with usually 4 narrow entire petals $\frac{2}{3}$ as
long as acute white-margined sepals. Stigmas 4, styles 4,
short recurved. Apr–Jun. Sandy grasslands. B, GB, F, D,
NL.

150 Water Chickweed *Myosoton aquaticum*
Straggling spreading or ascending downy perennial
20–120cm, with broadly elliptic pointed leaves, the lower

PINK FAMILY

short-stalked, the upper stalkless. Flowers 15mm across; petals white, deeply lobed, much longer than the lanceolate, glandular-hairy sepals. Stamens 10; styles 5. Jul–Sep. Streamsides, ditches, shallow ponds. Throughout area covered, except IRL, IS. **163**

SAGINA
PERENNIALS. VEGETATIVE STEMS PRESENT AT FLOWERING, PETALS 4–5

151 Knotted Pearlwort *Sagina nodosa*
Tufted perennial with stems of 15cm, linear leaves in basal rosettes, and short dense clusters of leaves up stem. Flowers white 5–10mm across. Petals 5, entire, 2–3-times as long as the ovate blunt sepals. Stamens 10. Jul–Sep. Damp sandy places. Throughout area covered.

152 Snow Pearlwort *Sagina intermedia*
Densely tufted cushion-forming perennial with many leafy flowering stems with linear leaves. Flowers white 3–6mm across, solitary on stalks up to 5mm. Petals 4–5, shorter than sepals, which are ovate with narrow papery often violet margins. Stamens usually 8 or fewer. Fruiting stalks curved outwards. Jul–May. Mountains. GB, SF, IS, N, S.

151

153 *Sagina caespitosa*
Differs from **152** in having 5 petals and sepals, with petals longer than sepals; stamens 10. Fruiting stalks straight. Jul–Aug. Mountains. IS, N, S.

154 Heath Pearlwort *Sagina subulata*
Mat-forming perennial with many erect flowering stems 2–8cm, each with a basal rosette of linear leaves and a solitary flower. Flowers white; petals 5, equalling the sepals; stamens 10. Jul–Sep. Dry sandy, gravelly or rocky places. Throughout area covered, except SF.

155 Alpine Pearlwort *Sagina saginoides*
Lax tufted perennial with numerous flowering stems up to 7cm, arising from a central rosette of linear, hairless leaves. Flowers white, solitary, 4–5mm across. Petals about equalling the blunt hairless white-margined sepals. Stamens usually 10, rarely 5. Capsule 4–5mm, fruit stalks at first recurved, later erect. Jul–Oct. Mountains and arctic regions. GB, SF, F, D, IS, N, S.

154

156 Procumbent Pearlwort *Sagina procumbens*
Differs from **155**: petals and sepals usually 4, rarely 5, and petals often minute or absent. Capsule less than 3mm. A widely distributed mat-forming perennial with a central rosette of leaves and many ascending stems up to 20cm. Flowers white, solitary, 4mm across; sepals ovate-blunt, hooded, spreading in ripe fruit. May–Sep. Grassy banks, paths, streamsides. Throughout area covered.

41

157 Annual Pearlwort *Sagina apetala*
Spreading, loosely tufted annual, with leafy stems up to
18cm, bearing several green flowers. Leaves linear
bristle-tipped, usually hairy. Flowers 4mm across; petals
absent or minute; sepals usually 4, ovate to oblong, often
hooded. May–Sep. Bare ground, dry places. Throughout
area covered, except SF, IS, N.

158 Sea Pearlwort *Sagina maritima*
Usually a hairless annual, with spreading or erect stems
2–12cm. Leaves fleshy, linear-lanceolate. Flowers 4mm
across, with 4 ovate-hooded sepals with purplish
margins; petals absent or minute. A very variable species.
May–Sep. Open places on coasts; rocks, cliffs,
sand-dunes. Throughout area covered, except D, IS.

157

159 Annual Knawal *Scleranthus annuus*
Small spiky-looking, much branched spreading or erect
annual or biennial up to 25cm, with linear blunt leaves
fused in pairs at the base, and with hairy bases. Flowers
green, 4mm across, with 5 triangular acute sepals with
very narrow papery margins and united below; petals
absent. Styles 2. Capsule enclosed in calyx-tube.
May–Oct. Dry sandy places. Throughout area covered,
except IS. **195**

160 Perennial Knawal *Scleranthus perennis*
Differs from **159** in having blunt sepals with wider papery
margins. Perennial with a woody rootstock. Variable
species, with spreading or erect stems. Jun–Sep. Dry
sandy places, grasslands, rocks. B, GB, DK, F, D, NL, N.
195

161 Strapwort *Corrigiola litoralis*
Small blue-green annual with many spreading stems
5–25cm, from rosettes of leaves. Leaves linear blunt,
alternate, somewhat fleshy. Flowers in dense terminal
and axillary clusters, minute, 1·5mm across; petals white
or red-tipped, nearly as long as sepals. Sepals and petals
5; stamens 5, anthers violet. Jul–Aug. Sandy and gravelly
places. B, GB, DK, F, D, NL. **163**

162 Smooth Rupturewort *Herniaria glabra*
Bright green annual or perennial; spreading stems to
15cm, with small elliptic to obovate alternate usually
hairless leaves. Flowers green, in clusters at the base of
the leaves. Petals linear, minute white; sepals c. 5mm,
ovate blunt, nearly hairless; stigmas 2. Jul. Sandy fields.
Throughout area covered, except IRL, IS.

163 Fringed Rupturewort *Hernaria ciliolata*
Like **162**, but stipules white, ovate pointed (ovate,

162

greenish in **162**). Flowers in rounded clusters; fruit blunt (acute in **162**). Dwarf evergreen shrublet, with spreading branches up to 20cm. Leaves ovate, usually fringed with hairs. Sepals fringed with hairs and bristly tipped; petals minute. Jul–Aug. Coastal sands and rocks. GB, F.

164 Hairy Rupturewort *Herniaria hirsuta*
Greyish or whitish prostrate annual covered with spreading hairs. Differing from **162** in having sepals with dense spreading hairs, each with a long terminal bristle. Leaves usually covered with stiff hairs. Flowers in dense clusters, opposite the leaves; stipules ciliate. Jul–Aug. Sandy ground. B, F, D. Int GB, NL.

165 Coral Necklace *Illecebrum verticillatum*
Small spreading hairless annual up to 30cm, with tiny ovate stalked leaves. Stipules small, papery. Flowers white, 1·5mm across, in axillary clusters. Sepals white, thick spongy with a fine awn; petals linear. Jun–Oct. Damp gravelly and sandy places. B, GB, F, D, NL. **163**

166 Four-leaved Allseed *Polycarpon tetraphyllum*
Much-branched spreading or prostrate annual, rarely biennial or perennial, 3–10cm, with ovate leaves, the upper on whorls of 4. Inflorescence lax, spreading and much branched. Flowers 4mm across, with minute white notched petals; sepals mostly less than 2mm. May–Sep. Sandy and rocky places. GB, F, D.

166

167 Corn Spurrey *Spergula arvensis*
Erect hairy or glandular-hairy annual up to 70cm, with linear pointed, fleshy glandular-sticky leaves up to 3cm. Inflorescence much-branched; flowers white, 7–8mm across. Petals little longer than ovate sepals. Seeds rounded, with broad wing. May–Sep. Weed of cornfields on acid soils. Throughout area covered. **163**

168 *Spergula morisonii*
Like **167** but a stiffer erect annual, with linear leaves not furrowed beneath (furrowed beneath in **167**), and seeds flattened, with a very narrow wing. Apr–Jun. Sandy ground. B, DK, SF, F, D, NL, N, S. Int GB, IRL.

SPERGULARIA
TAP-ROOT THICK, WOODY; SEPALS USUALLY 4MM OR MORE

169 Greater Sea Spurrey *Spergularia media*
Perennial with a stout branching rootstock, and many stout spreading or ascending stems up to 40cm. Leaves linear fine-tipped, fleshy, flat above, rounded beneath; stipules broadly triangular. Flowers white or pinkish, up to 12mm across, in a lax cluster; petals ovate, longer than the blunt hairy or hairless sepals. Jun–Sep. Salt-marshes. Throughout area covered, except SF, IS. **237**

170 Rock Sea Spurrey *Spergularia rupicola*
Much branched spreading perennial, with clusters of narrow linear, glandular-hairy leaves and long, triangular, somewhat silvery stipules. Flowers pink, up to 1 cm across; petals lanceolate equalling the glandular-hairy sepals which are c. 4mm. Stamens 10. Seeds without wings. Jun–Sep. Cliffs, rocks and walls by the sea. GB, F, IRL. **237**

SPERGULARIA
TAP-ROOT SLENDER; SEPALS USUALLY LESS THAN 4MM

171

171 Sand Spurrey *Spergularia rubra*
Annual to perennial, with spreading stems 5–25cm. Leaves narrow-linear, not fleshy, hairy, in clusters; stipules lanceolate-pointed, silvery. Flowers numerous in branched clusters; petals pink, 3–4mm, equalling the ovate-lanceolate sepals. Seeds not winged. May–Oct. Acid sandy and gravelly soils. Throughout area covered, except IS.

172 Lesser Sea Spurrey *Spergularia marina*
Much-branched spreading fleshy annual or biennial, up to 20cm or more, with fleshy linear leaves up to 2cm, and broad triangular sheathing stipules. Flowers 6–8mm, few in a sparsely branched cluster; petals pink, paler at base, about as long as sepals which are 2·5–4mm. Jun–Aug. Coastal salt-marshes. Throughout area covered.

173 *Spergularia segetalis*
Annual with slender ascending stems up to 15cm, with awned leaves, and long silvery stipules much divided at apex. Inflorescence very slender; petals white, shorter than the sepals, which are fine-pointed with wide papery margins, 1·5–2mm long. May–Jul. Cornfields. B, F, D, NL.

174 Ragged Robin *Lychnis flos-cuculi*
Erect hairless perennial up to 90cm, with oblong/spoon-shaped basal leaves, and upper leaves linear-lanceolate fused in pairs at the base. Flowers pink, 2·5cm across, with 5 irregularly 4-lobed petals giving a distinctive ragged appearance to the flowers. Inflorescence lax, branched. Calyx tubular, 10-veined, with 5 short teeth. May–Jul. Damp meadows, marshy places. Throughout area covered. **237**

175 Alpine Catchfly *Lychnis alpina*
Dwarf tufted perennial, with lanceolate to linear basal leaves, and stems up to 15cm with 2–3 pairs of wider leaves. Flowers pale pink, rarely white, up to 1cm across, in a dense terminal cluster. Petals deeply bilobed; calyx bell-shaped 4–5mm. Jun–Aug. Bare and stony places in mountains. GB, SF, F, IS, N, S. **256**

176 Sticky Catchfly *Lychnis viscaria*
Tufted perennial with simple or branched sticky stems up to 90cm. Leaves mostly basal, linear to broadly lanceolate. Flowers bright pink, 6–12mm across, numerous and appearing whorled, in a lax spike-like terminal cluster. Petals notched or entire, rarely white; calyx more than 6mm. Very variable species. May–Jul. Rocky places. B, GB, DK, SF, F, D, NL, N, S. **257**

177 Corncockle *Agrostemma githago*
Annual, with erect stems with long greyish hairs, 30–100cm. Leaves linear, in opposite pairs, fused together at base. Flowers purple, rarely white, 4–5cm across. Calyx-lobes linear, much longer than the petals, calyx-tube ovoid, hairy; petals obovate, slightly notched at apex and long-stalked. May–Aug. Cultivated fields. Throughout area covered but decreasing; casual IS. **257**

SILENE
FLOWERS ERECT OR INCLINED; FILAMENTS OF STAMENS HAIRLESS (see also **183**)

178 Italian Catchfly *Silene italica*
Slender, to 8cm, branched above, with ovate/spoon-shaped sticky-hairy leaves, mostly basal. Inflorescence lax; flowers white and reddish or greenish below, to 2cm across. Petals 2-lobed; calyx club-shaped, with acute teeth. May–Aug. Sands, copses, roadsides. F, D. Int GB. **163**

SILENE
FLOWERS NODDING; FILAMENTS OF STAMENS HAIRY

179 White Sticky Catchfly *Silene viscosa*
White flowers 2cm across, in a long terminal spike-like cluster. Petals deeply lobed; calyx hairy, teeth ovate-blunt. Densely glandular-hairy sticky perennial or biennial up to 60cm. Jun–Jul. DK, SF, D, S. **195**

180 Nottingham Catchfly *Silene nutans*
Differs from **178** in its horizontal or drooping white flowers (flowers more or less erect in **178**) and the capsule stalk half as long as the capsule (stalk as long as capsule in **178**). Branched perennial, glandular-sticky above. Petals inrolled, narrow and deeply cleft. Very variable species. May–Jul. Rocks, coastal shingle, walls, dry slopes. B, GB, DK, SF, F, D, NL, N, S. **238**

181 *Silene tatarica*
Almost hairless perennial to 60cm, with lanceolate to narrow spoon-shaped leaves. Flowers white or greenish-white, with linear lobes, inclined, in a narrow

inflorescence. Calyx hairless, with acute teeth. Jul–Aug.
SF, D, N.

182 Northern Catchfly *Silene wahlbergella*
Stem simple erect, bearing a solitary nodding flower with
large globular whitish inflated calyx, and dull reddish
petals. Small narrow-leaved perennial, hairy above.
Jul–Aug. Rocky and stony places in Arctic, SF, N, S.

183 *Silene furcata*
Differs from **182** in having a glandular-hairy stem, often
branched above. Flowers erect, small, with whitish petals
longer than the scarcely inflated calyx. Jul. Rocky and
stony places in Arctic SF, N, S.

184 Spanish Catchfly *Silene otites*
Numerous small, greenish-yellow flowers, in crowded
whorl-like clusters, in a long lax inflorescence. Stem up
to 50cm or more. Leaves narrowly spoon-shaped,
uppermost linear-lanceolate, all with short dense hairs.
Flowers 3–5mm across; petals with linear limb; calyx
ovoid, with blunt teeth, hairless. Jun–Jul. Sandy soils,
heaths. GB, DK, F, D, NL. Int B, SF. **195**

185 Bladder Campion *Silene vulgaris*
Perennial with stems up to 60cm, usually branched and
often blue-green. Leaves ovate to linear. Flowers white,
c. 18mm across, solitary or in branched clusters. Calyx
distinctive, inflated, ovoid to globular, net-veined with 20
conspicuous longitudinal veins. Petals usually white,
deeply lobed and with small scales at base of blade. Very
variable species. Jun–Sep. Grassy banks, fields.
Throughout area covered.
Sea Campion ssp. *maritima* is a spreading plant with
narrow leaves, and with solitary or 2–4 flowers 2–2·5cm
across. Growing on coastal rocks and shingle, and lead
mine spoil inland. **163**

186 Moss Campion *Silene acaulis*
Densely tufted perennial forming green moss-like
cushions. Leaves linear acute, with marginal hairs, in
dense rosettes. Flowers deep pink or whitish, 9–12mm
across, solitary on short stalks. Calyx bell-shaped, often
reddish; petals with notched or shallowly lobed limb.
Capsule up to twice as long as calyx. Jun–Aug. Mountain
rocks and cliffs. GB, SF, F, D, IRL, IS, N, S. **257**

187 Rock Catchfly *Silene rupestris*
Slender hairless erect perennial up to 25cm, with many
whorls of white or pink flowers in spreading branched
clusters. Basal leaves oblanceolate; stem leaves
lanceolate acute. Flowers small, long-stalked; calyx
obconical 10-veined; petals with ovate deeply lobed limb.
Jun–Sep. Rocks in mountains. SF, F, D, N, S. **164**

188 Sweet William Catchfly *Silene armeria*
Usually an unbranched annual 20–40cm, with oval-lanceolate, blue-green, hairless paired leaves fused round stem at base, leaves smaller up stem. Inflorescence branched, often dense flat-topped; flowers usually pink, c. 1·5cm across. Calyx club-shaped, with blunt teeth; petals obovate, notched, with lanceolate scales. Jul–Sep. Woods, rocks, uncultivated places. F, D. Int B, GB, DK, SF, NL, N, S. **257**

189 Night-flowering Catchfly *Silene noctiflora*
Hairy sticky erect annual up to 40cm, with ovate to lanceolate leaves fused at the base, the lower with winged leaf-stalks. Flowers pinkish above and white beneath, 12–17mm across, in short branched clusters. Calyx-tube conical, glandular-hairy, with slender teeth; petals deeply bilobed, with scales. Petals inrolled by day, spreading by night. Styles 3. Jun–Sep. Weed of cornfields. B, GB, F, D, NL. Int DK, IRL, IS, N, S.

189

190 White Campion *Silene alba*
Much branched short-lived perennial 30–100cm, densely and softly hairy. Lower leaves ovate to ovate-lanceolate, the upper narrower, stalkless. Flowers white, 2·5–3cm across, opening in the evening, in a lax branched inflorescence. Calyx of female flowers 20-veined, inflated to 3cm, calyx of male flowers 10-veined, to 2·2cm. Petals deeply lobed; styles 5. May–Oct. Hedgerows, waste places, cultivated ground. Throughout area covered, except IS; int IRL. **164**

191 Red Campion *Silene dioica*
Differs from **190** in having red flowers which open by day, and calyx 10–15mm with broadly triangular teeth. Perennial to 90cm, with leaves broadly ovate. Capsule with recurved teeth. Often forming hybrids with **190**. May–Jun. Woods on well drained soils, hedgerows, cliffs. Throughout area covered. **257**

192 Flax Catchfly *Silene linicola*
Pink-flowered annual. Stems rough, branched above up to 60cm, leaves linear. Flowers in a lax regularly branched inflorescence. Calyx club-shaped in fruit with ascending scales or hairs, teeth triangular-ovate blunt; petal limb 2–4mm, deeply lobed. Jun–Jul. Flax-fields. F, D.

193 Forked Catchfly *Silene dichotoma*
Annual up to 1m, branched above, with 5–10 white, rarely pink, flowers ranged along each branch. Leaves lanceolate. Flowers 1·5cm, with petals deeply lobed; calyx hairy, not glandular; stamens and style long-exserted. May–Aug. Fields, waste places. E. & S. Europe; int F, D.

194 Small-flowered Catchfly *Silene gallica*
Simple or much-branched annual 10–45cm, hairy and sticky above. Lower leaves spoon-shaped, upper narrowly lanceolate, hairy. Flowers white or pink, sometimes with a crimson spot on each petal, 10–12mm across, with entire or shallowly notched petals. Calyx is ovoid in fruit, rough-hairy, with long pointed teeth. Very variable species. May–Oct. Sandy places, cultivated ground. B, GB, DK, F, IRL, NL. **238**

195 Sand Catchfly *Silene conica*
Readily distinguished by its pink flowers, with large globular calyx developing after flowering. Annual up to 50cm, with densely glandular-hairy stem. Leaves linear-lanceolate acute, downy. Flowers 4–5mm across, short-stalked; calyx at first cylindrical, densely glandular-hairy, with long teeth. Filaments of stamens hairy. May–Oct. Sand-dunes, heaths, saline ground, waste places. GB, F, D, NL. Int DK.

195

196 Berry Catchfly *Cucubalus baccifer*
Straggling greyish-white perennial up to 1m, distinguished in fruit by its black globular berry, encircled by the persistent calyx. Leaves ovate pointed. Flowers c. 1·8mm across, drooping with widely bell-shaped calyx tube with 5 longer teeth recurved in fruit. Petals greenish-white, with deeply lobed blade with long basal scale. Jul–Sep. Shady places by coasts, hedges, woods, riversides. B, GB, F, D, NL.

197 Fastigiate Gypsophila *Gypsophila fastigiata*
Variable perennial, with a woody rootstock and stems 5–8cm. Leaves linear, 2–8cm, with ovate teeth. Flowers white, or pale purplish, 10–12mm across, glandular-hairy, many in a dense flat-topped inflorescence. Calyx 2–3mm, with ovate teeth; petals obovate notched, c. 1½ times as long as calyx. Jun–Sep. Dry rocks. SF, D, S. **164**

198 Annual Gypsophila *Gypsophila muralis*
Small nearly hairless annual 4–25cm, with linear acute, blue-green leaves. Flowers pink with darker veins, 4mm across, in a lax widely branched inflorescence. Petals twice as long as calyx which is 3–4mm. Jun–Sep. Damp woods, sandy fields, meadows. B, DK, SF, F, D, NL, S.

199 Soapwort *Saponaria officinalis*
Tall usually hairless perennial 30–90cm. Leaves ovate to ovate-lanceolate, hairless, 3-veined. Flowers pale pink, in dense clusters in a shortly branched inflorescence. Flowers 2·5–3cm across; petals spoon-shaped, entire, spreading; calyx with long cylindrical calyx-tube, and short triangular teeth. Capsule urn-shaped. Jul–Sep. Hedges, woods, waysides, by streams, often near villages. B, F, D. Int GB, DK, SF, IRL, N, S. **238**

200

200 Cowherb *Vaccaria pyramidata*
Hairless blue-green annual up to 60cm, with pink flowers
in a lax regularly branched inflorescence. Leaves oval,
blue-green. Flowers 1–1·5cm across; calyx-tube inflated
with 5 conspicuously winged angles; petals with ovate
entire or lobed limb which is long-stalked. Jun–Jul.
Fields. B, F, D. Int NL.

201 Proliferous Pink *Petrorhagia prolifera*
Erect annual up to 50cm, with paired linear-lanceolate
leaves 6–8mm wide, fused together at their bases.
Flowers pink, or purplish, 6–8mm across, in dense
clusters surrounded by brown papery bracts. Petal limb
heart-shaped. May–Sep. Dry banks and meadows,
roadsides. B, DK, F, D, NL, S. Int GB. **238**

202 Childling Pink *Petrorhagia nanteuilii*
Very like **201**, but middle part of stem often hairy.
Leaf-sheaths twice as long as wide (sheaths as long as
wide in **201**). May–Sep. Dry fields, waysides, coastal
shingle. GB, F.

203 Tunic Flower *Petrorhagia saxifraga*
Slender erect hairless perennial up to 45cm, with linear
leaves c. 1cm long. Flowers pale pink or white, usually
solitary on long leafy stems, in a lax cluster. Petals
notched to 1cm; calyx with oblong blunt teeth. Jun–Aug.
Dry sandy places, gravels, walls. F, D. Int GB, NL.

DIANTHUS
FLOWERS IN DENSE CLUSTERS, SURROUNDED BY INVOLUCRAL BRACTS

204 Deptford Pink *Dianthus armeria*
Stiff hairy green, not greyish, annual or biennial up to
40cm. Stem leaves linear, acute, shortly sheathing at
base. Flowers pink or red, in dense terminal clusters
surrounded by long green leafy bracts. Epicalyx-scales
lanceolate, about ½ as long as calyx; calyx up to 2cm,
narrowed above the middle; limb of petal c. 5mm,
toothed. Jun–Sep. Dry sandy places. B, GB, DK, F, D, NL,
S. **258**

205 Sweet William *Dianthus barbatus*
Nearly hairless perennial up to 60cm, with lanceolate
often short-stalked leaves with prominent mid-vein.
Flowers dark red or purple 2–3·4cm across, with petals
toothed, in a very dense many-flowered head surrounded
by leafy bracts as long as flowers; epicalyx with scales
longer than the calyx-tube. Calyx cylindrical, with narrow
awned teeth. May–Aug. Woods, grasslands; widely
cultivated. F, DK, SF, D, NL, N, S. **258**

206 Carthusian Pink *Dianthus carthusianorum*
Differs from **205** in having the epicalyx scales half as long

as the dark calyx-tube. Flowers pink or red, c. 2cm across, in a dense cluster surrounded by short brown bracts. Calyx 1–2cm, narrowed above the middle; petals toothed, bearded. Very variable species. May–Aug. Dry grassy places, open woods. B, F, D, NL; int GB. **258**

DIANTHUS
FLOWERS SOLITARY OR 2–3 IN A LAX CLUSTER

207 Jersey Pink *Dianthus gallicus*
Loosely tufted perennial up to 5cm with short leaves not more than 1·5cm. Flowers pink, 2–3cm across, fragrant, with petals deeply divided into narrow lobes, solitary or 2–3 on each stem. Epicalyx with 4 short obovate scales; calyx 2–2·5cm long. Jun–Aug. Sand-dunes. F.

208 Cheddar Pink *Dianthus gratianopolitanus*
Hairless, blue-green, densely tufted perennial up to 25cm, with linear-lanceolate rough-margined leaves; stems hairless. Flowers pale pink, fragrant, 2–3cm across, usually solitary. Epicalyx with 2–4 short pointed herbaceous lobes, to $\frac{1}{3}$ as long as the cylindrical calyx. Petals with broadly obovate shortly toothed lobes, unspotted. May–Aug. Limestone rocks. B, GB, F, D.

209 Maiden Pink *Dianthus deltoides*
Loosely tufted perennial, with lower stems downy and with rough hairy flowering stems up to 45cm. Leaves narrowly lanceolate, the upper narrower, acute, all with rough hairy margins. Flowers deep pink, spotted, 1·5–2cm across, with petals irregularly toothed. Epicalyx scales usually 2 long-pointed with papery margin about $\frac{1}{2}$ as long as cylindrical calyx. Jun–Sep. Grassy banks, fields, hill pastures. Throughout area covered, except IRL, IS. **258**

208

210 Clove Pink *Dianthus caryophyllus*
Hairless tufted perennial up to 80cm, with linear-pointed leaves with smooth margins. Flowers rose-pink, fragrant, 3·5–4cm across with petals with toothed margin, solitary or several in a lax cluster. Epicalyx $\frac{1}{4}$ length of calyx, with 4 broadly ovate scales; calyx cylindrical, usually 2·5–3cm. Jun–Aug. Old walls. Widely cultivated and locally naturalized in area covered. Possibly native in Mediterranean region.

211 *Dianthus arenarius*
Tufted perennial with slender, simple or branched stems up to 20cm, with linear leaves. Flowers white, with a green spot and often with a purplish margin, fragrant. Petals with limb 1–1·5cm deeply lobed to beyond the middle; calyx cylindrical, up to 2·5cm. Jun–Sep. Dry grassland. SF, D, S.

212 Superb Pink *Dianthus superbus*
Hairless branching perennial up to 90cm, with linear-lanceolate leaves. Flowers pink or purple, rarely white, fragrant, 3–5cm across. Petals divided almost to the base into many narrow lobes, bearded. Epicalyx ovate long-pointed; calyx narrowed upwards, 1·5–3cm. Jun–Sep. Dry meadows, woody hills. DK, SF, F, D, NL, N, S. **164**

210

211

WATER-LILY FAMILY

Nymphaeaceae

Aquatic herbs. Leaves large, ovate or orbicular. Flowers solitary, terminal; floral parts numerous.

213 White Water-lily *Nymphaea alba*
Aquatic perennial with stout rhizome below water, long-stalked floating leaves and large white floating flowers. Leaves with nearly rounded blade with deep narrow cleft to central leaf-stalk, with parallel or divergent lobes. Flowers 10–20cm across, both sepals and petals white; petals 20–25. Fruit obovoid, spongy to 4cm across, ripening below water. Jun–Sep. Ponds, lakes, slow-flowing rivers. Throughout area covered, except IS. **164**

214 *Nymphaea candida*
Differs from **213** in having strongly concave stigmas with 6–14 rays (stigmas flat with 14–20 rays in **213**) and filaments of innermost stamens lanceolate (thread-like in **213**). A smaller plant with fewer petals, and lobes of floating leaves touching or overlapping. Jun–Aug. SF, F, D, N, S.

215 *Nymphaea tetragona*
Differs from **213** in having 8–17 petals, and rays of stigmas 7–10; receptacle 4-angled. Flowers white, opening in the afternoon, with leathery sepals which persist in fruit. Jun–Aug. SF.

216 Yellow Water-lily *Nuphar lutea*
Aquatic perennial with oval floating leaves, and yellow flowers borne a little above water. Floating leaves up to 40cm with deep cleft, submerged leaves thin, heart-shaped. Flowers 4–6cm across, with 4–6 large outer yellowish sepals and numerous much smaller broadly spoon-shaped petals. Stigma rays 15–20. Jun–Sep. Still and slow-flowing waters. Throughout area covered, except IS. **206**

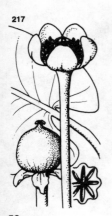

217

217 Least Yellow Water-lily *Nuphar pumila*
Like **216** but flowers smaller 1·5–3·5cm across, and stigma rays 8–10, reaching the margin of the stigmatic-disk (not reaching margin in **216**). Often hybridizes with **216**. Jun–Jul. Stagnant waters. B, GB, DK, SF, F, D, N, S.

Ceratophyllaceae

Aquatic herbs. Leaves in whorls, divided into very narrow segments. Flowers axillary, sessile, male and female at different nodes. Fruit a small nut.

218 Horn-wort *Ceratophyllum demersum*
Submerged aquatic plant with finely divided dark green leaves, and sparsely branched slender stems up to 150cm. Leaves in whorls of 3–8, densely crowded at top of stem and forming a cylindrical cluster. Flowers green, tiny, in axils of leaves; stamens 10–20; petals absent. Fruit 4–5mm, with a terminal spine and two basal spines. Jul–Sep. Still and slow-flowing waters. Throughout area covered, except IS.

219 Spineless Horn-wort *Ceratophyllum submersum*
Paler green plant than **218**, with leaves forked 3–4 times into thread-like lobes (leaves forked 1–2 times into rather stiff linear lobes in **218**). Fruit without basal spines and with or without short terminal spine. Jul–Sep. Ponds and ditches, often near the sea. B, GB, DK, F, D, NL, S.

219

218

BUTTERCUP FAMILY

Ranunculaceae

Annual or perennial herbs. Leaves alternate, often lobed, divided or compound. Flowers solitary, in branched clusters of spikes, variable in form. Perianth segments usually numerous, either forming a green whorl ('sepals' in text), coloured whorl ('petals' in text), or both; a whorl of nectaries may also be present. Stamens and 1- or many-seeded fruits usually numerous.

220 Stinking Hellebore *Helleborus foetidus*
A rather stout perennial, with a drooping cluster of large green bell-shaped flowers with purple margins to the petals, and with dark green, deeply divided leaves. Flowers 1–3cm across. Leaves with 9–11 narrow lanceolate toothed lobes, mostly basal; flowering stem 20–80cm. Carpels 3. Jan–Apr. Woods, scrub, grassy hills. B, GB, F, D. **188**

221 Green Hellebore *Helleborus viridis*
Distinguished from **220** by its few larger, open bowl-shaped, yellow-green flowers 4–5cm across, with spreading petals. Leaves once or twice deeply divided, dying down in winter (persistent in **220**); flowering stem 20–40cm. Feb–Apr. Woods and thickets on limestone. B, GB, F, D. **189**

222 Winter Aconite *Eranthis hyemalis*
Flower golden-yellow solitary, surrounded by a whorl of 3 deeply divided leaves and borne on an otherwise leafless stem 5–20cm. Flower 2–3cm across; petals 5–8. Basal leaves 1–2 with a rounded deeply lobed blade. Carpels 5–8, stalked. Feb–Mar. Damp woods, thickets. F; int B, GB, D, NL. **206**

223 Love-in-a-mist *Nigella damascena*
Flower blue, with conspicuous bluish stamens and long styles, terminal, solitary, and surrounded by a whorl of finely divided leaves. Flowers c. 3cm across, with 5 ovate-lanceolate stalked blue petals. Leaves deeply divided into linear lobes. Carpels fused and inflated, forming ovoid fruit. Jun–Jul. Dry open fields, hills. Native of Mediterranean region; int B, F, NL. **283**

224 *Nigella arvensis*
Differs from **223** in usually having a long-stalked solitary, blue often green-veined flower, without a surrounding whorl of leaves immediately beneath. Carpels fused to the middle only, not conspicuously inflated. Jun–Jul. Weed of cultivation, especially cornfields; decreasing. B, F, D, NL. **283**

BUTTERCUP FAMILY

226

225 Globeflower *Trollius europaeus*
Perennial 30–70cm with large terminal globular lemon-yellow flowers; leaves have deeply divided blades. Flowers up to 5cm across, usually with 10 rounded incurved petals. Leaves with 3–5 wedge-shaped lobes, further lobed and toothed; carpels many, not fused. May–Aug. Damp grassy places; in hills in south. Throughout area covered, except NL, IS. **206**

226 Baneberry *Actaea spicata*
Distinguished by its terminal dense cluster of tiny white flowers borne on a long stem up to 65cm, its large compound leaves with oval, toothed leaflets; and in autumn, by its globular shining black berries. Leaves once or twice divided, lower leaves much larger than upper. Berry 12–13mm. Mar–May. Damp woods. Throughout area covered, except IRL, IS.

227 *Actaea erythrocarpa*
Differs from **226** in its smaller red berries, and its usually more divided leaves. Mar–May. Damp woods. SF, S.

228 Marsh Marigold *Caltha palustris*
Early-flowering perennial of damp places with a conspicuous cluster of glossy yellow flowers and large rounded leaves. Flowers with 5–8 petals, 1·5–5cm across, in a lax leafy branched cluster. Leaves kidney-shaped, toothed, shiny, long-stalked; stems hollow, spreading or ascending 5–30cm. Carpels several, beaked. Mar–May (–Aug in mountains). Damp places, marshes, fens, ditches. Throughout area covered. **206**

229 Common Monk's-hood *Aconitum napellus*
Tall perennial 0·5–1m with a long spike of blue, mauve or rarely white, hooded flowers, and with leaves divided into narrow lobes. Petals 5, the upper hood broader than long, to c. 2cm high. Leaves twice divided into narrow pointed lobes; stem very leafy, simple or branched. Carpels 3. May–Sep. Woods, damp meadows, streamsides. B, GB, F, D, S. **272**

230 Northern Wolfsbane *Aconitum septentrionale*
Perennial up to 2m with a long spike of dark violet or rarely yellowish flowers, each with a tall upright cylindrical hood, with a much broader base. Flowers c. 3cm long, hairy. Leaves dark green, divided into 4–6 segments which are further divided into 3 narrow toothed lobes. Jun–Aug. Bushy places. SF, N, S. **273**

231 Wolfsbane *Aconitum vulparia*
Differs from **230** in having yellowish flowers in a relatively short, few-flowered, terminal spike, and leaf segments more deeply cut to the middle into 3 lobes. Hood of flower not conspicuously broader below. Jun–Aug. Woods, damp meadows. B, F, D, NL. **195**

55

232 Forking Larkspur *Consolida regalis*
Widely branched annual up to 50cm, the flowers with
spreading petals and a long slender
backward-projecting spur up to 2·5cm long. Leaves
divided into many narrow linear segments; bracts
subtending flowers linear, shorter than the flower-stalks;
carpel 1. Jun–Aug. Arable weed, waste places.
Throughout area covered northwards to c. 60°N., except
GB, IRL, IS. **273**

233 Larkspur *Consolida ambigua*
Distinguished usually by its slender inflorescence and by
lobed bracts of the lower flowers. Flowers deep blue;
spur 13–18mm. Fruit hairy. Jun–Jul. Cornfields, waste
places. Mediterranean region; int F, B.

234 Eastern Larkspur *Consolida orientalis*
Like **233** but distinguished by its short spur to 12mm, and
its hairless carpels, which very abruptly narrow at apex.
Apr–May. Cornfields, waste places. S-E. Europe; int GB,
F, D.

235 Wood Anemone *Anemone nemorosa*
Perennial with a solitary white flower borne above a
whorl of 3-stalked palmately-lobed leaves. Flowers
2–4cm with usually 6–7 white, pink or purple petals
flushed on undersides. Basal leaves 1–3, deeply lobed,
long-stalked; flowering stem 6–30cm. Mar–May. Woods,
shady places, mountain meadows. Throughout area
covered except IS. **164**

236 Yellow Wood Anemone *Anemone ranunculoides*
Like **235** but flowers bright yellow, usually 1–2, each
1·5–2cm across. Stem-leaves short-stalked. Mar–May.
Woods, damp places. B, DK, SF, F, D, NL, N, S.

237 Blue Anemone *Anemone apennina*
Like **235** but flowers blue, and petals more numerous
8–14, finely hairy beneath. Fruiting head erect (nodding
in **235**). Mar–Apr. S. Europe; int DK.

238 Snowdrop Windflower *Anemone sylvestris*
Distinguished by its large white solitary flower 4–7cm
across, with usually only 5 rounded petals. Stem leaves
deeply lobed, short-stalked, basal leaves long-stalked;
flowering stem 15–50cm. Carpels woolly-haired, in a
globular head. May–Jun. Dry woods on limestone. F, D, S.
Int B.

239 Hepatica *Hepatica nobilis*
Distinguished by its solitary bluish-violet or purple, rarely
white or pink, flowers borne on leafless stems, and its
long-stalked basal leaves with 3 conspicuous rounded
lobes. Flowers 1·5–2·5cm across; petals usually 6–7;
sepals 3 green, and with 3 green ovate sepal-like bracts

238

beneath; flowering stems 5–15cm. Mar–May. Mountain woods, bushy places. DK, SF, F, D, N, S. **273**

240 Pasque Flower *Pulsatilla vulgaris*

Flowers erect, purple, large solitary, with finely-dissected stalkless leaves below the flower; in fruit the long feathery styles are very conspicuous. Flowers somewhat bell-shaped, 5·5–8·5cm across, with 6 acute petals, hairy outside. Basal leaves at first silver-haired, divided into 7–9 segments which are further divided 2–3 times into narrow stalked lobes, leaves stalked; flowering stem 10–30cm. Mar–Jun. Pastures, grassy hills. B, GB, DK, F, D, NL, S.

240

241 Small Pasque Flower *Pulsatilla pratensis*

Like **240** but with smaller nodding flowers 3–4cm across, with petals recurved above and less than 1½ times as long as the stamens (petals 2–3 times as long as stamens in **240**). Flowers usually dark purple. Apr–May. Grasslands. DK, D, N, S. **273**

242 Spring Anemone *Pulsatilla vernalis*

Flower solitary, at first drooping then erect, with white petals flushed pink, violet or blue outside, and with silvery stem-leaves cut into narrow segments. Basal leaves once divided into 3–5 oval coarsely toothed segments; flowering stem 5–15cm, lengthening in fruit. Apr–Jun. Mountain meadows. DK, SF, F, D, N, S.

243 Eastern Pasque Flower *Pulsatilla patens*

Like **242** but basal leaves cut into broad lanceolate toothed lobes and flowers bluish-violet with wide-spreading petals. Apr–Jun. SF, D, S.

244 Alpine Clematis *Clematis alpina*

A low scrambling woody climber 1–2m, with large solitary showy nodding violet flowers with silky-haired petals 2·5–4cm. Leaves twice divided into narrow ovate coarsely toothed leaflets. Fruit distinctive, with long silky styles. Jun–Aug. Woods, rocky hills, largely on limestone. SF, F, D, N. **273**

245 Erect Clematis *Clematis recta*

Erect herbaceous perennial up to 1·5m, with branched clusters of fragrant white flowers, each c. 2cm across. Leaves large, to 25cm, with 5–7 oval leaflets, each 5–9cm; stem hollow. May–Jun. Woods, bushy places, dry hills. F, D. Int N. **164**

246 Summer Pheasant's Eye *Adonis aestivalis*

Annual with terminal solitary red or rarely yellow flowers, with a dark or black centre and black anthers. Sepals hairless, green, spreading. Leaves 3-times divided into narrow pointed segments; stem often branched above, 10–40cm. Fruit a cylindrical cluster of many achenes

57

each with a transverse ridge and 2 projections on the inner margin. Jun–Jul. Fields on limestone. B, F, D.

247 Large Pheasant's Eye *Adonis flammea*
Like **246** but flowers large, 2–3cm across with usually deep scarlet, narrowly oblong petals, and hairy sepals, adpressed to petals (sepals spreading in **246**). Distinguished by its achenes which have a rounded projection just below the black-tipped beak. May–Jul. Fields on limestone. F, D.

248 Yellow Pheasant's Eye *Adonis vernalis*
Perennial up to 30cm, with stem scaly below, distinguished by its large solitary yellow flower 4–8cm across, with more than 10 petals. Leaves deeply dissected with narrow segments. Sepals half as long as the petals, hairy. Achenes densely hairy, with curved beak. Apr–May. Dry grasslands. F, D, S. **206**

RANUNCULUS
FLOWERS WHITE, PINK OR PURPLE; LAND PLANTS

249 Glacier Crowfoot *Ranunculus glacialis*
Distinguished by its white, often purple- or pink-flushed flowers, and sepals with red-brown hairs. Flowers few, c. 2cm across; petals 5, broad. Leaves slightly fleshy, 3-times divided into elliptic or oblong lobes; flowering stem 4–25cm. Achenes with very short straight beak. Jul–Aug. Mountains, near the snow-line, on acid rocks. SF, F, D, IS, N, S. **165**

250 Large White Buttercup *Ranunculus platanifolius*
A tall, erect perennial 50–130cm, with a terminal branched cluster of long-stalked white flowers, each 1–2cm across, and with hairless reddish or purple sepals. Petals 5, ovate. Leaves 5–7-lobed, the mid-lobe not free to the base. Achenes slightly flattened, with a slender beak. May–Aug. Damp woods. B, F, D, N, S.

RANUNCULUS
AQUATIC PLANTS; LEAVES WITH FLATTENED BLADES ONLY

251 Ivy-leaved Crowfoot *Ranunculus hederaceus*
Annual or biennial, creeping on damp mud, distinguished by its kidney-shaped lobed leaves, and its small axillary white flowers, c. 5–8mm across with spreading widely-spaced petals. Sepals and petals equal in length. Leaves 1–2cm wide, with 3–5 shallow lobes; stems rooting at the nodes, 10–40cm. Apr–Aug. Mud, ditches, shallow still waters. Throughout area covered, except SF, IS. Int N.

251

252 Round-leaved Crowfoot *Ranunculus omiophyllus*
Like **251** but differing in the leaf-lobes which are narrower at their base (lobes broader at base in **251**), and petals twice as long as sepals. Jun–Aug. Muddy neutral or acid streams. GB, F, IRL, NL.

RANUNCULUS
AQUATIC PLANTS; LEAVES DIVIDED, SOMETIMES WITH FLATTENED BLADES

253 Common Water-crowfoot *Ranunculus aquatilis*
Aquatic annual or perennial with much divided submerged leaves with thread-like segments, with or without rounded floating leaves with wedge-shaped, toothed lobes. Flowers white, stalks usually shorter than the opposed leaf-stalk. Nectaries circular. Apr–Jul. Still and running waters. Throughout area covered, except IS.

254 Pond Water-crowfoot *Ranunculus peltatus*
Submerged aquatic plant with usually floating leaves and dissected submerged leaves, but differing from **253** by its longer flower-stalks more than 5cm (usually less than 5cm in **253**), longer than the opposed leaf-stalk. Petals usually more than 1cm; nectaries pear-shaped. May–Aug. Ponds, slow streams. Throughout area covered, except IS. **165**

255 *Ranunculus pseudofluitans*
Similar to **254** but a larger more robust plant with submerged leaves longer than the stem internodes (shorter than internodes in **254**), and usually growing in fast-flowing waters. Flower-stalks very long, to 15cm. Flowing waters. Throughout area covered, except SF, IS, N. **165**

256 Brackish Water-crowfoot *Ranunculus baudotii*
Brackish coastal water annual or perennial, with robust submerged dissected leaves, which do not collapse when removed from the water. Flowers white, with petals touching, variable in size but usually more than 6mm long. Floating leaves deeply 3-lobed, the lobes entire or 3-toothed, sometimes absent. Achenes usually winged, hairless. May–Sep. Brackish ditches and pools. Throughout area covered, except N, IS.

257 Three-lobed Water-crowfoot
Ranunculus tripartitus
Like **256** but with smaller petals less than 6mm long, widely spaced and not touching. Receptacle globular, (ovoid in **256**), achenes hairless. Submerged leaves with very slender segments, collapsing out of water, sometimes absent; floating leaves deeply 3–5-lobed. Apr–Jun. Muddy ditches and shallow ponds. GB, F, D, IRL, NL.

258 *Ranunculus ololeucos*
Differs from **257** in its larger petals usually more than
6mm long and touching. May–Jul. Pools in peat-bogs. B,
F, D, NL.

259 River Water-Crowfoot *Ranunculus fluitans*
Submerged aquatic perennial without floating leaves,
with submerged leaves 8–30cm much longer than the
stem-internodes, which collapse when removed from the
water. Flowers white 2–3cm across. Differs from **256** and
252 in having almost hairless receptacle. May–Aug.
Fast-flowing waters. B, GB, F, D, NL, S. **165**

260 Fan-leaved Water-crowfoot
Ranunculus circinatus
Perennial without floating leaves: submerged leaves
rounded in outline, 0·5–3cm across, with leaf-segments in
one plane only and shorter than the stem internodes, not
collapsing out of water. Flowers white, 8–18mm across,
petals to 10mm. Jun–Aug. Ponds, lakes, ditches, slow
streams. Throughout area covered, except IS, N. **166**

261

261 Thread-leaved Water-crowfoot
Ranunculus trichophyllus
Differs from **260** in having leaf-segments lying in several
planes rarely more than 4cm long. Flowers small, usually
8–10mm across; petals rarely more than 5mm long,
widely spaced not touching; nectaries moon-shaped.
May–Jun. Ponds, ditches, slow streams. Throughout
area covered.

RANUNCULUS
LAND PLANTS; FLOWERS YELLOW; LEAVES ENTIRE OR TOOTHED

262 Lesser Celandine *Ranunculus ficaria*
Perennial 5–30cm with bright yellow flowers, and
distinctive triangular heart-shaped shiny stalked leaves.
Flowers solitary, usually 1·5–3cm across, but sometimes
larger; petals 8–12, spreading, glossy, narrow ovate
sepals 3 green. Roots with swollen tubers. Sometimes
tuber-like bulbils borne in axils of leaves. Feb–May.
Woods, shady banks, meadows. Throughout area
covered, except IS. **207**

263 *Ranunculus cymbalaria*
Slender perennial with ascending and creeping stems,
kidney-shaped toothed leaves, and small bright yellow
flowers on ascending stems to 25cm. Flowers 6–9mm
across; petals and sepals 5. Roots not tuberous. Achenes
longitudinally ribbed, with short slender beak. Jun.
Native of N. America. Int SF, N, S.

264 Lesser Spearwort *Ranunculus flammula*
Erect or creeping rather fleshy perennial, 10–50cm with

265

267

lanceolate to broadly ovate leaves, and one or several yellow flowers 7–20mm across. Sepals 5, greenish-yellow; petals 5 obovate, pale glossy yellow. Uppermost stem leaves stalkless, lower stalked, all entire or toothed. May–Sep. Damp meadows, marshes, bogs. Throughout area covered. **207**

265 Creeping Spearwort *Ranunculus reptans*
Slender creeping perennial like **264**, rooting at the nodes but with smaller solitary flowers 5–10mm across, borne at apex of creeping stems. Leaves all stalked, spoon-shaped to narrowly elliptic; stems very slender, rooting at each node. Jun–Aug. Lake margins. GB, DK, SF, F, D, IS, N, S.

266 Adder's-tongue Spearwort
Ranunculus ophioglossifolius
Like **263** but an erect branched annual with numerous small yellow flowers 5–9mm across and leaves ovate to heart-shaped. Petals obovate, nearly twice as long as sepals. Achenes with minute swellings. Jun–Jul. Marshes. GB, F, S.

267 Greater Spearwort *Ranunculus lingua*
Robust hollow-stemmed perennial 50–120cm, usually growing in shallow water, with few large shining yellow flowers, and long spear-shaped stem-leaves. Flowers 3–5cm across; petals 5 rounded ovate. Basal leaves ovate heart-shaped, long-stalked, the lower stem leaves stalked, the upper stalkless, all toothed. Achenes relatively large, c. 2·5mm, pitted, bordered. Jun–Aug. Marshes, lake, ditches. Throughout area covered, except IS. **207**

RANUNCULUS
LAND PLANTS; LEAVES DISTINCTLY LOBED OR DEEPLY DIVIDED; STEMS
CREEPING BELOW, AND ROOTING AT THE NODES

268 Creeping Buttercup *Ranunculus repens*
Erect perennial, with creeping and rooting runners, and with glossy yellow flowers 2–3cm across. Petals 5; sepals 5, erect. Basal leaves triangular-ovate divided into 3 stalked segments which are further divided into 3 toothed lobes, and upper leaves smaller, less divided. Fruit in a globular head; flattened, bordered, with a curved beak. May–Sep. Wet meadows, woods, damp places. Throughout area covered. **207**

269 *Ranunculus hyperboreus*
A small slender creeping or floating water plant, with yellow flowers c. 5mm across and 3 petals. Flowers solitary, axillary; sepals 3. Leaves 5-lobed, ovate, short-stalked. Jul. SF, IS, N, S.

270 *Ranunculus lapponicus*
Slender creeping perennial, with long-stalked axillary
yellow flowers with 6–8 petals, and 3 deflexed sepals.
Leaves kidney-shaped in outline, 3-lobed, the lobes
obovate wedge-shaped, toothed or shallowly lobed. Jul.
SF, N, S.

RANUNCULUS
LAND PLANTS; STEMS NOT CREEPING OR ROOTING AT THE NODES; ACHENES
DISTINCTLY FLATTENED

271 Meadow Buttercup *Ranunculus acris*
Perennial 30–100cm, usually hairy with terminal
branched clusters of golden-yellow flowers each
1·5–2·5cm across, and with deeply divided leaves. Sepals
spreading; flower-stalks smooth. Leaves with 5–7
stalkless segments which are toothed or further divided.
Achenes with a short hooked beak. Very variable species.
Apr–Oct. Damp grassy places, meadows. Throughout
area covered. **207**

272 Corn Buttercup *Ranunculus arvensis*
Readily distinguished in fruit by its cluster of flattened
achenes covered with long spines, and with a broad
straight beak 3–4mm. Flowers pale yellow, 4–12mm
across in leafy branched cluster; sepals spreading.
Annual 15–60cm; leaves 3-lobed often further divided
into narrow entire toothed lobes. May–Jul. Cultivated
fields, often in damp places. Throughout area covered,
except IS; int SF.

273 Small-flowered Buttercup *Ranunculus parviflorus*
Hairy spreading branched annual to 40cm with tiny pale
yellow flowers 3–6mm across, with deflexed sepals.
Lower leaves rounded in outline, 3–5-lobed, lobes further
cut into broad toothed segments; the upper leaves
unlobed or with entire oblong lobes. Achenes bordered
and with hooked spines; beak short, hooked. Apr–Jun.
Cultivated and open ground, often by the sea. GB, F, IRL.

273

274 Hairy Buttercup *Ranunculus sardous*
Hairy annual with pale yellow flowers 1·2–2·5cm across,
with reflexed sepals and flower-stalks furrowed. Basal
leaves kidney-shaped, toothed, the upper 3–5-lobed,
toothed; stem branched above, 10–45cm. Achenes with a
ring of swellings near the margin, beak short, curved.
Jun–Oct. Damp cultivated ground, waste places.
Throughout area covered, except SF, IRL, IS, N.

275 Bulbous Buttercup *Ranunculus bulbosus*
Hairy perennial 10–50cm with glossy long-stalked yellow
flowers with conspicuous down-turned sepals, and with
large bulb-like swelling at the base of the stem. Flowers
2–3cm across. Leaves 3-lobed, the lobes further lobed

and toothed, the mid-lobe usually stalked. Achenes smooth, beak short, curved. A variable species. Apr–Jun. Dry pastures, grassy slopes, sand-dunes. Throughout area covered, except IS. **207**

276 Woolly Buttercup *Ranunculus lanuginosus*
Very hairy perennial up to 50cm, covered with long brownish or yellowish hairs, and with bright orange-yellow flowers usually 2–3cm across and deeply divided. Leaves deeply divided with 3–5 broad rounded, toothed lobes. Fruiting head globular, with flattened bordered achenes, and strongly curved beaks. Jun–Aug. Montane woods. B, DK, F, D.

277 Mountain Buttercup *Ranunculus montanus*
Small variable perennial rarely more than 15cm, with usually 1–3 yellow flowers, with spreading sepals. Flowers 2–4cm across; sepals finely hairy. Basal leaves 3–5-lobed, the lobes ovate, toothed; stem-leaves linear to elliptic, toothed. Lobes often half-clasping stem. Achenes hairless, with short curved beak. May–Aug. Montane pastures and woods. F, D.

277

278 *Ranunculus polyanthemos*
Flowers golden-yellow, 1·8–2·5cm across, with spreading sepals, in much-branched cluster, on stems 10–130cm. Leaves divided into 5 narrow linear-lanceolate toothed lobes. Distinguished by its globular fruiting cluster with achenes 3–5mm, flat-sided, bordered, and with a short curved beak. May–Jul. Damp woods. B, DK, SF, F, D, NL, N, S.

279 Wood Buttercup *Ranunculus nemorosus*
Distinguished from **278** by its 3-lobed leaves with broadly ovate lobes, and the beak of the achenes sharply curved, 1·5mm (beak 0·5mm in **278**). Petals golden-yellow, 1·5–2cm long (7–14mm long in **278**). May–Jun. Meadows. DK, F, D, NL, S.

RANUNCULUS
LAND PLANTS; STEMS NOT CREEPING OR ROOTING AT THE NODES; ACHENES NOT FLATTENED FROM SIDE TO SIDE

280 Goldilocks Buttercup *Ranunculus auricomus*
Distinguished by rounded kidney-shaped stalked basal leaves with 5 ovate toothed lobes, and stalkless upper leaves with linear entire lobes. Flowers yellow, 1·2–2·2cm across, often with unequal petals, or some or all petals absent; sepals yellowish, spreading. Perennial with many stems 10–40cm. Achenes 3·5–4mm, downy, with hooked beak. Variable species, often divided into many microspecies. Apr–Jun. Woods, hedges. Throughout area covered.

281 Celery-leaved Buttercup *Ranunculus sceleratus*
Rather stout, erect, nearly hairless branched annual up
to 60cm, with numerous small yellow flowers 5–10mm
across, with down-curved sepals. Basal leaves
kidney-shaped, deeply 3-lobed, the lobes further lobed
and with rounded teeth; upper leaves with lanceolate
sparsely toothed lobes; stem hollow. Fruiting head
ovoid, with numerous very small achenes c. 1mm.
May–Sep. Marshes, ditches, shallow ponds. Throughout
area covered, except IS.

282 *Ranunculus pygmaeus*
Tiny unbranched perennial usually not more than 4cm,
with tiny greenish-yellow flowers 5–10cm across, and
sepals shaggy-haired at base. Basal leaves
kidney-shaped, 3-lobed, the lobes wide, blunt, and
usually shallowly lobed; flowering stem about as long as
basal leaves. Achenes c. 1mm; beak short, hooked.
Jul–Aug. Wet places in mountains. SF, NL, IS, N, S.

283 *Ranunculus nivalis*
Perennial, taller and with larger flowers than **282**.
Flowers solitary long-stalked, c. 15mm across with
spreading shaggy-haired sepals; flowering stem 8–15cm
or more, unbranched, much longer than basal leaves.
Basal leaves rounded, kidney-shaped, deeply lobed,
stem-leaves with narrower lobes. Fruit with beak as long
as achene. Jul–Aug. SF, N, S.

283

284 *Ranunculus sulphureus*
Perennial like **283** but a stouter plant with basal leaves
wedge-shaped and shallowly lobed. Receptacle densely
hairy (nearly hairless in **284**); sepals covered with dense
brown hairs. Fruit with beak ½ as long as achene. Jul–Aug.
SF, N, S.

285 Mousetail *Myosurus minimus*
Small hairless annual with a basal rosette of linear leaves,
and leafless stems 5–12cm with a terminal small
greenish-yellow flower. Petals 3–4mm, spurred at base,
nectaries long, tubular. Receptacle lengthening in fruit,
forming a slender spike of tiny achenes. Mar–Jun. Damp
and seasonally flooded fields. Throughout area covered,
except IRL, IS. 195

286 Columbine *Aquilegia vulgaris*
Readily distinguished by its large nodding, usually violet
flowers, with 5 backward-projecting spurs with hooked
tips. Outer petals to 2·5cm, inner petals with spur
1·5–2·2cm long. Leaves twice divided into ovate leaflets
which are further 2–3 lobed; flowering stem 30–60cm.
Carpels large, glandular-hairy. May–Jul. Woods, scrub.
B, GB, F, D, IRL, NL; int DK, SF, N, S. 274

287 Common Meadow-rue *Thalictrum flavum*
Tall perennial up to 1m, with densely crowded terminal clusters of numerous yellowish, fragrant flowers, and compound leaves with rounded, wedge-shaped, lobed leaflets. Flowers tiny, with 4 narrow whitish petals and with much longer yellow stamens. Leaves 2–3-pinnate, the upper leaves stalkless. Jun–Aug. Damp places, marshes. Throughout area covered, except IS. **196**

288 Great Meadow-rue *Thalictrum aquilegifolium*
Tall perennial 50–140cm with hairless stems and a much-branched, flat-topped cluster of numerous tiny whitish or lilac flowers. Petals greenish, soon falling; stamens violet or less commonly whitish, with swollen filaments as broad as the anthers. Leaves 2–3-ternate wedge-shaped toothed leaflets. Achenes 8–12, c. 7mm with 3 winged angles, long-stalked, pendulous. May–Jul. Damp shady places in mountains. SF, F, D, S. **238**

289 Alpine Meadow-rue *Thalictrum alpinum*
Small delicate perennial with single lax spike of tiny purplish flowers, borne on slender leafless stem 5–20cm. Petals c. 3mm; stamens much longer with pale violet filaments and yellow anthers. Leaves basal, long-stalked, twice 3-lobed. Jun–Jul. Dry rocky grasslands, mainly in mountains. GB, SF, F, IRL, IS, N, S.

289

THALICTRUM
STAMENS PENDENT

290 Lesser Meadow-rue *Thalictrum minus*
Variable perennial with numerous tiny yellowish to purple flowers, in lax branched terminal clusters borne on a leafy stem 15–150cm. Flowers with 4 small petals, and numerous much longer drooping stamens. Leaves much divided into oval to wedge-shaped lobed or toothed ultimate leaflets. Fruit cluster erect, with 3–15 stalkless achenes with short beaks. May–Jul. Damp shady places, wood margins, rocky ground, sand-dunes. Throughout area covered, except IS.

291 Small Meadow-rue *Thalictrum simplex*
Distinguished from **290** by its 2–3-pinnate leaves which are distinctly longer than wide (leaves 3–4 times 3-lobed, about as long as wide in **290**). Inflorescence usually narrow oblong, with short branches; flowers yellowish, at first pendent, then erect. Achenes ribbed, with arrow-shaped stigma. Apr–May. Mountain meadows. DK, SF, F, D, N, S.

65

BARBERRY FAMILY

Berberidaceae

Perennial herbs and shrubs. Flowers in clusters; perianth segments in 3–6 differentiated whorls. Stamens 4–6. Fruit a capsule or berry.

292 Barren-wort *Epimedium alpinum*
Perennial with many stems up to 30cm and small dull reddish-purple flowers in a lax branched terminal nodding cluster. Flowers 9–13mm across; inner petals boat-shaped yellow contrasting with the outer brownish petals and lying on top of the latter. Leaves usually twice divided into groups of 3 oval/heart-shaped leaflets with bristly toothed margins. Rootstock creeping. Mar–May. Shady places, damp woods. Native of south-central Europe; int B, GB, F, D.

292

POPPY FAMILY

Papaveraceae

Annual and perennial herbs, often with milky juice (latex). Flowers either large, regular and solitary; or small, asymmetrical, the upper petal spurred or sac-like, in clusters of up to 30. Fruit a capsule or a 1-seeded nut. Many species are weeds of cultivation.

PAPAVER
FRUITING CAPSULE HAIRLESS

293 Opium Poppy *Papaver somniferum*
Robust unpleasant-smelling blue-green annual up to 1 m or more, with large white or purple flowers with dark blotches at the base of the petals, and with lobed leaves. Flowers somewhat globular, with rounded petals 3·5–4·5cm long; stamens with white filaments and yellow anthers. Leaves oblong–ovate deeply lobed, the upper clasping the stem. Capsule ovoid to nearly globular, 5–9cm long, with stigma disk deeply lobed. Jun–Aug. Fields, waste places, waysides. Cultivated and naturalized throughout area covered, except B, DK, SF, IS. **274**

294 Corn Poppy *Papaver rhoeas*
Hairy annual with few large red flowers, sometimes with dark blotches at base of petals, and with 1–2-lobed pinnate leaves with narrow coarsely toothed and lobed leaflets. Petals rounded, 3–4·5cm; filaments of stamens purple, anthers bluish. Stem erect, branched,

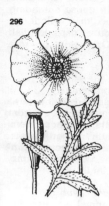

296

bristly-hairy, 25–90cm. Capsule nearly globular or obovoid, 1–2cm long, hairless, usually with 8–12 rays on the disk. A very variable species. May–Aug. Cultivated ground, waste places. Throughout area covered, except IS. **233**

295 Long-headed Poppy *Papaver dubium*
Like **294** but petals usually paler red and shorter, 1·5–3cm, sometimes with a dark spot at the base. Capsule at least twice as long as wide, 1·5–2cm long and rays on disk usually 7–9. Upper part of stem and flower-stalks with appressed hairs. Apr–Jul. Cultivated ground. Throughout area covered, except IS. **233**

296 Yellow-juiced Poppy *Papaver lecoqii*
Differs from **295** in having yellow latex (latex white in **295**) and yellow anthers (anthers violet in **295**). Leaves less glaucous and more deeply divided. Jun–Jul. Cultivated ground, roadsides. B, GB, F, IRL.

PAPAVER
FRUITING CAPSULE BRISTLY–HAIRY

297 Prickly Poppy *Papaver argemone*
Readily distinguished by its oblong–cylindrical ribbed fruit up to 2cm covered with stiff erect bristles. Flowers with red obovate petals sometimes dark-blotched at base, 2–2·5cm; filaments of stamens violet, anthers bluish. Leaves much divided into narrow bristly hairy segments; stems bristly. Annual up to 50cm. May–Jul. Fields, sandy places, waste ground. Throughout area covered, except IS. **238**

298 Rough Poppy *Papaver hybridum*
Like **297** but capsule nearly globular, ribbed and covered with stiff bristles. Petals obovate, usually 1–2cm, with dark blotch at base. A bristly annual 10–50cm. May–Jul. Cultivated and waste ground. B, GB, F, D, NL, N.

299 Arctic Poppy *Papaver radicatum*
Tufted perennial usually with yellow flowers and an ellipsoid capsule with spreading or adpressed bristles. Flowers sometimes whitish or rarely pink; petals mostly 1·5–2cm. Leaves pinnately lobed, with 2–5 pairs of ovate–lanceolate to linear acute segments; old leaf-bases persistent, forming a tunic at base of stem. A very variable species. Jul. Open stony ground. IS, N, S.

300 *Papaver lapponicum*
Like **299** but distinguished by its capsule which is club- or pear-shaped and widest towards the apex (capsule widest in the middle in **299**), and stigma-disk which is more or less pyramidal. Jul. Open stony ground. N.

301 *Papaver laestadianum*
Differs from **299** in having yellowish bristly leaves less finely divided into lanceolate or ovate–lanceolate pointed segments. Flower-stalk with dense spreading bristles curved at base. Capsule 11–12mm, cylindrical, disk flat or slightly concave, as wide as capsule (disk narrower than capsule in **299**). Jul. Open stony ground. Arctic Scandinavia: N, S.

302

302 Welsh Poppy *Meconopsis cambrica*
Tufted perennial with long-stalked solitary yellow flowers, and pinnate leaves glaucous beneath. Flowers from axils of upper leaves; petals 4 obovate, 2–4cm; stamens yellow. Leaves with ovate to lanceolate toothed leaflets. Flowering stems several, 30–60cm. Fruit narrowly cylindrical 4–6 ribbed, hairless, 2–4cm. May–Aug. Damp, shady and rocky places. GB, F, IRL. Int D, NL.

303 Yellow Horned Poppy *Glaucium flavum*
Distinctive silvery-grey glaucous biennial or perennial, 30–100cm with large yellow flowers, and very long seed-pods. Flowers solitary, at the ends of branched stems; petals obovate, 3–4cm; stamens yellow. Leaves pinnately-lobed, the lobes toothed; upper leaves clasping stem. Seed-pods linear, 15–30cm, hairless, often curved. Jun–Aug. Sandy and shingly sea-shores; waste land inland. B, GB, DK, F, D, IRL, NL, N. **196**

304 Red Horned Poppy *Glaucium corniculatum*
Differs from **303** in having smaller orange or reddish flowers often with dark blotch at base. Petals mostly 3cm. Stems 20–40cm. Seed-pod hairy, up to 20cm. May–Jun. Waste places. Native of S. Europe. F; int DK, D. **233**

305 Greater Celandine *Chelidonium majus*
Glaucous leafy perennial up to 90cm with lax terminal umbels of few bright yellow flowers, and with pinnate leaves. Flowers 2–2·5cm across, 2–6 in each umbel; petals 4, obovate; stamens yellow. Leaflets 5–7, ovate to oblong, toothed, the terminal lobe 3-lobed. Capsule linear, 1-celled, 3–5cm. May–Aug. Walls, banks, waste ground, often near houses. Throughout area covered, except IS; int IRL. **208**

CORYDALIS
FLOWER CLUSTERS AXILLARY; STEM LEAVES MANY

306 Climbing Corydalis *Corydalis claviculata*
Slender annual climbing by leaf tendrils, and with stalked clusters of 6–8 two-lipped cream-coloured flowers. Petals 4, 5–6mm long upper petal, with small sac-like spur at base and usually broadened to wings at the apex. Leaves twice divided into elliptic segments, some leaves

with branched tendrils at the apex; stem much branched, 20–100cm. Capsule c. 1cm, hairless. Jun–Sep. Shady rocks, open woods. B, GB, DK, F, D, IRL, NL, N. **166**

307 *Corydalis ochroleuca*
Differs from **306** in having leaves without tendrils, and more numerous flowers, 14–22 in each cluster. Flowers cream-coloured with yellow apex, c. 15mm long. Leaf-stalks winged; a non-climbing perennial, up to 40cm. Capsule erect. Jun–Oct. Rocks, walls. Native of S-E. Europe; int. B, F, D, NL.

308 Yellow Corydalis *Corydalis lutea*
Distinguished from **306** and **307** by larger golden-yellow flowers which are darker at the tips. Flowers 12–20mm long, with spur 2–4mm. Leaves green above, blue-green beneath; leaf-stalk not winged; stem 10–40cm. Capsule drooping. Apr–Sep. Rocks, shady walls; widely cultivated. Native of Alps; nat B, GB, F, D, IRL, NL. **208**

CORYDALIS
FLOWER CLUSTERS TERMINAL; STEM LEAVES FEW; BRACTS BELOW LOWER FLOWERS LOBED

309 *Corydalis solida*
Perennial up to 20cm, with a conspicuous terminal cluster of 10–20 usually pinkish-purple flowers borne on unbranched stem with divided leaves. Flowers sometimes white or yellow, each 1·5–2cm or more long, with a nearly straight spur. Lower bracts subtending flowers lobed. Leaves mostly twice 3-lobed, lobes oblong to obovate. Plant with a rounded tuber below ground. Variable species. Mar–May. Woods, hedges. Throughout area covered, except IRL, IS. Int GB, DK, N. **239**

310 *Corydalis pumila*
Like **309** with bracts below lower flowers lobed, but with smaller purplish flowers 12–17mm in dense clusters of 4–8 and flower-stalks less than 5mm. (Flower-stalks 1–2cm in **309**.) Mar–Apr. Woods, hedges. DK, F, D, N, S.

309

CORYDALIS
FLOWER CLUSTERS TERMINAL; STEM LEAVES FEW; BRACTS BELOW LOWER FLOWERS ENTIRE

311 Bulbous Corydalis *Corydalis bulbosa*
Distinguished from **309** by all bracts subtending flowers entire oval, stem without bracts below the lowest leaf (bract below lowest leaf in **309**), and fruit-stalk much shorter than capsule. Flowers white, cream or pinkish-purple, 18–30mm. Spurs curved at apex. Stem 10–35cm. Mar–May. Woods, hedges, cultivated ground. DK, F, D, NL, S; int B. **239**

312 *Corydalis intermedia*
Perennial up to 20cm, with short terminal cluster of 2–8, purple spurred flowers, subtended by entire bracts. Flowers 1–1·5cm long; spur straight or curved. Stem-leaves 1–2, twice 3-lobed, with an oval scale below lowest leaf. Capsule 1·5–2cm, and short stalk. Mar–Apr. Woods, calcareous soils. DK, SF, F, D, N, S.

FUMARIA
FLOWERS AT LEAST 9MM LONG

313 White Ramping Fumitory *Fumaria capreolata*
White or cream-coloured flowers with red or blackish-red tips; a robust climbing annual up to 1m. Flower-clusters axillary, up to 20-flowered. Flowers 10–12mm long, lower petal with narrow margins; sepals toothed near base. Leaves pinnate with obovate 3–5-lobed stalked leaflets. Fruit globular smooth, on down-curved stalks. Apr–Sep. Hedges, walls, cultivated ground; often near the coast. B, GB, F, D, IRL; int DK, NL, N. **239**

314 Purple Ramping Fumitory *Fumaria purpurea*
Like **313** but petals purple in rather lax up to 24-flowered clusters, upper petal wider and not laterally compressed (laterally compressed in **313**), and wings exceeding keel (not exceeding keel in **313**). Jul–Oct. Cultivated fields, waste places. Endemic to GB, IRL.

315 Western Ramping Fumitory *Fumaria occidentalis*
Like **313** but more robust and flowers 12–14mm long; petals white to pink, with blackish-red tips, lower petals with broad spreading margins. Fruit 3mm, wrinkled when dry (smooth in **313**). May–Oct. Cultivated ground, waste places. Endemic to GB (Cornwall).

316 Tall Ramping Fumitory *Fumaria bastardii*
Distinguished by its pink flowers with the upper petal laterally compressed and the lower with narrow spreading wings, and with lax flowering clusters longer than the flower-stem. Flowers 15–25, corolla 9–12mm long; sepals toothed. Rather robust erect or spreading annual, with leaves 2-pinnately lobed with oblong lobes. Fruit wrinkled when dry on ascending or erect stalks. Apr–Oct. Cultivated ground, waste places. GB, F, IRL.

317 Wall Fumitory *Fumaria muralis*
Erect, spreading or climbing, slender or robust annual, distinguished by its pink flowers with acute or long-pointed sepals. Flower clusters as long or little longer than the flower-stem; flowers 9–12mm, lower petal with narrow erect margin. Fruit-stalks ascending, fruit sometimes somewhat wrinkled when dry. A variable species. Apr–Aug. Cultivated ground, hedges, walls. B, GB, F, D, IRL, NL, N; int DK.

FUMARIA
FLOWERS NOT MORE THAN 9MM LONG; SEPALS 0·5–1MM LONG

318 Few-flowered Fumitory *Fumaria vaillantii*
Slender blue-green annual. Flowers pale pink, 5–6mm
long, in clusters of 6–12, the clusters longer than the
flower-stem. Tips of inner petals and wings often flushed
blackish-red; lower petal spoon-shaped with spreading
margins; sepals 0·7–1mm, deeply toothed. Bracts shorter
than the fruit-stalks. Fruit globular, 2–2·5mm. May–Jul.
Cultivated and waste ground. B, GB, SF, S.

319 Fine-leaved Fumitory *Fumaria parviflora*
Like **318** but flowers white, in nearly stalkless, up to
20-flowered clusters and bracts as long or longer than
the fruit-stalks. Sepals mostly 0·5–1mm, not more than $\frac{1}{3}$
as long as petals. Jun–Jul. Cultivated and waste ground.
B, GB, F, D.

320 *Fumaria schrammii*
Like **318** but more slender and flowers paler pink, with
flower-stalks up to 2·5mm and bracts half as long (bracts
$\frac{3}{4}$ as long as flower-stalks in **318**). Fruit smaller,
1·75–2mm. Jun–Jul. Cultivated ground. F, D.

321 *Fumaria schleicheri*
Like **319** but flower-stalks 4mm, and bracts not more than
$\frac{1}{3}$ as long. Flowers 5–6mm, deep pink, wings of upper
petal and tip of inner petal dark purple. May–Jul.
Cultivated ground. F, D; int DK.

FUMARIA
FLOWERS NOT MORE THAN 9MM LONG; SEPALS 1·5–3·5MM LONG

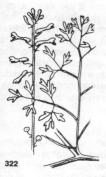

322 Common Fumitory *Fumaria officinalis*
Robust, erect or climbing annual, 20–70cm, branched
above, with clusters of numerous pink flowers on stems
shorter than flower cluster. Leaves much-dissected with
lanceolate or linear-oblong segments. Flowers 7–9mm
long, pink with blackish-red tips to the petals; sepals
ovate, irregularly toothed; bracts linear-lanceolate,
shorter than fruit-stalks. Fruit usually broader than long,
blunt, 2–2·5mm. May–Oct. Cultivated and waste ground.
Throughout area covered except IS. **267**

323 Dense-flowered Fumitory *Fumaria densiflora*
Flowers pink with blackish tips, in 20- to 25-flowered
clusters, without or with very short flower-stalk. Flowers
6–7mm; lower petal with spreading margins; sepals
2·5–3·5mm broader than the corolla, entire or deeply cut
into narrow lobes. Bracts longer than fruiting-stalks.
Leaves with narrow linear channelled lobes. Jun–Oct.
Dry cultivated ground. B, GB, F; int D, N, S.

71

MUSTARD FAMILY

Cruciferae

Annual, biennial or perennial herbs. Leaves alternate. Flowers usually grouped in a raceme. Sepals and petals 4; petals usually white or yellow. Stamens 6; ovary of 2 fused carpels. Fruit a capsule more than 3 times as long as wide (silicula); or less than 3 times as long as wide (siliqua); sometimes breaking into jointed segments (lomentum). Ripe fruit is important for identification. Often weeds and plants of open habitats such as seashores and mountains.

SISYMBRIUM
FLOWERS WHITE; INFLORESCENCE WITH LEAVES AND BRACTS

324 Rocket *Sisymbrium supinum*
Distinguished from other species by its tiny white flowers borne in axils of leaves. Hairy annual to 35cm, with pinnate leaves, the lateral lobes linear to oblong, terminal lobe broader. Petals 3–4mm. Pod 1–3cm, 5–6 times as long as broad, hairy, with mid-vein and branched lateral veins. Jun–Aug. Damp sands. B, F, D, NL, S; int SF, N.

SISYMBRIUM
FLOWERS YELLOW; INFLORESCENCE WITHOUT BRACTS

325 London Rocket *Sisymbrium irio*
Annual up to 60cm with pinnately lobed basal leaves, the terminal lobe larger and stem leaves entire or lobed arrow-shaped. Inflorescence clustered with young pods overtopping the flowers. Flowers 3–4mm across, petals yellow, little longer than sepals. Pods 2·5–6·5cm with slender stalks. May–Aug. Waste places. S. Europe; int throughout area covered, except the extreme north. **208**

326 False London Rocket *Sisymbrium loeselii*
Distinguished from **325** by its long inflorescence, with young pods not overtopping the yellow flowers. Annual up to 1m; leaves pinnately lobed. Flowers bright yellow, petals 4–7mm, about as long as sepals. Pod up to 4–5cm. Jul–Sep. Mostly casual. D: int B, GB, DK, SF, F, NL, N, S.

326

327 *Sisymbrium volgense*
Distinguished from **325** by its lower leaves which are ovate to arrow-shaped with prominent basal lobes. Petals yellow, 6–10mm. Pod 2·5–5cm. Aug. Casual. S-E. Russia. Int B, GB, DK, SF, F, D, NL, N, S.

328 *Sisymbrium strictissimum*
Leafy erect branched perennial up to 1m, with stout rootstock and relatively large, scented, bright yellow

flowers in a terminal branched cluster. Leaves ovate-acute, entire or toothed, uppermost lanceolate, stalkless. Petals 4·5mm–1cm. Pod 3–8cm. Jun–Aug. Damp hedges, roadsides, rocks. F, D; int B, GB, IRL.

329 *Sisymbrium austriacum*
Variable biennial or perennial up to 1m, with pinnately lobed leaves. Flowers golden-yellow; petals 4–7mm, twice as long as sepals. Pod up to 6cm, with club-shaped curved twisted stalks about as long as the pod. May–Aug. Stony ground. F, D; int GB, NL, N, S. **208**

330 Tall Rocket *Sisymbrium altissimum*
Annual up to 1m with lower stem-leaves pinnately lobed, the lobes with wavy margins, upper leaves with linear lobes and stalkless. Flowers pale yellow, c. 11mm across; petals twice as long as sepals. Pods 5–10cm, spreading on rather stout stalks as thick as the pod. Jun–Aug. Waste places. D; int B, GB, DK, SF, F, NL, IS, N, S.

330

331 Eastern Rocket *Sisymbrium orientale*
Distinguished from **330** by its uppermost leaves which are stalked and simple or 3-lobed with the terminal lobe linear or lanceolate. Sepals not horned (horned in **330**); petals 8–10cm (petals 5–8mm in **330**). May–Aug. Dry banks, river-banks, waste ground. S. Europe; int B, GB, DK, SF, F, NL, IS, N, S.

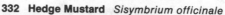
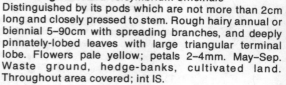

332 Hedge Mustard *Sisymbrium officinale*
Distinguished by its pods which are not more than 2cm long and closely pressed to stem. Rough hairy annual or biennial 5–90cm with spreading branches, and deeply pinnately-lobed leaves with large triangular terminal lobe. Flowers pale yellow; petals 2–4mm. May–Sep. Waste ground, hedge-banks, cultivated land. Throughout area covered; int IS.

333 Flixweed *Descurainia sophia*
Erect annual or biennial up to 1m, branched above, with grey-green leaves 2–3 times divided into narrow lobes. Flowers pale yellow, 3mm across, very numerous in terminal clusters. Petals smaller than sepals which are 2–2·5mm; stamens usually longer than sepals. Pod 1–4cm cylindrical, curved upwards, very short stalked. Jun–Aug. Waste places. Throughout area covered.

332

334 Treacle Mustard *Erysimum cheiranthoides*
Erect branched sparsely or densely hairy annual to 1m, with oblong-lanceolate entire wavy-margined leaves. Flowers deep yellow, c. 6mm across, in erect terminal and lateral leafless spikes. Petals hairy on outer side, longer than hairy lanceolate sepals. Pods 1–5cm, 4-angled. Jun–Sep. Waste places. Throughout area covered. **208**

335 Wallflower *Cheiranthus cheiri*
Perennial up to 90cm with entire narrowly lanceolate
leaves covered with flattened forked hairs. Flowers
yellow, c. 2·5cm across, fragrant. Sepals erect, the inner
with sac-like base. Pod 2·5–7·5cm, compressed.
Apr–Jun. Walls, limestone cliffs. S-E. Europe; int B, GB,
F, D, IRL, NL.

336 Winter-cress *Barbarea vulgaris*
Erect, usually much branched, hairless perennial up to
1m. Lower leaves pinnate with 2–5 pairs of lobes and
much larger terminal lobe; uppermost leaves simple,
toothed. Flowers yellow, with notched petals 7–9mm,
longer than the unequal hairless sepals, in an elongate
branched inflorescence. Pod 1·5–3cm, rounded in
section and with a long style. May–Aug. Damp places,
hedges, streamsides, waysides. Throughout area
covered; int IS. **208**

338

337 Small-flowered Winter-cress *Barbarea stricta*
Differs from **336** in its fruit which has a short style 1·5mm
(style 2–3mm in **336**) and hairy buds (buds hairless in
336). Flower yellow, 5–6mm across. Leaves with 1–3 pairs
of lateral lobes, and much larger elliptic terminal lobe,
larger than the rest of the leaf. May–Jun. River-banks.
GB, DK, SF, D, NL, N, S; int F.

338 Medium-flowered Winter-cress
Barbarea intermedia
Differs from **336** in having uppermost leaves
pinnately-lobed and yellow flowers with petals 5–6mm,
twice as long as sepals. Pods 1–3cm, with short style.
May–Jun. Cultivated fields, waste places. F, D; int B, GB,
DK, IRL, NL.

339 American Winter-cress *Barbarea verna*
Slender branched biennial up to 75cm, with rosette
leaves with 6–10 pairs of lateral lobes and oblong/
heart-shaped terminal lobe, with uppermost leaves
deeply narrowly lobed. Flowers bright yellow, 7–10mm
across, in a dense inflorescence; petals 3 times as long as
sepals. Pods 3–7cm, curved, with short thick style.
Apr–Jul. Waste ground. F; int B, GB, DK, IRL, N. **209**

340 Creeping Yellow-cress *Rorippa sylvestris*
Erect nearly hairless perennial 20–50cm, with spreading
creeping runners at base. Leaves pinnate or
pinnately-lobed, with oval to lanceolate toothed lobes.
Flowers yellow, 7–8mm across, in short lax clusters.
Petals ovate, twice as long as sepals. Pod linear,
5–18mm. Jun–Sep. Waste places, river-banks.
Throughout area covered; int IS.

341 Marsh Yellow-cress *Rorippa islandica*
Annual or biennial up to 60cm, with pinnately-lobed

340

leaves with lobed segments, upper leaves stalkless, nearly entire. Flowers pale yellow with petals 1–2mm shorter or equalling sepals. Pod 4–7mm, oblong, slightly curved. Jul–Oct. Damp places. Throughout area covered.

342 Great Yellow-cress *Rorippa amphibia*
Perennial up to 120cm, usually hairless, and often with stolons. Leaves very variable, entire, toothed or pinnately-lobed, the upper lanceolate, stalkless. Petals yellow, twice as long as the sepals. Pod ovoid, 3–6mm. Jun–Sep. Wet places, margins of streams. Throughout area covered, except IS. **209**

343 Austrian Yellow-cress *Rorippa austriaca*
Erect or spreading perennial up to 90cm, distinguished by its elliptic toothed leaves, the upper leaves with basal clasping lobes. Flowers yellow, 5mm across; petals slightly longer than sepals. Pod globular, with style as long, borne on slender stalks. Jun–Sep. Damp places, fields. C. & E. Europe; int B, GB, DK, F, D, NL, N, S.

344 *Rorippa pyrenaica*
Perennial up to 40cm, with lower leaves in a rosette, ovate entire, or pinnately-lobed with rounded segments, long-stalked. Stem leaves narrow with 2–8 pairs of linear lobes, stalkless with basal clasping lobes. Petals yellow, 2–3mm, little longer than sepals. Pod elliptic. May–Jul. Dry sandy places. F, D; int B. **209**

345 Hare's-ear Mustard *Conringia orientalis*
Hairless annual up to 50cm, with entire ovate stalked lower leaves, upper stalkless and clasping stem. Flowers yellowish or greenish-white in an elongated unbranched cluster; petals 8–13mm, longer than sepals. Pod 6–10cm, 4-angled. May–Jul. Arable fields, waste land, cliffs by sea. D; int B, GB, DK, SF, F, NL, IS, N.

345

346 Annual Wall-rocket *Diplotaxis muralis*
Small annual or perennial, with lax rosette of leaves, and several flowering stems to 50cm with yellow flowers. Leaves conspicuously lobed or toothed, or entire. Flowers bright yellow, 14–17mm across; petals ovate, twice as long as hairy sepals. Pod linear 1·8–4·5cm, with conical beak. Very variable species. Jun–Sep. Sandy and waste places. F, D; nat GB, IRL, NL, S.

347 Perennial Wall-rocket *Diplotaxis tenuifolia*
Distinguished from **345** by its more or less fleshy blue-green leaves, which are strong-smelling when crushed. Perennial to 80cm, with woody base; lower leaves stalked, with long narrow lobes, upper leaves almost entire, lanceolate. Flowers sulphur-yellow; petals 7·5–14mm. Pod linear, 2–6cm, hairless. Jun–Sep. Dry waste ground, walls. B, F, D, NL, S; int GB, IRL, DK, SF, N, S.

MUSTARD
FAMILY

348 *Diplotaxis viminea*
Slender hairless annual up to 30cm, with leaves in basal
rosettes, pinnately-lobed, stalked. Petals sulphur- or
lemon-yellow, 3–4mm; outer stamens sterile. Pod
1–3.5cm. Apr–Sep. Fields, vineyards. F; int D.

349 Rape *Brassica napus*
Stout or slender annual or biennial up to 150cm. Leaves
pinnately lobed with larger terminal lobe, with few bristly
hairs on veins, stalked, upper leaves stalkless, entire.
Flowers yellow, not overtopping the flower buds; petals
10–18mm; pod 5–10cm, with a long slender beak.
May–Aug. Banks, streamsides and ditches. Cultivated
and naturalized throughout area covered. **209**

350 Wild Turnip *Brassica rapa*
Like **348** but basal leaves bright green, with bristly hairs;
upper stem-leaves blue-green. Open flowers
overtopping buds of younger flowers. Petals 6–10mm,
yellow; sepals spreading. May–Aug. Weed of cultivation.
Int GB, DK, SF, D, NL, IS, N, S.

351 Black Mustard *Brassica nigra*
Stout annual with flowering stems up to 1m or more,
branched from the middle or near the base. Lower leaves
with 1–3 pairs of lateral lobes and much larger terminal
lobe, bristly-hairy. Flowers yellow, 8–10mm across, with
petals 7–9mm, in elongated clusters. Pod 1–2cm, with
slender beak. Jun–Sep. Waste places, waysides, cliffs,
stream-banks. Throughout area covered, except IS.

351

352 Wild Cabbage *Brassica oleracea*
Stout biennial or perennial, with thick blue-green leaves,
and much branched stem becoming woody at base,
1–3m, with pale yellow flowers in elongated clusters.
Basal leaves pinnately-lobed with a much larger terminal
lobe, upper leaves entire, stalkless. Flowers 3–4cm
across; sepals pointed, erect, ½ as long as petals. Pod
5–7cm, with conical beak. May–Aug. Sea-cliffs; varieties
of this species are widely cultivated as vegetables
(cabbage, cauliflower, etc.). GB, F; int D, NL.

353 White Mustard *Sinapis alba*
Annual up to 80cm, branched above, usually with stiff
hairs, and leaves lobed with terminal lobe ovate-stalked.
Flowers yellow, 12–15mm across; petals twice as long as
spreading sepals. Pod 2–4cm, with long narrow flattened
beak 1–3cm. Jun–Jul. Field verges, often cultivated.
Throughout area covered; casual in SF, IS. **209**

354 Charlock *Sinapis arvensis*
Differs from **353** in having pod with a cylindrical or
conical beak (not flattened as in **353**). Pod with 8–13
seeds (seeds 4–8 in **353**). Usually a rough-hairy annual to
80cm, with upper leaves stalkless, lanceolate toothed.

354

Flowers golden-yellow, 14–17mm across; petals 3 times as long as sepals. Pod 2·5–4·5cm, usually hairless. May–Sep. Cultivated fields, waste places. Throughout area covered; casual in IS. **209**

355 Hairy Rocket *Erucastrum gallicum*
Densely rough-hairy biennial or perennial up to 80cm, with pinnately-lobed leaves, the lower stalked. Flowers pale yellow or whitish, 1–1·5cm across, in a lax branched cluster; sepals erect. Pod 3–4·5cm, not stalked; beak seedless. May–Sep. Waste places, dry rocks. F, D, NL; int GB, DK, N, S.

356 *Erucastrum nasturtiifolium*
Like **355** but flower clusters without bracts below (with bracts below in **355**). Sepals spreading; pods stalked, 2·3–4·5cm, with conical beak with 1 or 2 seeds. May–Sep. Waysides, banks, waste places, moraines. F, D; int GB.

357 Wallflower Cabbage *Rhynchosinapis cheiranthos*
Rather slender annual to short-lived perennial, with stems up to 90cm, rough-hairy below. Leaves deeply pinnately-lobed, the lobes further lobed or toothed, sparsely hairy or with dense bristly hairs, uppermost leaves lanceolate. Flowers bright yellow with darker veins, 1·8cm across. Sepals 5–10mm. Pod 3–8cm, hairless, with slender beak up to 2cm with 1–3 seeds. A very variable species. Jun–Aug. Cultivated ground, rocks, waste places, gravel. B, F, D; int GB, NL. **210**

358 Isle of Man Cabbage *Rhynchosinapis monensis*
Biennial with usually hairless stems to 30cm. Leaves mostly basal, deeply pinnately lobed, hairless, blue-green. Flowers pale yellow with darker veins, c. 1·8cm across; petals twice as long as sepals. Pod 4–9cm, stalked, with long beak with up to 5 seeds in beak. Jun–Aug. Endemic to GB (west coast).

359 Lundy Cabbage *Rhynchosinapis wrightii*
Distinguished from **357** by being perennial with stout stems with deflexed hairs, and pod 3–4mm wide (pod 2mm wide in **357**). Sepals shorter than flower-stalks. Ovary hairy (hairless in **357**). Jun–Aug. Cliffs. Endemic to GB (Lundy Island, N. Devon).

360 Hoary Mustard *Hirschfeldia incana*
Rather stout annual or perennial up to 1m, usually branched and densely white-hairy below. Leaves in a rosette, pinnately-lobed, rough-hairy; upper stem leaves lanceolate. Flowers pale yellow, c. 5mm across, in elongated clusters. Pods 8–17mm with thick swollen beak, pressed against stem. Jun–Aug. Waste places, cultivated ground. F; int B, GB, DK, D, IRL, NL.

361 *Braya linearis*
Loose tufted perennial, with flowering-stems up to 20cm.
Leaves linear, the lower in a basal rosette, stem leaves 1
or several. Petals purplish. Pod linear, 8–15mm, more
than 7 times as long as wide. Jun–Jul. Calcareous screes,
gravelly places in mountains. N, S.

362 *Braya purpurascens*
Differs from **361** in having no or 1 stem leaf and pod
elliptic or oblong-ovate 4–10mm. Petals purplish,
3–4mm. Jul. Arctic Europe. IS, N.

363 Dame's Violet *Hesperis matronalis*
Stout erect somewhat branched biennial or perennial,
40–120cm. Leaves ovate-lanceolate acute, toothed, the
upper smaller. Flowers lilac or white, very fragrant,
2–2·5cm across. Petals notched; sepals with hairy ribs.
Pod to 10cm, curved upwards. May–Aug. Damp places,
meadows, hedgerows, grassy verges. Introduced
throughout area covered. **166**

361

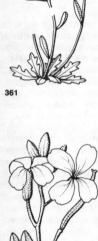

364 Hoary Stock *Matthiola incana*
Grey hairy annual or perennial up to 80cm, with leafless
stems, with purple, pink or white flowers 2·5–5cm across
in a lax cluster. Leaves linear-lanceolate, entire, densely
downy. Petals 2–3cm long; sepals hairy with papery
margins. Pod 4–16cm, flattened, hairy. Apr–Jul.
Sea-cliffs. GB, F; often casual elsewhere.

365 Sea Stock *Matthiola sinuata*
Differs from **364** in having lower leaves pinnately-lobed
with wavy margins. Pods glandular (not glandular in **364**).
Densely white-woolly, usually biennial, to 60cm, with
pale purple flowers to 2–5cm across. Sand-dunes,
sea-cliffs. GB, F, IRL.

366 *Cardaminopsis arenosa*
Annual to perennial with robust usually branched hairy
stems 5–80cm. Basal leaves pinnately-lobed, stem leaves
lanceolate, shallow-lobed or toothed. Flowers white
becoming pale pink to purplish or lilac, 8–10mm across.
Pod 1–4·5cm, strongly flattened. Apr–Jul. Sands, walls,
rocks. B, DK, SF, F, D, NL, N, S.

364

367 Northern Rock-cress *Cardaminopsis petraea*
Differs from **366** in having basal leaves almost entire,
toothed or shallowly lobed, and stem leaves entire.
Perennial with stolons, and stems up to 30cm. Flowers
purplish or white, few, c. 6mm across. Jun–Aug.
Calcareous mountain rocks, sometimes at sea level. GB,
D, IRL, N, S.

368 Sea Rocket *Cakile maritima*
Stout branched annual 20–60cm, with fleshy blue-green
hairless leaves which are linear or with a few short lobes.

Flowers violet, pink or white, in elongated clusters. Petals 4–14mm; sepals half as long. Pod 1–2·5cm, with unequal 1-seeded joints, the upper longer and mitre-shaped. Jun–Sep. Coastal sands and shingle. GB, DK, SF, F, D, IRL, NL, N, S. **239**

369 *Cakile edentula*
Very like **368**, but upper segment of pod contracted towards base and without a papery margin, lower segment without projections (upper segment with membraneous margined base, lower segment with 2 projections at apex in **368**). Jul–Sep. Coastal sands. IS, N.

370 Garlic Mustard *Alliaria petiolata*
Erect biennial 20–120cm, smelling strongly of garlic when crushed, with ovate-triangular deeply toothed leaves with shallow heart-shaped base, stalked. Flowers white, in dense terminal cluster, on main stem and lateral branches. Flowers 6mm across; petals twice as long as sepals; stamens 6. Pod linear 2–7cm, somewhat 4-angled. Apr–Jun. Hedgerows, open woods. Throughout area covered, except IS. **166**

371 Thale Cress *Arabidopsis thaliana*
Slender annual 5–40cm, sparsely hairy below, with basal rosette of elliptic toothed, hairy leaves; stem-leaves few, lanceolate stalkless. Flowers white c. 3mm across, in a lax inflorescence. Petals 2–4mm, about twice as long as sepals. Pod slender, somewhat curved, laterally compressed, 5–20mm, narrowed to the style. Mar–Jun. Open ground, banks, walls. Throughout area covered, except IS.

372 *Arabidopsis suecica*
Like **371** but with basal leaves toothed to pinnately-lobed, and lower stem-leaves usually toothed. Petals white, 4–8mm. Pod 2–3mm, not strongly compressed. Jun. Gravelly places. SF, N, S.

373

ARABIS
FLOWERS WHITE

373 Hairy Rock-cress *Arabis hirsuta*
Stiffly erect, bristly-hairy perennial up to 60cm or more, with often several hairy flowering stems. Basal leaves lanceolate, narrowed to a short stalk, toothed stem leaves erect, more or less heart-shaped and clasping stem at base. Flowers white, in a dense spike-like cluster; petals 4–5·5mm, twice as long as sepals which are often violet with a white margin. Pod 1·5–3·5cm, straight, hairless. A variable species. May–Aug. Dry grasslands, rocks, walls, sand-dunes; calcareous soils. Throughout area covered, except IS.

376

374 *Arabis pauciflora*
Differs from **373** in having blue-green, hairless, ovate entire basal leaves with long stalks, and stem leaves fiddle-shaped, the uppermost lanceolate, clasping at base; stem up to 1m. Flowers white or pink; petals 4–7mm. Pod 3–8cm, with spreading stalks. May–Jul. Rocky meadows, open woods. B, F, D.

375 *Arabis recta*
Annual to 30cm, lower leaves ovate to obovate, stalked, withered at flowering; stem leaves ovate to oblong, clasping stem at base. Petals 2–3·5mm. Pod 1–3·5cm, spreading in lax cluster. Apr–May. Rocks in mountains, calcareous hills. F, D; int B.

376 Bristol Rock-cress *Arabis stricta*
Rough hairy perennial 5–25cm, with several flowering stems bearing 3–9 creamy flowers. Basal leaves lanceolate deeply toothed, leathery, glossy-green in a compact rosette; stem leaves few, oblong with heart-shaped clasping base, all leaves bristly hairy. Petals 5–8mm. Pod 3·5–5cm, erect. Mar–Jul. Screes, stony places, rocks. GB, F.

377 Alpine Rock-cress *Arabis alpina*
Loosely tufted perennial with rosettes of oblong to obovate toothed leaves, sparsely covered with branched hairs; upper leaves clasping, erect. Flowering stem up to 40cm, with white flowers 1–1·2cm across. Sepals hairless. Pod 2–3·5cm, spreading. Apr–Jul. Rocky places in mountains. GB, SF, F, D, IS, N, S. **166**

378 Grey Rock-cress *Arabis caucasica*
Spreading perennial with many rosettes of softly hairy leaves. Basal leaves greyish-green to whitish, with blunt teeth; stem leaves clasping at base. Petals white, notched, 9–18mm, with a spreading limb and long stalk; sepals shorter. Pod 4–7cm, somewhat constricted between seeds. Mar–May. Dry rocks, walls. Widely cultivated and naturalized in B, GB, F, D, NL.

ARABIS
FLOWERS YELLOW

379 Tower Cress *Arabis turrita*
Hairy biennial or perennial up to 80cm, with pale yellow flowers. Basal leaves long-stalked, obovate and regularly toothed; stem leaves stalkless, fiddle-shaped with clasping base, to oblong above. Petals 6–8mm. Fruits in a long one-sided cluster; pods 10–14cm, curved when ripe. Apr–Jul. Rocks, walls. B, F, D; int GB. **196**

380 Tower Mustard *Arabis glabra*
Tall erect, unbranched, almost hairless biennial

MUSTARD FAMILY

30–120cm. Basal leaves in a rosette, lanceolate, toothed, with star-shaped hairs; stem leaves arrow-shaped, clasping stem, grey-green. Flowers yellow, 5–6mm across, in erect spike-like cluster. Pod 4–6cm, erect. May–Jul. Dry banks, roadsides, open woods. Throughout area covered, except B, IRL, IS.

381 Water-cress *Nasturtium officinale*
Creeping or floating perennial of ponds and wet places, rooting at the nodes, and with ascending stems up to 60cm with pinnate leaves. Leaves with rounded or broadly elliptic leaflets, the upper leaves with 5–9 or more leaflets. Flowers white, 4–5mm across; petals nearly twice as long as sepals. Pod 13–18mm, ascending, straight or curved. May–Oct. Shallow streams, springs, ditches with running water. Throughout area covered, except SF, IS. **167**

380

382 One-rowed Water-cress
Nasturtium microphyllum
Differs from **381** in having longer pods 16–22mm, with one row of seeds on each side (seeds in 2 rows on each side in **381**). Flowers white and slightly larger. Jun–Oct. Shallow streams, springs, running water. Throughout area covered, except SF, IS, N.

383 Cuckoo Flower *Cardamine pratensis*
Erect hairless perennial 15–60cm; pinnate basal leaves in a rosette, each with 1–7 pairs of broadly elliptic rounded leaflets and a larger terminal leaflet. Upper stem leaves with more numerous and narrower leaflets. Flowers white, tinged pink or purple, 12–18mm across; petals veined, up to 3 times as long as erect sepals; anthers yellow. Pod linear, 2·5–4cm. Apr–Jun. Damp grassy places. Throughout area covered, except SF, IS. **239**

382

384 *Cardamine nymanii*
Like **383** but a tufted perennial with thick leaves with impressed veins, and often with adventitious shoots. Petals pale lilac, 9–12mm. SF, IS, N, S.

385 *Cardamine palustris*
Like **383** but leaflets of stem leaves all distinctly stalked (leaflets of upper leaves stalkless in **383**). A smaller plant than **383**, often branched below. Sepals 4–5mm; petals 12–18mm. Throughout area covered, except IS.

386 Large Bitter-cress *Cardamine amara*
Differs from **383** in having more than 5 stem leaves, and anthers blackish-violet or yellowish-white (anthers yellow in **383**). Hairless perennial up to 60cm, with angled stems. Basal leaves not in a rosette, pinnate with 2–4 pairs of ovate to rounded leaflets, stem leaves with narrower leaflets. Flowers c. 1cm across; petals white,

81

rarely purplish. Pod 2–4cm. Apr–Jun. Wet meadows, streamsides. Throughout area covered, except IS. **167**

387 Narrow-leaved Bitter-cress *Cardamine impatiens*
Hairless annual or biennial up to 60cm, with stalked lower leaves with 3–5 pairs of ovate 2–5-lobed leaflets. Upper stem leaves stalkless, with 5–9 pairs of lanceolate toothed leaflets, and a larger terminal leaflet, and clasping stem at base. Flowers c. 6mm across; petals whitish, about as long as sepals; anthers greenish-yellow. Pod 1·8–3cm. May–Aug. Damp shady places. Throughout area covered, except IRL, IS.

388 *Cardamine parviflora*
Hairless annual up to 30cm. Leaves pinnate with 11–17 oblong to linear entire leaflets, and leaf-stalks without basal lobes. Petals white obovate, 2·5mm or less, longer than sepals. Pod 12–20mm, erect. May–Sep. Flooded areas, coasts. B, SF, F, D, S.

387

389 Hairy Bitter-cress *Cardamine hirsuta*
Annual with erect simple hairless stem or stem branched from base, 5–30cm. Basal leaves in rosette, stalked, pinnate with 1–5 pairs of rounded or obovate leaflets and a larger kidney-shaped terminal leaflet; stem leaves few, smaller. Inflorescence branched, at first flat-topped; flowers c. 3mm across with white petals or petals absent, not longer than sepals. Stamens 4. Pod 1·8–2·5cm, erect. Apr–Aug. Disturbed and cultivated ground, rocks, screes, walls. Throughout area covered. **239**

390 Wavy Bitter-cress *Cardamine flexuosa*
Differs from **389** in being usually biennial or perennial with curved hairy stems, branched above, and few basal leaves, not in a distinct rosette. Stem to 50cm; leaves pinnate, with 3–6 pairs of ovate to kidney-shaped leaflets. Petals white, not longer than sepals. Stamens usually 6. Apr–Sep. Shady places, woods, river-banks. Throughout area covered, except IS.

390

391 Coralroot *Cardamine bulbifera*
Distinguished by large pale purple or lilac flowers, and brownish-purple bulbils in axils of upper leaves. Hairless perennial up to 70cm; lower leaves pinnate with 1–3 pairs of lanceolate toothed leaflets, uppermost leaves entire. Petals 1·2–1·6cm. Pods 2–3·5cm. Apr–Jun. Woods. Throughout area covered, except IRL, IS. **240**

392 *Cardamine bellidifolia*
Tiny hairless perennial up to 8cm, with thick, usually entire leaves, all spoon-shaped and long stalked. Flowers 2–5; petals white 3·5–5mm. Pod 1–2·5cm, erect purplish-brown. Jul–Aug. SF, F, D, IS, N, S.

MUSTARD FAMILY

393

398

393 Wild Radish *Raphanus raphanistrum*
Branched, bristly-hairy annual 15–150cm. Basal and lower leaves pinnately-lobed with terminal lobe triangular, upper leaves usually entire. Flowers white with purple veins, or pale yellow or purple; petals about twice as long as elliptic-lanceolate blunt sepals. Pod 3–9cm, with beak 1–3cm, jointed. May–Sep. Cultivated land, waste places, sandy and rocky shores. Throughout area covered.
Sea Radish ssp. *maritimus* differs in being perennial, with bristly-hairy leaves in a rosette and lobes of leaves overlapping. Petals usually yellow, to 2·5cm. Pod 1·5–4·5cm, beak 8–20mm. Sea-shores.

394 Mitre Cress *Myagrum perfoliatum*
Blue-green annual 15–100cm with oblanceolate stalked basal toothed or lobed leaves and stalkless, toothed or entire, stem-leaves clasping at base. Flowers yellow; petals 3–5mm. Fruiting clusters long; pods club-shaped as long as broad, with thick stalk, 1-seeded. May–Jul. Damp places, calcareous fields. F; int B, SF, D, NL, N, S.

395 Woad *Isatis tinctoria*
Hairless biennial or perennial, branched above, 30–120cm. Lower leaves obovate to lanceolate, upper arrow-shaped with clasping base, blue-green. Flowers yellow, up to 4mm, many in dense spreading cluster; petals twice as long as ovoid sepals. Pod pendulous, 10–30mm, with a broad thick wing. Jun–Aug. Dry places, rocks. Naturalized throughout area covered (formerly widely cultivated), except IRL, IS. **210**

396 Warty Cabbage *Bunias orientalis*
Hairless or sparsely glandular perennial 25–120cm. Leaves lanceolate, pinnately lobed. Flowers yellow, in branched clusters; sepals lanceolate, spreading or bristly-haired; petals 4–8mm. Pod ovoid, covered with irregular swellings. May–Sep. Waste places. Native of E. Europe; int B, GB, DK, SF, F, D, NL, N, S.

397 *Bunias erucago*
Like **396** but pods with 4 longitudinal wings. Petals larger, 8–13mm. Glandular-hairy annual or biennial up to 60cm, with upper leaves entire or toothed. May–Jul. Damp places, cultivated fields. F; int GB, D. **210**

398 Small Alison *Alyssum alyssoides*
Erect or ascending grey hairy annual or biennial 5–30cm, with star-shaped hairs. Lower leaves obovate to oblanceolate, upper narrower. Flowers yellow, 3mm across, in clusters, elongating in fruit. Petals lanceolate notched; sepals lanceolate, nearly as long. Pod rounded, with flattened margin, hairy. Apr–Jun. Sandy open ground, cornfields. Throughout area covered, except IRL, IS.

399 Mountain Alison *Alyssum montanum*
Spreading or erect green to rather whitish perennial
5–25cm, with non-flowering rosettes of leaves on short
stems. Basal leaves oblong, upper linear, all with
star-shaped hairs. Flowers bright yellow in simple
elongate cluster; petals notched 3·5–4mm. Pod globular,
without persistent sepals. Apr–Jun. Sands, rocks. F, D.

400 Gold of Pleasure *Camelina sativa*
Slender branched erect annual up to 80cm, with narrow
arrow-shaped usually hairless leaves, the upper clasping
stem. Flowers yellow; petals c. 5mm. Fruiting clusters
elongate, rather dense; pod pear-shaped 7–9mm, with
conspicuous style. May–Jul. Waste places, arable fields.
Throughout area covered, except IS; casual in GB. **196**

401 *Camelina microcarpa*
Like **400** but stems and leaves densely hairy. Flowers pale
yellow. Pod smaller 5–7mm, with usually hard woody
valves. May–Jul. Arable fields, sandy and gravelly places.
Throughout area covered, except GB, IRL.

402 *Camelina alyssum*
Differs from **400** in having a flattened globular pod,
almost as long as wide, and leaves strongly toothed or
lobed. Slender hairless annual 15–50cm. Flowers pale
yellow; petals 4–5mm. May–Jul. Flax-fields. Throughout
area covered, except GB, IRL, IS.

403 *Camelina macrocarpa*
Like **400** but pods larger, usually 10–15mm, obovoid or
pear-shaped. Tall erect hairless annual up to 60cm or
more, with entire or obscurely toothed leaves. Petals pale
yellow, 4–5mm. Pods with long often spreading stalks.
May–Jul. Flax-fields. DK, SF.

404

404 Ball Mustard *Neslia paniculata*
Downy annual up to 60cm, with oblong to lanceolate,
sometimes toothed leaves, the lower stalked, the upper
clasping stem. Flowers yellow, 3–4mm across, in
branched clusters, elongating in fruit. Pod rounded,
often somewhat flattened, wrinkled, with distinct style.
Jun–Sep. Waste places. F, D; int B, GB, DK, SF, NL, N, S.

406

405 Steppe Cabbage *Rapistrum perenne*
Densely rough-hairy biennial or perennial up to 80cm,
branched above. Leaves pinnately-lobed or toothed.
Petals bright yellow, 5–7mm. Pod to 1cm, upper segment
ovoid, strongly ribbed, gradually narrowed into a beak;
lower segment narrower, cylindrical. Jun–Aug.
Cultivated land, waste ground. D; int B, GB, F, NL.

406 Bastard Cabbage *Rapistrum rugosum*
Like **405** but annual, and upper segment of fruit abruptly
contracted into a beak up to 3mm (beak up to 1mm in

405). Flowers pale yellow; petals 6–10mm. May–Sep. Waste ground. F; int B, GB, IRL, D, NL.

407 Buckler Mustard *Biscutella laevigata*
Simple or branched perennial up to 50cm or more. Basal leaves may be in a rosette; linear to ovate, entire or toothed; stem leaves smaller, entire. Flowers yellow, 5–10mm across, in a lax or dense cluster. Pod distinctive, much wider than long with two rounded flattened lobes which eventually break off. May–Jul. Limestone rocks, waste places. B, F, D.

408 Perennial Honesty *Lunaria rediviva*
Perennial to 140cm, with hairy stems. Leaves ovate pointed, sharply toothed, stalked. Flowers pale purple or violet, in branched clusters; petals 1·2–2cm, spreading; sepals with sac-like base. Pod flat, elliptic pointed, 3·5–9cm. May–Jul. Damp woods. B, DK, F, D, S; int GB. **240**

409 Honesty *Lunaria annua*
Biennial up to 1m with leaves broadly heart-shaped, coarsely toothed, the upper stalkless. Flowers reddish-purple, rarely white, 1·5–2·5cm. Pod 2–7cm, oblong–elliptic flattened to nearly rounded, with rounded base and apex, style 4–8mm (style 1–5mm in **408**). Apr–Jun. Cultivated; often escaped from gardens. Native of S-E. Europe; int B, GB, F, D, NL, N, S. **258**

410 Hoary Alison *Berteroa incana*
Annual or perennial 20–70cm; lanceolate to oblong entire leaves with grey star-shaped hairs. Flowers white, 5–8mm across; petals deeply lobed, more than twice as long as hairy sepals. Pod oval inflated, 4·5–8mm, style long. Jun–Sep. Waste places. DK, D; int B, GB, SF, F, NL, N, S. **167**

411 Horse-radish *Armoracia rusticana*
Robust much branched leafy perennial 50–125cm, with massive fleshy pungently aromatic roots. Basal leaves large ovate, toothed, long-stalked, upper stem-leaves narrow lanceolate, toothed or entire. Flowers white, 8–9mm across, in a much-branched spreading flat-topped cluster. Petals twice as long as sepals. Pod spherical or obovoid, inflated, 4–6mm. May–Jun. Waste places; often cultivated. Int throughout area covered, except IS. **167**

412 Sweet Alison *Lobularia maritima*
Short densely hairy greyish annual or perennial to 40cm, branched below. Leaves linear-lanceolate, usually acute. Flowers white c. 6mm across, fragrant, in terminal clusters. Petals rounded, spreading, longer than sepals. Pod obovate to 3·5mm, borne on spreading stalks, finely hairy. Jun–Sep. Coastal sands, waste places. F; int B, GB, DK, NL, N. **167**

413 Wall Whitlow-grass *Draba muralis*
Short hairy simple or branched annual up to 30cm, with broadly ovate toothed basal leaves in a rosette, the upper clasping stem at base. Flowers white, 2–3mm across, many in branched clusters. Pod elliptic-oblong, hairless, with spreading stalks. Apr–Jun. Rocks, walls. Throughout area covered, except IS; casual in NL.

414 *Draba nemorosa*
Differs from **413** in usually having hairy pods, and leaves which are wedge-shaped at base, not clasping stem. Petals pale yellow, fading to whitish. Pod rough with hairs, borne on slender spreading stalks longer than the pod. May–Jun. Dry pastures, wood margins. SF, F, D, N, S.

415 Hoary Whitlow-grass *Draba incana*
Distinguished by its narrow elliptic pod which is often twisted when ripe. Stout or slender biennial or perennial up to 35cm, with simple or branched leafy flowering stems with basal leaves lanceolate, hairy. Flowers white, 3–5mm across. A very variable species. May–Jul. Rocks, sand-dunes, mountains. GB, DK, SF, F, IRL, IS, N.

416

416 Rock Whitlow-grass *Draba norvegica*
Loosely tufted variable perennial, with rosettes of lanceolate hairy leaves, and short often leafless flowering-stem up to 20cm. Flowers white, 3–5mm across, in a dense inflorescence becoming lax in fruit. Petals notched, nearly twice as long as sepals. Pod ovate 5–7mm, usually hairless. Jul–Aug. Alpine rocks. GB, SF, IS, N, S.

417 *Draba nivalis*
Dense cushion-like perennial, with flowering stems up to 5cm. Basal leaves wedge-shaped, entire, with dense covering of star-shaped hairs; stem leaves absent. Inflorescence dense; petals c. 3mm. Pod usually hairless. Jun–Jul. SF, IS, N, S.

418 *Draba daurica*
Differs from **416** in having leafy flowering stems, and pods 6–12mm (flowering-stem usually leafless and pods 5–7mm in **416**). Stems to 25cm. Petals creamy, c. 5mm; filaments of stamens with enlarged base. SF, IS, N, S.

419 *Draba fladnizensis*
Differs from **418** in having white petals 2·5–4mm, and flowering stem rarely more than 8cm, entirely hairless. Stem leaves oblong–obovate, fringed with hairs, otherwise hairless or sparsely hairy. Pod elliptic, hairless. Jun–Jul. SF, F, D, IS, N, S.

DRABA
FLOWERS YELLOW (see also **414**)

420 Yellow Whitlow-grass *Draba aizoides*
Tufted often cushion-shaped perennial, with hairless
flowering-stems 5–10cm. Leaves stiff, in compact
rosettes, linear with hairy margins, otherwise hairless.
Flowers yellow, 8–9mm across; petals obovate, longer
than the sepals. Pod ellipsoid, flat, usually hairless, with
persistent style, 1·5–3mm or more. Mar–May. Limestone
rocks, usually in mountains. B, GB, F, D. **210**

421 *Draba alpina*
Variable perennial with entire densely hairy leaves in
compact rosettes, and flowering stems up to 20cm,
dense in fruit. Leaves entire, densely hairy. Petals bright
yellow, 3·5–5mm. Pod hairless. Jun–Jul. SF, IS, N, S.

421

422 *Draba crassifolia*
Dwarf hairless perennial with flowering stems up to 6 cm
and leaves oblong/spoon-shaped with few unbranched
hairs. Flowers pale yellow; petals narrow, scarcely longer
than sepals. Pod hairless, 4–7mm. Jul. N, S.

423 Common Whitlow-grass *Erophila verna*
Small variable annual, with one or several stems 2–20cm,
and basal rosette of spoon-shaped to lanceolate leaves
covered with branched hairs. Flowers white, c. 3mm
across, sepals shorter than petals. Pod flat, narrow
elliptic to oblanceolate, 6–10mm, hairless. Mar–Jun. Dry
places, walls, sand-dunes. Throughout area covered. **167**

424 Common Scurvy-grass *Cochlearia officinalis*
Robust biennial with stout much-branched stems
10–50cm. Leaves fleshy; basal leaves kidney-shaped
stalked, the upper elliptic clasping stem. Flowers white,
scented, 6–10mm across, in lax cluster; sepals rounded
half as long as petals. Pod 4–7mm, nearly globular,
netted; style short. Mar–Aug. Banks and cliffs by sea,
salt-marshes. B, GB, DK, F, D, IRL, NL, N, S. **168**

425

425 Scottish Scurvy-grass *Cochlearia scotica*
Compact dwarf perennial up to 10cm with basal fleshy
leaves with kidney-shaped or cut-off base. Petals white,
or often purplish, 2–3mm, abruptly contracted to a short
stalk. Pod 3mm, ovoid or broadly ellipsoid. May–Aug.
Coastal sands and rocks. GB, IRL.

426 Danish Scurvy-grass *Cochlearia danica*
Annual 2–20cm, the upper leaves entire stalked, the
lower 3–7-lobed. Flowers whitish or purplish, 4–5mm
across. Pod ellipsoid, narrowed at both ends, finely
netted when mature. Mar–Jun. Coasts, sometimes on

disturbed ground inland. Throughout area covered, except IS. **240**

427 *Cochlearia aestuaria*
Perennial with broadly ovate basal leaves with cut-off or heart-shaped base. Petals white, 5–7mm. Pod 5–6mm, obovoid, narrow at base, cut-off or sometimes slightly notched at apex. Apr–Jun. Atlantic coast. F.

428 **English Scurvy-grass** *Cochlearia anglica*
Robust biennial or perennial 10–40cm, with long-stalked ovate to oblong entire basal leaves with wedge-shaped bases, upper leaves elliptic and clasping stem. Flowers white or pale mauve 10–14mm across. Sepals broadly oblong; petals spoon-shaped. Pod ovoid–oblong, strongly compressed, conspicuously net-veined. Apr–Jul. Salt-marshes, estuaries, muddy sea-shores. GB, DK, D, IRL, NL, N, S.

429 *Cochlearia fenestrata*
Distinguished by its long narrow ellipsoid pod 3–4 times as long as broad. Petals white, rarely purplish, 2·5–6mm. Biennial or perennial, leaves ovate with heart-shaped or cut-off bases. Jun–Jul. SF, IS, N.

430 **Shepherd's-purse** *Capsella bursa-pastoris*
Erect annual or biennial with leafy stem 5–60cm and with basal leaves in a rosette. Leaves oblanceolate, deeply pinnately-lobed to entire, the upper clasping stem with acute lobes. Flowers white, 2–5mm across; petals entire, twice as long as sepals. Pod distinctive, triangular with two keeled valves with short central style. A very variable species. Feb–Nov. Cultivated ground, waste places, waysides. Throughout area covered. **168**

431 *Capsella rubella*
Like **430** but petals tinged reddish, scarcely longer than sepals. Pod triangular with elongated base and fairly deeply notched apex. Mar–May. Cultivated ground, dry banks. S. & C. Europe; int D, GB, F.

432 **Hutchinsia** *Hornungia petraea*
Low hairless branched annual with leaves in a rosette and sparingly leafy stem 3–15cm. Leaves all pinnate with ovate to lanceolate acute leaflets. Flowers greenish-white, minute up to 2mm across; petals not notched. Pod elliptic to obovate, with valves flattened, to 2·5mm. Mar–May. Sandy ground, limestone rocks. B, GB, DK, F, D, N, S.

432

433 **Shepherd's Cress** *Teesdalia nudicaulis*
Hairless annual 5–45cm, with basal ascending branches and almost leafless stems. Leaves in a basal rosette, pinnately-lobed, with broader 3-lobed terminal lobe. Flowers white, c. 2mm across; petals unequal. Pod to

4mm, oval hairless, narrowly-winged above. Apr–Jun.
Open sandy places. B, GB, DK, F, D, IRL, NL, N, S.

434 Field Penny-cress *Thlaspi arvense*
Hairless, sparsely branched annual up to 60cm, with
basal leaves oblanceolate to obovate, toothed, the upper
oblong with arrow-shaped base clasping stem. Flowers
white, 4–6mm across; petals notched; sepals shorter,
ovate, hairless. Pod rounded, 1–1·5cm, and flattened
with a broad wing, with deep narrow notch. May–Aug.
Cultivated ground. Throughout area covered. **168**

435 Garlic Penny-cress *Thlaspi alliaceum*
Differs from **434** in being hairy below, and pod inverse
heart-shaped 6–7mm across, narrowly winged. Annual,
smelling of garlic, up to 60cm; basal leaves in a rosette,
hairless and blue-green. Petals white 2·5–3mm. Apr–Jun.
Fields, hedges, vineyards. F, D; int GB.

433

436 Perfoliate Penny-cress *Thlaspi perfoliatum*
Low grey hairless annual, with rosettes of leaves each
bearing a flowering-stem up to 20cm. Lower leaves
obovate stalked, the upper ovate clasping stem, toothed.
Flowers white; petals 2–3mm, longer than sepals which
have broad white margins. Pod inverse heart-shaped
with wing broadening upwards. Apr–May. Calcareous
pastures, cultivated fields, waste places. B, DK, F, D, NL,
S.; casual in GB.

437

437 Alpine Penny-cress
Thlaspi caerulescens (*T. alpestre*)
Small hairless, blue-green biennial or perennial, with
branched rootstock, with crowded rosettes of leaves;
flowering stems to 50cm. Basal leaves spoon-shaped,
long-stalked, stem leaves ovate/heart-shaped, clasping
stem. Petals white or purplish, longer than sepals;
anthers usually reddish or dark violet. Fruiting stems
much elongating; pod inverse ovate or heart-shaped,
5–10mm, with wings broadening upwards. Variable
species. Apr–Jul. Rocks, screes, mountain woods, lead
mine spoil heaps. B, GB, F, D, NL; int DK, SF, IS, N, S.

438 Wild Candytuft *Iberis amara*
Much-branched, slightly hairy annual up to 40cm, with
spoon-shaped, lobed or toothed leaves fringed with
hairs. Flowers white or purplish, 7mm across, in short
clusters in flat-topped inflorescence. Petals unequal,
twice as long as ovate sepals. Pod rounded, 3–5mm, with
broad wing. A variable species. May–Sep. Calcareous
fields, woodland clearings. B, GB, F, D, NL. **168**

439 Garden Candytuft *Iberis umbellata*
Differs from **438** in having linear-lanceolate pointed,
usually entire leaves, and pod ovate, to 1cm, broadly

89

winged from the base, with triangular-pointed lobes, and deeply notched. Annual with pink-purplish flowers in a flat-topped inflorescence. May–Sep. Bushy places, rocks; widely cultivated and often escaping. F; int B, GB, D, NL. **258**

440 Field Pepperwort *Lepidium campestre*
Densely hairy, unbranched annual or biennial up to 60cm. Basal leaves ovate to obovate entire or slightly lobed; stem leaves numerous overlapping, ovate to oblong with acute basal lobes. Flowers white, 3–4mm across, in elongate cluster; petals little longer than sepals; sepals c. 1·5mm. Pod oval, winged, with shallow apical notch, covered with scaly swellings. May–Sep. Cornfields, waste places. Throughout area covered; int IS.

441 Smith's Pepperwort *Lepidium heterophyllum*
Like **440** but perennial, with pod hairless with few or no swellings, winged for about ⅓ of the total length; fruit-stalks hairy. May–Sep. Cornfields, waste places. GB, DK, F, IRL; int B, D, NL, N, S.

442 Garden Cress *Lepidium sativum*
Annual with single erect hairless stem up to 40cm. Basal leaves long-stalked, pinnately lobed with terminal lobe larger, upper stem leaves linear entire, stalkless. Flowers white or reddish; petals twice as long as sepals. Pod broadly elliptic 5–6mm, narrowly winged above, with deep apical notch, hairless, short-stalked. Jun–Jul. Waste places; escape from cultivation. Introduced throughout area covered, except IS.

443 Poor Man's Pepperwort *Lepidium virginicum*
Distinguished by its downwardly directed hairs, and its toothed leaves not clasping stem. Unbranched annual or biennial up to 50cm, with basal leaves rough with short bristles, and stem leaves sharply toothed and fringed with hairs. Pod rounded narrowly winged above with broad apical notch. May–Jul. Native of N. America. Casual in B, GB, DK, SF, F, D, NL, N, S.

444 *Lepidium densiflorum*
Annual or biennial with grey hairy stem up to 50cm, branched above and covered with minute swellings. Basal leaves elliptic, usually deeply toothed, long-stalked, upper leaves linear-lanceolate, remotely toothed. Petals thread-like, shorter than sepals which are 1mm, or petals absent. Pod 3–4mm, rounded–ovate, narrowly winged in upper third, shallowly notched, with a very short style. May–Jul. Native of N. America. Casual in B, GB, DK, SF, F, D, NL, N, S.

445 Least Pepperwort *Lepidium neglectum*
Differs from **444** in having upper stem-leaves linear

entire. Petals rudimentary; sepals c. 1·25mm. Pod 3mm, rounded, with a deep apical notch and much shorter style. May–Jun. Native of N. America. Casual in B, GB, DK, SF, F, D, NL, N, S.

446 *Lepidium bonariense*
Distinguished by having all leaves pinnate and more or less hairy; stem with long unbranched hairs. Sepals c. 0·5mm, petals shorter. Pod tiny 2–3·5mm, with narrow shallow apical notch. Aug. Native of S-E. & S. America. Casual in B, GB, D, NL, N.

447 Narrow-leaved Pepperwort *Lepidium ruderale*
Strong-smelling erect annual or biennial to 30cm. Basal leaves long-stalked, 1–2-pinnately lobed with linear lobes, upper leaves linear entire. Flowers c. 1mm across; petals absent; sepals ovate, green; stamens 2. Pod ovate to broadly elliptic, 2–2·5mm, narrowly winged above, deeply notched. May–Sep. Waste places, near coasts. Throughout area covered, except IRL.

447

448 *Lepidium divaricatum*
Annual; stem covered with small swellings, up to 50cm. Basal leaves pinnate, upper leaves oblong–lanceolate pointed, toothed. Sepals up to 0·75mm; petals shorter. Pod 2–3mm with shallow narrow apical notch and fruit stalk 2–4mm. Native of Africa. Int B, GB, F, D.

449 Dittander *Lepidium latifolium*
Robust hairless perennial up to 130cm, much branched above, with white flowers in a pyramidal cluster. Leaves leathery, the lower ovate, toothed or lobed, long-stalked, the upper entire, stalkless, often bract-like. Petals rounded–ovate, twice as long as broadly white-margined hairy sepals. Pod rounded, up to 2mm, not winged or notched. Jul–Sep. Salt-marshes, river-banks, damp places. Throughout area covered; except SF, IS, N.

450 Tall Pepperwort *Lepidium graminifolium*
Distinguished from **449** by its basal leaves which are oblanceolate to oblong, toothed, or pinnately lobed with broad lobes; long-stalked and upper leaves linear to narrowly spoon-shaped, entire. Petals equalling or up to 1½ times as long as sepals. Jun–Jul. Native of S. & C. Europe. Casual in B, GB, NL.

449

451 *Lepidium perfoliatum*
Distinguished by its two forms of leaves; basal leaves long-stalked 2–3 times pinnately lobed, with narrow lobes; upper nearly rounded–acute, entire, with broad overlapping basal lobes encircling stem. Annual or biennial up to 40cm. Petals pale yellow, little longer than sepals. Pod c. 4mm, narrowly winged above, with short exserted style. May–Jun. Naturalized throughout area covered, except SF, IRL.

91

452 Hoary Cress *Cardaria draba*
Perennial with erect flowering stems 20–80cm, bearing a
dense branched rather flat-topped cluster of tiny white
flowers. Leaves obovate, with wedge-shaped base and
wavy-toothed margin, hoary; the upper, toothed and
clasping stem. Flowers 5–6mm across; petals white,
twice as long as broadly ovate sepals. Pod rounded/
heart-shaped, inflated; style long. May–Jun. Cornfields,
waste places. F; naturalized throughout rest of area
covered, except IS. **168**

453

453 Swine-cress *Coronopus squamatus*
Annual or biennial with many spreading leafy branches
up to 30cm. Leaves deeply pinnately lobed, the lower
leaves with lobes further lobed. Flowers white, c. 2·5mm
across in clusters in axils of leaves; petals longer than
sepals; fertile stamens 6. Pods crowded in fruit, almost
kidney-shaped, netted or ridged. May–Sep. Waste
ground. Throughout area covered, except IS.

454 Lesser Swine-cress *Coronopus didymus*
Differs from **453** in having pod with apical notch, and
fruit-stalk longer than pod (pod with pointed apex with
short stalk in **453**). Flowers in elongate lateral clusters.
Petals greenish-white, shorter than sepals, or sometimes
absent; fertile stamens usually 2. Jun–Oct. Waste
ground, cultivated land. Probably native of S. America;
naturalized in B, GB, F, D, IRL, NL. **189**

455

455 Awlwort *Subularia aquatica*
Dwarf aquatic hairless annual growing submerged in
shallow water. Leaves linear pointed, rounded in section
in a basal rosette, and with leafless flowering stems to
8cm. Flowers white, c. 3mm across; petals longer than
lanceolate sepals. Pod elliptic–oblong, 2–5mm long.
Jun–Aug. Lakes and pools in hills. Throughout area
covered, except NL.

456 Sea Kale *Crambe maritima*
Stout glaucous hairless perennial up to 75cm; large
rounded fleshy leaves with crinkly lobes or teeth.
Uppermost leaves narrow, entire. Flowers white
12–18mm across, in dense, branched, flat-topped clusters. Petals ovate with short stalk. Pod 2-jointed, with
small stalk-like seedless lower segment and globular or
ovoid upper seeded segment. May. Sea-shores, sand-
dunes, cliffs. Throughout area covered, except IS. **169**

457 White Ball Mustard *Calepina irregularis*
Hairless annual up to 80cm, with basal leaves in a rosette,
obovate entire or with broad lobes. Stem leaves
arrow-shaped with spreading basal lobes clasping stem.
Flowers white 2–4mm; petals unequal. Pod spherical,
shortly beaked, becoming net-veined when dry. Apr–Jul.
Waste places. B, F; int GB, D, NL.

MIGNONETTE FAMILY

Resedaceae

Annual or perennial herbs. Leaves alternate, usually pinnately lobed. Flowers in terminal spikes or racemes, yellowish or white; petals with lobed distal portion. Fruit a capsule, which is open at the top, with numerous seeds. Plants of disturbed ground.

458 Weld *Reseda luteola*
Distinguished from other members of genus by its entire leaves, its petals and sepals both 4, and carpels 3. Erect branched biennial up to 130cm, with long slender terminal spikes of yellowish-green almost stalkless flowers. Flowers 4–5mm across; petals very unequal, the upper deeply divided, the lower entire. Pod globular, with 3 teeth. Jun–Sep. Disturbed ground, stony and sandy places. B, GB, DK, F, IRL, NL, S; int D. **196**

459 White Mignonette *Reseda alba*
Distinguished by its pinnate leaves, with 5–15 narrow lobes on each side. Erect annual to perennial up to 80cm, branched above, with white flowers, with 5–6 sepals and petals, in a long dense spike. Petals 3-lobed. Pod narrowly obovate to elliptic, with 4 short teeth. Jun–Aug. Dry waste places; F; int GB, D, IRL, NL. **196**

460 Wild Mignonette *Reseda lutea*
Erect or ascending annual to perennial up to 70cm, with diffusely branched stem. Leaves mostly pinnately-lobed with 1–3 pairs of lobes. Flowers yellow, c. 6mm across, in a long terminal spike. Sepals 6; petals 6, the upper 3-lobed, the lower 2 petals entire. Pod obovoid, 3-lobed, with 3 very short teeth. Jun–Aug. Waste places, arable land. GB, F, IRL, NL; int B, DK, D. **197**

461 Corn Mignonette *Reseda phyteuma*
Distinguished by its drooping whitish flowers and pods. Annual or biennial 10–50cm, branched from near base. Leaves oblong or spoon-shaped, entire or with one pair of narrow blunt lobes. Sepals 6, enlarging in fruit; petals 6, deeply divided into narrow linear lobes. Pod ovoid–oblong, with 3 terminal lobes. Jun–Aug. Disturbed ground. S. Europe, F; int D, NL. **169**

SUNDEW FAMILY

Droseraceae

Perennial herbs, notable for their insectivorous habit.
Leaves basal, covered with long gland-tipped hairs that
are irritable and mobile, entrapping and digesting
insects. Acid, boggy places: the digested insects are a
source of nutrients on the poor soil of such habitats.

462 Round-leaved Sundew *Drosera rotundifolia*
Readily distinguished by its basal rosette of long-stalked
leaves with rounded blades covered with long red
glandular hairs. Flowers white, 5mm across, several
borne on slender leafless stems to 8cm. Petals usually 6,
5mm long; sepals hairless. Capsule smooth, with 3 styles,
longer than sepals. Jun–Aug. Peat-bogs, wet acid moors.
Throughout area covered.

463 Great Sundew *Drosera anglica*
Distinguished by its linear–oblanceolate glandular-hairy
leaf-blades, with long hairless leaf-stalks. Flowering
stem leafless, 10–18cm bearing 3–6 white flowers; petals
6mm. Capsule toothed. Jun–Aug. Peat-bogs. Throughout area covered, except IS.

464 Oblong-leaved Sundew *Drosera intermedia*
Differs from **462** by its flowering stems which arise
laterally from the lowest leaves, and are little longer than
the leaves (flowering stems arising terminally, and much
longer than leaves in **463**). Blade of leaf obovate,
glandular-hairy. Flowers white; petals 4–5mm. Capsule
longitudinally grooved. Plants often gregarious.
Jun–Aug. Peat-bogs, moors; drier habitats than **462** and
463. Throughout area covered, except IS. 233

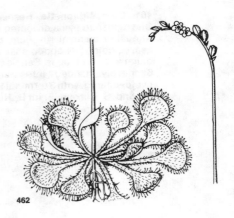

462

STONECROP FAMILY

Crassulaceae

Annual or perennial herbs. Leaves entire, more or less succulent. Flowers solitary or in clusters. Fruit a follicle, with 2 to many seeds. *Crassula* species are characteristic of wet places or seasonally flooded ground. Other genera usually occur on rocks.

465 Mossy Stonecrop *Crassula tillaea*
Tiny moss-like reddish annual, with opposite paired tiny crowded leaves and with tiny clusters of pale pink flowers in their axils. Leaves ovate, concave, 2mm. Flowers stalkless; sepals and petals 3; petals 1mm, shorter than sepals. Capsule usually 2-seeded. May–Sep. Sandy places that are damp in winter. B, GB, F, D, NL.

465

466 Water Tillaea *Crassula aquatica*
Like **465** but leaves broadly linear, flat and spreading, and flowers usually with 4 sepals and petals. Leaves 4–6mm. Flowers white, solitary in leaf-axils; petals longer than sepals. Capsule with many seeds. May–Jul. Mud on margins of pools and lakesides. GB, DK, SF, D, IS, N, S.

467 *Crassula vaillantii*
Differs from **466** in having flower-stalks longer than the subtending linear–oblong leaves. Stems erect or ascending to 6cm. Petals pink, ovate–lanceolate acute, longer than sepals. May–Aug. Marshes. F.

468 Navelwort *Umbilicus rupestris*
Succulent perennial with rosette of rounded leaves with long leaf-stalks attached to the undersides of the leaves. Flowering-stem stout, erect up to 50cm, with progressively smaller kidney-shaped leaves, and a slender spike on numerous greenish-yellow, sometimes whitish-pink, pendulous flowers. Flowers tubular to 1cm, fused below and with 5 lobes; sepals ovate acute. Carpels 6, with long style. A very variable species. May–Jul. Rocks, walls, banks, trees. GB, F, IRL. **197**

469 House Leek *Sempervivum tectorum*
Distinguished by its fleshy leaves in large rosettes 3–8cm across. Leaves oblong–lanceolate to obovate, with stout apical spine and white marginal hairs. Flowering stem stout, to 50cm, with large lax inflorescence with many dull pink or purple flowers. Petals usually 13, lanceolate acute, hairy beneath; stamens twice as many. A very variable species. Jun–Aug. Rocks, walls; often cultivated. F, D; locally naturalized elsewhere. **240**

SEDUM
LEAVES FLATTENED, FLESHY, NOT CYLINDRICAL IN SECTION

470 Orpine *Sedum telephium*
Tufted perennial with many leafy flowering stems
30–80cm, with ovate flat fleshy toothed leaves. Flowers
pale pink to white, in branched flat-topped cluster.
Sepals triangular; petals 5, lanceolate, 1–5mm, twice as
long as sepals. Carpels boat-shaped, erect. A variable
species. Jul–Sep. Woods, banks, shady rocks.
Throughout area covered, except IS.

471 Caucasian Stonecrop *Sedum spurium*
Differs from **470** in having spreading rooting stems with
short non-flowering shoots. Flowers reddish-purple,
pink or white, with erect petals 10–12mm (petals
spreading 3–5mm in **470**). Jul–Aug. Naturalized on walls
and screes. Native of Caucasus. Int throughout area
covered, except IS.

470

SEDUM
FLOWERS YELLOW OR YELLOWISH-WHITE; LEAVES CYLINDRICAL IN SECTION,
NOT FLATTENED

472 Reflexed Stonecrop *Sedum reflexum*
Stout perennial with flowering stems up to 35cm, and
many shorter densely leafy, cylindrical non-flowering
shoots. Leaves blue-green, linear to lanceolate, fleshy.
Inflorescence umbel-like compact and convex in flower,
concave in fruit. Flowers yellow c. 1·5cm across, with 5–9
linear–lanceolate spreading petals; stamens 10–14.
Jun–Aug. Rocks, walls. B, DK, SF, F, D, NL, N, S; int GB,
IRL. **210**

473 Rock Stonecrop *Sedum forsteranum*
Like **472** but non-flowering shoots with leaves confined
to a terminal globular cone-like rosette, and with
persistent dead leaves on rest of shoot. Sepals blunt,
2·5mm. (Sepals more or less acute, 3–4mm in **472**).
Jun–Jul. Sands, screes (often damper places than **472**).
B, GB, F, D.

474 Biting Stonecrop *Sedum acre*
Small tufted peppery-tasting perennial with creeping
stems, and erect branched flowering stems up to 10cm or
more. Leaves ovoid, broadest towards base, thick and
fleshy, hairless. Flowers bright yellow, 1–1·2cm across,
with 5 narrowly triangular spreading petals twice as long
as the lanceolate whitish sepals; stamens 10. Variable
species. May–Jul. Dry grassland, walls, sand-dunes,
coastal shingle. Throughout area covered. **210**

475 *Sedum alpestre*
Differs from **474** in having dull yellow flowers with petals

3·5mm, little longer than sepals (petals 6–8mm, bright yellow in **474**). Carpels dark red. Jun–Aug. Rocks, moraines. F, D.

476 Tasteless Stonecrop *Sedum sexangulare*
Like **474** but leaves parallel-sided (broadest towards base in **474**). Petals bright yellow, 4–5mm (petals 6–8mm in **474**). Jun–Sep. Rocks, sands, walls. B, DK, SF, F, D, NL, S; int GB.

477 Annual Stonecrop *Sedum annuum*
Low hairless annual or biennial, often spotted or streaked with red, with stems branching fron the base, up to 12cm. Leaves alternate, distant, linear–oblong, thick but flattened on both sides. Flowers yellow, in a lax compound cluster; petals oblanceolate pointed, twice as long as sepals. Jun–Jul. Mountains. SF, F, D, IS, N, S. **211**

476

SEDUM
FLOWERS WHITE OR PINKISH; LEAVES CYLINDRICAL IN SECTION

478 White Stonecrop *Sedum album*
Rather robust, matted, often reddish perennial with many non-flowering leafy stems, and with erect flowering stems up to 18cm. Leaves cylindrical, flattened on upper side, to 12mm. Flowers white, rarely pink, 6–9mm, in a much-branched somewhat flat-topped inflorescence. Petals 2–4mm; sepals fused at base; stamens twice as long as petals. Very variable species. Jun–Aug. Rocks, walls. Throughout area covered, except IS. **169**

479 English Stonecrop *Sedum anglicum*
Low tufted greyish or reddish perennial, with cylindrical to nearly globular leaves up to 5mm, with flowering stems usually less than 15cm. Flowers white or pink, 12mm across, crowded in a small cluster; petals twice as long as ovate sepals which are not fused below. Jun–Sep. Rocks and sandy soil, near sea. GB, F, IRL, N, S.

480 Thick-leaved Stonecrop *Sedum dasyphyllum*
Reddish tufted perennial, with usually hairless rounded, thick fleshy opposite leaves. Flowering stems up to 8cm, with few white flowers streaked with pink, 5–6mm across. Petals 3mm much longer than the tiny ovate sepals; stamens twice as long as petals. Jun–Jul. Old walls, limestone rocks. F, D; int B, GB, DK, IRL, NL.

481 Hairy Stonecrop *Sedum villosum*
Glandular-hairy perennial 5–15cm, with pink or lilac flowers. Stem erect, often branched from base; leaves alternate, linear–oblong, 6–12mm. Flowers c. 6mm across, in a lax cluster. Petals ovate pointed, spreading; sepals lanceolate blunt. Jun–Jul. Streamsides, wet places in mountains. GB, SF, F, D, IS, N, S.

481

482 *Sedum rubens*
Erect glandular-hairy, usually reddish annual up to 12cm.
Leaves linear, rounded in section, spreading. Flowers
white or pink, in a leafy flat-topped cluster; petals 5mm
long, pointed; stamens usually 5. May–Jun. Fields,
vineyards, walls, gravelly places. B, F, D.

483 *Sedum hispanicum*
Distinguished by its 6 white petals with pink veins.
Usually annual, hairless or glandular-hairy. Flowers
numerous, in one-sided clusters; petals 5–7mm,
lanceolate pointed. Leaves linear, rounded in section,
blue-green. Stem branched ascending up to 15cm.
Jun–Jul. Rocks, screes, walls. Native of S-E. Europe; int
D, S. **240**

484 Roseroot *Rhodiola rosea*
Perennial with fleshy rhizome, fragrant when cut, and
with many erect leafy flowering stems 5–35cm, with
rounded to linear–oblong, toothed, fleshy, blue-green
leaves. Flowers dull yellow, in flat-topped cluster, with
male and female flowers. Petals 4, linear, 3–4mm,
sometimes absent; stamens 8. Fruits 4, reddish.
May–Aug. Cliffs, rocks in mountains. GB, SF, F, IRL, IS,
N, S.

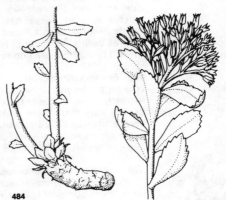

484

SAXIFRAGE FAMILY

Saxifragaceae

Perennial or rarely annual herbs. Leaves simple, but often deeply dissected, fleshy. Flowers grouped in cymes (or sometimes solitary or in racemes). Petals 4–5, or absent; carpels 2, united below. Fruit a capsule, with numerous seeds. *Saxifraga* is typically a genus of rocks, especially in the mountains.

SAXIFRAGA
LEAVES ENCRUSTED WITH LIME

485 Purple Saxifrage *Saxifraga oppositifolia*
Small spreading perennial, forming loose mats or compact cushions, with tiny opposite rounded to obovate, thick leaves in 4 rows, with 1 or several lime-secreting pits. Flowers solitary, pink or deep purple, 8–10mm across, on stem 1–2cm; sepals ovate, with hairy margin. A very variable species. Mar–May. Damp rocks, stony ground in mountains. GB, SF, F, D, IRL, IS, N, S.

486 *Saxifraga paniculata*
Densely tufted perennial with obovate to oblong blue-green finely toothed lime-encrusted leaves, in hemispherical rosettes. Flowering stems to 30cm, branched above. Flowers 8–11mm across; petals white or cream, 4–6mm, sometimes with red spots. May–Aug. Stony places, screes in mountains. F, D, IS, N. **169**

SAXIFRAGA
FLOWERS YELLOW OR ORANGE; LEAVES NOT LIME-ENCRUSTED OR WITH LIME PITS

487 Marsh Saxifrage *Saxifraga hirculus*
Loosely tufted reddish-brown hairy perennial up to 35cm, with stems leafy in lower half. Leaves lanceolate blunt, entire. Flowers bright yellow, sometimes red-spotted, 2–3cm across, solitary or 2–4; sepals recurved in fruit. Jul–Sep. Wet places, bogs. Throughout area covered, except B, NL.

488 Yellow Saxifrage *Saxifraga aizoides*
Loose tufted perennial, with short hairy shoots, and erect leafy flowering-stems, branched above, up to 25cm. Leaves linear–oblong, entire or with few teeth. Flowers yellow or orange, often spotted with red, 12mm across, in lax branched leafy clusters. Petals lanceolate, not touching, little longer than blunt, hairless sepals. Jun–Sep. Stream-sides and damp rocks in mountains. GB, SF, F, D, IRL, IS, N, S. **211**

487

489 Meadow Saxifrage *Saxifraga granulata*
Erect perennial with stems branched above, 10–50cm. Long-stalked leaves in a lax rosette, kidney-shaped rounded–lobed with bulbils in leaf-axils. Flowers 1·5cm across, in a lax cluster; petals obovate, twice as long as triangular-ovate to oblong, glandular sepals. May–Jul. Grasslands. Throughout area covered, except IS. **169**

490 Drooping Saxifrage *Saxifraga cernua*
Erect perennial up to 30cm, with kidney-shaped 5- to 7-lobed, long-stalked leaves, with reddish bulbils in leaf-axils. Flowers white, usually solitary, with petals 8–12mm, but flower often abortive; reproduction by bulbils. Jul–Aug. Rocks in mountains. GB, SF, IS, N, S. **170**

491 Highland Saxifrage *Saxifraga rivularis*
Densely tufted perennial up to 18cm; basal leaves in a rosette with rounded blades with 3–7 ovate lobes, long-stalked; lobes of stem leaves narrower or absent. Petals white obovate, 3–5mm. Jul–Aug. Rocks and screes in northern mountains. GB, SF, IS, N, S.

491

492 Alpine Saxifrage *Saxifraga nivalis*
Leaves in one or several rosettes, rounded to oblong, toothed or shallowly-lobed, hairy on margin, often reddish beneath, leaf-stalk broad and short. Flowering stem 5–20cm, glandular-hairy, with clusters of white or pink flowers. Petals c. 3mm, little longer than sepals. Jul–Aug. Wet rocks in mountains. GB, SF, IRL, IS, N, S.

493 *Saxifraga tenuis*
Very like **492** but flowers distinctly stalked in a rather lax cluster (almost stalkless in a dense cluster in **492**). Flowering stem more slender, less densely hairy, and without long hairs. Jul. Arctic and sub-arctic parts of area covered. SF, IS, N, S.

495

494 Kidney Saxifrage *Saxifraga hirsuta*
Densely tufted perennial with branched inflorescence up to 30cm. Leaves in rosettes, long-stalked, with rounded or kidney-shaped toothed blades, hairy on both sides. Flowers white with orange spots at base, in a lax cluster. Petals elliptic c. 4mm; sepals oblong blunt, deflexed, shorter than petals. May–Jul. Calcareous rocks by mountain streams. F, IRL; int GB. **170**

495 St Patrick's Cabbage *Saxifraga spathularis*
Distinguished from **494** by its leaves which are hairless on lower side, and broad distinctly flattened leaf-stalk. Leaves rather leathery, rounded to spoon-shaped, coarsely toothed. Petals white, with many red spots. May–Jul. Acid rocks and mountains. IRL.

SAXIFRAGA
BLADES OF LEAVES LONGER THAN BROAD, NOT CONSPICUOUSLY LOBED

496 Starry Saxifrage *Saxifraga stellaris*
Small densely-tufted perennial, with rosettes of obovate to spoon-shaped toothed leaves, and erect slender leafless, sparsely branched stems up to 20cm, with few white flowers. Leaves slightly fleshy, bristly–hairy. Flowers 1cm across; petals narrowly lanceolate, with 2 yellow spots at base; sepals oblong, reflexed, anthers pink. Jun–Aug. Wet rocks, beside springs in mountains. GB, SF, F, D, IRL, IS, N, S. **170**

497 *Saxifraga foliolosa*
Like **496** but smaller rosette usually solitary. Leaves narrower than **496**, hairless except on margin. Inflorescence narrow, with usually a single terminal flower and dense clusters of reddish bulbils below. Jul. SF, IS, N, S.

498 *Saxifraga hieracifolia*
Flowering-stem leafless 10–40cm, densely glandular-hairy, with a narrow congested spike of greenish-red flowers. Leaves in a basal rosette, oblong–ovate, entire or somewhat toothed, with broad leaf-stalk. Petals to 3mm, about as long as sepals which are recurved in fruit. Jul. Damp rocks, moraines, by streams. F, N.

499 *Saxifraga cotyledon*
Leaves in a large rosette, obovate to tongue-shaped, finely toothed, blue-green, 2–6cm. Flowering stem up to 50cm, branched with a large pyramidal cluster of numerous white flowers. Petals 6–10mm; sepals glandular-hairy. Jul–Aug. Rocks. D, IS, N, S.

SAXIFRAGA
BLADE OF LEAVES LONGER THAN BROAD, CONSPICUOUSLY LOBED

500 Tufted Saxifrage *Saxifraga cespitosa*
Forming lax or dense cushions, with short more or less erect leafy shoots; flowering stems up to 8cm, bearing 1–3 dull white flowers. Flowers 10–12mm across; sepals blunt, glandular. Leaves wedge-shaped, usually 3-lobed, with a broad leaf-stalk, all covered with glandular hairs. May–Jun. Arctic and sub-Arctic; rocks in mountains. GB, SF, IS, N, S. **170**

501 Irish Saxifrage *Saxifraga rosacea*
Cushion-forming perennial or with spreading stems forming a loose mat. Leaves broad wedge-shaped, usually 5-lobed, densely glandular-hairy or nearly hairless. Flowering stem slender up to 25cm, nearly leafless, with few long-stalked white flowers 15 mm across. Petals ovate; sepals triangular–ovate. A very

501

variable species. Jun–Jul. Damp rock-ledges, stream-sides. B, F, D, IRL, IS.

502 Mossy Saxifrage *Saxifraga hypnoides*
Perennial forming mats with flowering rosettes and with numerous spreading sterile shoots bearing leafy bulbils. Lower leaves with 3–5 lobes, the basal in rosettes, the upper stem leaves entire. Flowering stems up to 30cm. Flowers 1–1·2cm across; petals white; sepals triangular–pointed. May–Jul. Rock ledges, screes, stony grasslands. B, GB, F, IRL, IS, N.

503 Rue-leaved Saxifrage *Saxifraga tridactylites*
Small slender often reddish annual 3–20cm with 3–5-lobed stem-leaves, and simple spoon-shaped small basal leaves, all glandular. Flowers white, in a branched cluster; petals 2–3mm, notched, about twice as long as sepals. Apr–Jun. Sandy grasslands, rocks, walls. Throughout area covered, except IS.

503

504 *Saxifraga adscendens*
Perennial with simple or branched stem up to 25cm, with basal leaves in a compact rosette with blades wedge-shaped with 2–5 broad short triangular teeth. Petals white, rarely yellowish, 3–5mm, flowers borne on stalks not more than twice as long as petals. Jun–Aug. Pastures, damp rocks, screes. SF, F, N, S.

505 Opposite-leaved Golden Saxifrage
Chrysosplenium oppositifolium
Low creeping perennial forming large patches on wet soils, with rather long-stalked leaves with rounded, shallowly blunt-toothed blades. Flowering stems 10–15cm, 4-angled, with opposite leaves, with a dense terminal cluster of tiny yellow flowers surrounded by rounded leaves. Flowers c. 4mm across, with ovate or triangular–ovate yellow sepals; petals absent. Apr–Jun. Damp and shady places, by streams and springs. B, GB, DK, F, D, IRL, NL, N. **211**

506 Alternate-leaved Golden Saxifrage
Chrysosplenium alternifolium
Differs from **505** in having alternate stem-leaves, and basal leaves with heart-shaped bases (base broadly wedge-shaped in **505**). Rather larger plant than **505**, with flowers 5–6mm across. Apr–Jul. Damp and shady places by streams and often in wetter sites than **505**. Throughout area covered, except IRL, IS.

507 *Chrysosplenium tetrandrum*
Like **506** with alternate stem-leaves, but a hairless perennial with green flowers with erect sepals and with 4 stamens (stamens 8 in **505**, **506**). Jun–Jul. Wet places in Arctic part of area covered. SF, N, S.

506

GRASS-OF-PARNASSUS FAMILY

Parnassiaceae

Perennial herbs. Leaves simple, undivided. Flowers solitary; petals 5. Carpels 4. Fruit a capsule.

508 Grass of Parnassus *Parnassia palustris*
Hairless perennial with several flowering stems 5–50cm, each with a conspicuous encircling leaf and long-stalked solitary white flower. Basal leaves ovate, heart-shaped at base, long-stalked; stem leaf 1, stalkless and clasping stem. Flower 1·5–3cm across; petals ovate spreading, with conspicuous veins, and with a ring of large sterile fringed stamens with nectaries opposite the petals. Fertile stamens 5. Jun–Sep. Marshes, moors, damp places in sand-dunes. Throughout area covered. **170**

ROSE FAMILY

Rosaceae

Perennial (or rarely annual) herbs, or shrubs. Leaves often compound. Stipules usually present. Flowers regular, usually 5-merous, with numerous stamens. Fruit often numerous, variable in structure, free or fused: follicles, achenes, drupes, and structures derived from persistent and swollen receptacle.

509 Goat's-beard Spiraea *Aruncus dioicus*
Perennial 1–2m, with large twice-pinnate leaves to 1m, leaflets ovate acute, double-toothed; stipules absent. Inflorescence large, branched and pyramidal, with numerous small white or yellowish-white flowers c. 5mm across. Petals oblong; stamens numerous. Fruit pendulous. Jun–Aug. Damp shady woods in mountains. B, F, D. **197**

510 Dropwort *Filipendula vulgaris*
Erect perennial with nearly hairless stems up to 80cm, usually branched and with few leaves; roots with ovoid tubers. Basal leaves with 8–25 pairs of large oblong pinnately-lobed leaflets; stipules present. Inflorescence broader than long; petals usually 6, white usually purplish beneath, 5–9mm; stamens about as long. May–Aug. Grassland, open woods. Throughout area covered, to 64° north, except IS. **197**

511 Meadowsweet *Filipendula ulmaria*
Distinguished from **510** in having basal leaves with not more than 5 pairs of leaflets, which are more than 2cm; petals smaller, 2–5mm. Hairy perennial with simple or branched stems up to 2m; roots without tubers. Inflorescence usually longer than broad. Flowers white, with stamens longer than petals. Jun–Sep. Damp places, marshes, wet woods. Throughout area covered. **197**

RUBUS
STEMS NOT WOODY OR NEARLY SO; STIPULES NOT FUSED TO LEAF-STALK

512 Cloudberry *Rubus chamaemorus*
Small perennial with creeping rhizome, and erect annual stems up to 20cm. Leaves kidney-shaped, with 5 blunt, toothed lobes. Flowers white, solitary, 2·5–4cm across; petals hairy, larger than sepals. Fruit with many red or orange, fleshy, 1-seeded drupelets. Jun–Aug. Moors, bogs, in mountains. GB, DK, SF, D, IRL, N, S. **233**

513 Arctic Bramble *Rubus arcticus*
Distinguished by its leaves with 3 ovate, toothed leaflets or leaves 3-lobed. Stems to 30cm, spineless, with 1–3 stalked, red or pink flowers, 1·5–2·5cm across; stamens purple. Fruit dark red, with numerous drupelets. Jun–Jul. Moors. †GB, SF, N, S. **233**

514 Stone Bramble *Rubus saxatilis*
Like **513** but flowers white, and all stems with prickles (flowering stems without prickles in **513**) and some stems not flowering. Flowering stems up to 50cm; leaves with 3 ovate–elliptic, unevenly toothed leaflets. Inflorescence branched, with 3–10 flowers, each 8–10mm across. Petals narrow, white, not or scarcely longer than lanceolate sepals; stamens white. Fruit red with 2–6 shining drupelets. May–Aug. Shady, rocky ground, thickets. Throughout area covered.

514

RUBUS
STEMS WOODY; STIPULES FUSED TO LEAF-STALK

515 Bramble *Rubus fruticosus* agg.
Stems usually arching to 3m or more, or spreading, usually sharply 4-angled, with prickles of different sizes and curvature. Leaves commonly with 3–5 stalked leaflets, with prickles on leaf-stalk. Flowers white or pink, 2–3cm across, in terminal and axillary branched clusters; sepals usually hairy. Fruit red, then black–purple, with many fleshy drupelets. An aggregate of numerous micro-species in Europe. Jun–Oct. Woods, scrub, waste ground, hedges. Throughout area covered. **170, 267**

516 Dewberry *Rubus caesius*
Stems rounded in section, grey-bloomed, with few or many prickles, trailing and with runners. Leaves with 3 leaflets, the terminal often 3-lobed, leaf-stalk grooved; stipules lanceolate. Flowers white or pink 2–2·5cm across, in terminal and axillary clusters of 2–5. Sepals ovate–lanceolate, grey-woolly, with white margin; petals longer, broader. Fruit with large, black bloomed drupelets. Jun–Sep. Grasslands, scrub, fens. Throughout area covered, except IS. **171**

517 Raspberry *Rubus idaeus*
Stems erect 1–2m, rounded, and usually with slender straight weak prickles. Leaves normally with 3–5 ovate–lanceolate irregularly toothed leaflets, densely white-woolly beneath. Flowers white, 1cm across, in dense terminal and axillary clusters. Petals erect, widely spaced, about as long as lanceolate pointed sepals. Fruit red or orange, with hairy drupelets. May–Aug. Woods, heaths, in mountains. Throughout area covered, except IS.

517

518 Burnet Rose *Rosa pimpinellifolia*
Low shrub usually less than 1m, forming dense patches
and with stems covered in numerous prickles mixed with
stiff bristles. Leaves with 6–11 small rounded to broadly
elliptic toothed leaflets. Flowers white, rarely pink,
2–4cm across, solitary; sepals narrowly lanceolate
pointed, without glands. Fruit globular black. May–Jul.
Sand-dunes, sandy heaths, limestone rocks. Throughout
area covered, except SF, S. **197**

519 Provence Rose *Rosa gallica*
Shrub up to 80cm, forming large patches, with stems
with prickles and glandular hairs. Leaves with 3–7
rounded to narrowly elliptic, double toothed,
bluish-green leathery leaflets. Flowers deep pink, usually
solitary, 6–9cm across; sepals glandular. Fruit globular
or spindle-shaped, bright red. May–Jul. Margin of woods,
copses, uncultivated ground. B, F, D.

520 Field Rose *Rosa arvensis*
Shrub with weak trailing spreading stems forming low
bushes up to 1m, stems with more or less equal hooked
bristles. Leaves with 5–7, ovate, toothed leaflets. Flowers
white. 3–5cm across, 1–3 in a terminal cluster; flower
stalks with stalked glands. Sepals ovate pointed, often
purplish, reflexed after flowering. Fruit globular to ovoid,
red. Jun–Jul. Woods, hedgebanks, scrub. B, GB, F, D,
IRL, NL. **171**

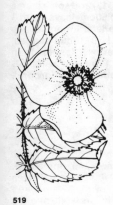
519

521 Agrimony *Agrimonia eupatoria*
Erect perennial up to 150cm, with stems densely leafy
below, sparse above. Basal leaves in a rosette, pinnate
with 3–6 pairs of large elliptic, coarsely toothed leaflets
and 2–3 pairs of smaller leaflets in between, all dark
green above and whitish or greyish-woolly beneath.
Flowers yellow, 6–8mm across, in a long terminal spike.
Calyx tube with hooked spines, half encircling the carpels. Fruit obconical, deeply furrowed and with terminal
erect and spreading bristles. Jun–Sep. Wood verges,
thickets, meadows. Throughout area covered, except IS.
198

522 Fragrant Agrimony *Agrimonia procera*
Like **521**, but leaves with numerous stalked glands
beneath (not or rarely glandular in **521**), and fruit
bell-shaped, furrowed for $\frac{1}{2}$ its length (furrowed for $\frac{3}{4}$ of
length in **521**) and lower bristles of fruit reflexed.
Flowering stem up to 120cm, with long non-glandular
hairs. Petals golden-yellow, often notched. Jun–Sep.
Hedges, woods, ravines, pastures. Throughout area
covered, except IS.

523 Bastard Agrimony *Aremonia agrimonoides*
Differs from **521** in having few flowers in branched
spreading clusters. Flowering stem slender 5–35cm;
leaves usually with 3–5 pairs of leaflets, the 3 terminal
ones much larger. Flowers 7–10mm across, each with
lobed involucre some not opening; calyx-lobes 2·5mm
on open flowers; petals ovate, shorter than sepals. Fruit
without bristles. May–Jun. Mountain woods, waysides.
D; int GB.

524 Great Burnet *Sanguisorba officinalis*
Hairless perennial up to 1m, with erect branched stems.
Leaves pinnate, with 3–7 pairs of ovate/heart-shaped
leaflets, blue-green beneath. Flowers in globular or
oblong dull crimson heads, 1–3cm across, long-stalked.
Sepals dull crimson; petals absent; stamens 4, anthers
dark crimson. Fruit with 4 narrow wings. Jun–Sep. Damp
grasslands. Throughout area covered; int SF. **267**

525 Salad Burnet *Sanguisorba minor*
Differs from **524** in having upper flowers of flower
clusters female, and fruit netted or irregularly ridged.
Stems up to 90cm; basal leaves in a rosette. Leaves with
3–12 pairs of rounded to elliptic toothed leaflets, all
similar in size (not larger towards apex of leaf as in **524**).
Flower heads globular; flowers green, often
purple-tinged. A variable species. May–Sep. Dry
grasslands. Throughout area covered, except IS; int SF,
N. **198**

526 Mountain Avens *Dryas octopetala*
Low creeping, much-branched mat-forming dwarf shrub
up to 50cm, with woody stems and oblong to obovate
rounded-toothed leaves, dark green above and densely
white-woolly beneath. Flowers white, 3–3·5cm across,
solitary long-stalked, with usually 8 oblong petals, twice
as long as the woolly-haired sepals. Stamens and carpels
numerous. Fruit a cluster of achenes each with long hairy
style. May–Aug. Screes and rocky places on limestone,
usually in mountains in southern part of area covered.
GB, SF, F, D, IRL, IS, N, S. **171**

527 Wood Avens *Geum urbanum*
Erect leafy hairy perennial, branched above, up to 60cm,
with pinnate leaves and yellow flowers. Leaves with 1–5
pairs of unequal leaflets, and with rounded deeply lobed
terminal leaflet. Inflorescence with 2–5 long-stalked
flowers, each 1–1·5cm across. Petals obovate or oblong,
spreading, little longer than calyx. Fruit hairy, in a
globular head, each achene with persistent hooked style.
May–Sep. Woods, shady places, by paths. Throughout
area covered, except IS. **211**

528 Water Avens *Geum rivale*
Erect branched perennial to 30cm, distinguished by its
107

nodding pink or cream flowers with dark brownish-purple calyx. Leaves pinnate, the basal with 3–6 pairs of unequal leaflets, and with terminal rounded lobed leaflet; stem leaves 3-lobed. Petals 1–1·5cm, spoon-shaped, notched. Fruit with hairy achenes with long hooked beaks. Often hybridizes with **527**. May–Sep. Marshes, wet hedge-banks, shady places. Throughout area covered. **240**

529 Alpine Avens *Geum montanum*
Low perennial with thick creeping rhizome, and flowering stems up to 10cm, with 1–3 golden-yellow erect flowers 2·5–4cm across. Basal leaves pinnately-lobed with large terminal lobe. Achenes numerous, with feathery styles to 2cm, not hooked. Jun–Aug. Fields, rocks, open woods in mountains. F, D. **213**

530 *Geum hispidum*
Glandular-hairy perennial with erect stems up to 40cm, with basal leaves lanceolate in outline with 3–5 pairs of leaflets, and a terminal deeply 3-lobed leaflet. Flowers pale yellow, erect, long-stalked; petals 5–8mm, oblong to obovate, spreading. Achenes numerous in a globular head, styles short, hairless. Jul. S.

POTENTILLA
FLOWERS WHITE, PINK OR PURPLISH; BASAL LEAVES WITH 3 LEAFLETS

531 Barren Strawberry *Potentilla sterilis*
Small, hairy spreading perennial with stolons and leaves in a rosette; flowering stems 5–15cm with 1–3 white flowers. Leaves with 3 obovate, coarsely toothed leaflets, silvery-grey beneath. Flowers 1–1·5cm across with petals slightly longer than sepals; epicalyx segments lanceolate, shorter than sepals. Achenes minutely wrinkled. Feb–May. Dry grasslands, open woods. B, GB, DK, F, D, IRL, NL, S. **171**

533

532 *Potentilla montana*
Distinguished from **531** by its larger flowers 1·5–2cm across, with petals twice as long as sepals. Leaves toothed only towards apex, with silvery hairy margins and undersides. May–Jun. Woods, waste land. F. **171**

533 *Potentilla micrantha*
Differs from **532** in having white petals shorter or as long as the sepals, and leaflets which are toothed almost to the base (leaflets only toothed towards apex in **531**). Petals 3–5mm, white or rarely pink, as long or slightly shorter than ovate–lanceolate sepals which are dark reddish on inner side towards base. Perennial with flowering stems up to 5cm or more. Apr–May. Woods, rocks, walls, lawns. F, D.

POTENTILLA
BASAL LEAVES WITH 5 OR MORE LEAFLETS ARISING FROM APEX OF
LEAF-STALK

535

534 Marsh Cinquefoil *Potentilla palustris*
Erect rather robust perennial to 50cm, with pinnate
leaves and purplish flowers. Rhizome woody,
long-creeping. Leaves with 5–7 oblong toothed leaflets
and with long leaf-stalk; upper leaves smaller. Flowers in
lax terminal cluster, each 3–3·5cm across; sepals
purplish, 5, ovate pointed, fused at the base and with
linear epicalyx segments; petals half as long, purple,
spoon-shaped, toothed. Stamens and carpels purple.
May–Jul. Fens, marshes, bogs, wet heaths. Throughout
area covered. **267**

535 *Potentilla alba*
Flowering stems up to 15cm, hairy. Leaves with 5
oval–lanceolate terminal leaflets each with few teeth at
apex, green, hairless above, silvery-hairy beneath; upper
leaves few, with 3 leaflets. Flowers white; petals slightly
notched, 7–10mm, longer than lanceolate sepals.
Stamen filaments hairless. Apr–Jul. Rocks, open woods,
lawns. F, D.

536 Rock Cinquefoil *Potentilla rupestris*
Stout erect hairy perennial 20–60cm, branched above,
with a terminal cluster of smallish white flowers. Leaves
pinnate, with 5–7 ovate to nearly rounded irregularly
toothed leaflets; upper leaves with 3 narrower leaflets.
Flowers 1·5cm across, one or many, with 5 obovate petals
little longer than the triangular sepals. May–Jun.
Limestone rocks. B, GB, F, D, N, S. **171**

POTENTILLA
FLOWERS YELLOW; BASAL LEAVES USUALLY WITH 3 LEAFLETS

537 Ternate-leaved Cinquefoil *Potentilla norvegica*
Annual or short-lived perennial, with hairy stems
10–70cm. Leaves mostly with 3 leaflets, rarely 5; leaflets
obovate to oblong, coarsely toothed, green. Flowers
yellow, numerous; petals 4–5mm, usually shorter than
ovate–acute sepals which enlarge in fruit. Epicalyx
oblong, longer than sepals in fruit. Jun–Aug. Waste
places, walls. DK, SF, D, N, S; int B, GB, F, NL.

538 *Potentilla hyparctica*
Differs from **537** in being perennial with numerous
non-flowering rosettes, and epicalyx shorter or as long
as sepals in fruit. Flowering stems lateral, ascending to
10cm. Leaflets obovate to triangular–oblong, toothed,
hairy and often glandular beneath. Flowers yellow, 1–3;
petals 1½ times as long as sepals. S.

539

539 Tormentil *Potentilla erecta*
Perennial with stout stock, and with rosettes of leaves, which are often absent at flowering; flowering stems spreading or ascending 10–30cm. Leaves with 3 lanceolate toothed leaflets, silvery-hairy beneath. Flowers yellow, usually many in terminal cluster; petals usually 4, 4–6mm, little longer than the ovate–lanceolate sepals; stamens 14–20. Jun–Sep. Grasslands, heaths, bogs, lowlands to mountains. Throughout area covered.

540 Trailing Tormentil *Potentilla anglica*
Like **539** but with persistent rosettes of leaves; flowering stems spreading up to 80cm, and lower leaves with 5 leaflets. Flowers yellow, with 4–5 sepals and petals, mostly solitary, axillary. Petals 5–8mm, up to twice as long as sepals. Often hybridizes with **539**. Jun–Sep. Grasslands, heaths, hedge-banks. Throughout area covered, except IS, N.

541 *Potentilla nivea*
Perennial with flowering stems up to 20cm, with leaves with 3 ovate to obovate, toothed leaflets, densely white-woolly beneath and leaf-stalks with curled hairs. Flowers yellow, in terminal clusters; petals 6–9mm, slightly longer than the lanceolate to ovate sepals; epicalyx segments linear–lanceolate. Jul. F, SF, N, S.

542 Grey Cinquefoil *Potentilla cinerea*
Mat-forming with short creeping rooting woody, densely grey-hairy stems. Leaves with 3–5 grey-green oblong–obovate toothed leaflets. Flowers yellow 1–1·5cm across, with 4 petals little longer than the ovate–lanceolate sepals and narrow epicalyx. Apr–May. Dry grassy and rocky places. B, DK, F, D, S.

POTENTILLA
LEAVES WITH 5 OR MORE LEAFLETS FROM APEX OF LEAF-STALK

543

543 Creeping Cinquefoil *Potentilla reptans*
Stems trailing up to 1m, rooting at the nodes, and leaves usually with 5 obovate toothed leaflets with rounded apex. Flowers yellow, 1·5–2cm across, long-stalked from axils of leaves. Sepals 5, lanceolate; epicalyx narrower, as long. Petals 5, more or less heart-shaped, longer than sepals. Jun–Sep. Waste places, hedge-banks, grasslands. Throughout area covered, except IS.

544 *Potentilla collina*
Spreading or erect perennial; flowering stems up to 30cm, and leaves with 5–7 oblong to oblanceolate, toothed leaflets, white or silvery-hairy beneath. Flowers yellow, 8–10mm across; petals about same length as ovate sepals; epicalyx linear. A variable species. Apr–Jul. Sands, gravels, dry fields, woods. B, DK, F, D, S. **211**

545 *Potentilla neglecta*
Flowering stems usually erect up to 50cm, with leaves
with 5 obovate leaflets with acute teeth, grey-green
above. Petals yellow, 5–7mm, almost overlapping; calyx
and flower-stalks white-woolly. Throughout area
covered, except IRL, IS.

546 Hoary Cinquefoil *Potentilla argentea*
Very like **545** but leaflets of basal leaves with 2–7 blunt
teeth or lobes (leaflets with 9–11 acute teeth in **545**), and
petals 4–5mm, not overlapping. May–Aug. Open woods,
screes, sandy ground. Throughout area covered.

547 Alpine Cinquefoil *Potentilla crantzii*
Small spreading perennial with ascending flowering
stems up to 20cm, with one or few yellow flowers. Leaves
with 5 ovate to rounded, toothed leaflets, all nearly equal,
and with adpressed hairs beneath. Flowers 1–2·5cm
across, long-stalked. Petals heart-shaped, often with
basal orange spot, twice as long as sepals and epicalyx.
Very variable species. May–Jul. Rocks in mountains. GB,
SF, F, D, IS, N, S. **211**

548 *Potentilla intermedia*
Biennial or perennial with flowering stems up to 50cm,
and leaves with usually 5 obovate–oblong toothed
leaflets. Flowers numerous; petals yellow, 4–5mm, as
long or slightly longer than ovate–oblong sepals which
enlarge up to 2cm in fruit. Jun–Sep. Casual. Native of
USSR; int throughout area covered, except IRL, IS.

549 Sulphur Cinquefoil *Potentilla recta*
Rather stout erect perennial up to 70cm, with numerous
yellow flowers in lax branched rather flat-topped cluster.
Leaves with 5–7 oblong to obovate, toothed or
shallowly-lobed leaflets. Flowers 2–2·5cm across; petals
as long or longer than triangular–ovate sepals; epicalyx
segments linear. Jun–Sep. Waste places. F, D; int B, GB,
SF, NL, N, S. **212**

550 Spring Cinquefoil *Potentilla tabernaemontani*
Mat-forming perennial with spreading woody stems
rooting at the nodes. Leaves with 5–7 oblanceolate to
obovate toothed leaflets. Flowers yellow, in a lax
few-flowered cluster, not or slightly raised above the
leaves. Flowers 1–1·3cm across, long-stalked; petals
longer than sepals; epicalyx segments usually much
shorter than sepals. Variable species. May–Jun. Dry grasslands, rocky places. B, GB, DK, SF, F, D, NL, N, S. **212**

551 *Potentilla heptaphylla*
Perennial with short slender ascending branches, and
flowering stems up to 40cm, with dense thick hairs and
soft spreading hairs. Leaves with 5–7 ovate-lanceolate
toothed leaflets. Flowers yellow, solitary or up to 10;

petals 5–7mm; sepals ovate–lanceolate, epicalyx segments linear–lanceolate as long or shorter than sepals. May–Jun. Dry grasslands. DK, F, D, S.

POTENTILLA
LEAVES PINNATE

552 Shrubby Cinquefoil *Potentilla fruticosa*
Much-branched deciduous shrub 0·5–1m, with pinnate leaves with usually 5 oblong–lanceolate entire, silky-haired leaflets. Flowers yellow, 2cm across, one or few in terminal branched clusters. Petals longer than triangular–ovate sepals; epicalyx segments about as long as sepals. Jun–Jul. Rocky and bushy places on limestone. GB, F, IRL, S; int N. **212**

553 Silverweed *Potentilla anserina*
Leaves pinnate, in a rosette, with creeping rooting stems up to 80cm, and solitary axillary yellow flowers. Leaves with 7–25 oblong to ovate, coarsely toothed, silvery-silky leaflets. Flowers 1·5–2cm across, long-stalked; petals twice as long as the ovate to broadly elliptic sepals. May–Sep. Damp grassy places, waste ground, seashores. Throughout area covered. **212**

554 Sibbaldia *Sibbaldia procumbens*
Dwarf tufted spreading branched perennial, distinguished by its tiny yellow petals which are $\frac{1}{4}$ as long as the hairy sepals. Leaves in rosettes, each with 3 obovate blunt hairy leaflets, toothed or lobed at apex. Flowers 5–7mm across, few in almost stalkless cluster; sepals 5, lanceolate; epicalyx linear, shorter than sepals; stamens 5. Jun–Aug. Grassland, rock-crevices in mountains. GB, SF, F, D, IS, N, S.

554

555 Wild Strawberry *Fragaria vesca*
Perennial with long arching rooting runners, and leaves with 3 leaflets, in a basal rosette. Leaflets ovate to rhombic, coarsely toothed, bright green and sparsely silky-hairy above. Flowers white, 1–1·8cm across, borne on stems 5–30cm, little longer than the leaves. Petals obovate; sepals lanceolate acute, epicalyx narrower and longer than sepals. Fruit fleshy scarlet, globular, 1–2cm, with scattered greenish achenes. May–Jul. Woods, scrub, grasslands. Throughout area covered. **172**

556 Hautbois Strawberry *Fragaria moschata*
Differs from **555** in having flowering stems to 40cm, conspicuously longer than the leaves, and stolons few or absent. Flowers white c. 2cm across, usually one-sexed; flower-stalks with spreading hairs. Fruit reddish-purple, without achenes near its base. May–Jul. Forest clearings, open woodlands. B, F, D; int GB, DK, SF, NL, N, S.

557 *Fragaria viridis*
Differs from **555** in having sepals pressed together or down-curved after flowering (sepals spreading or down-curved in **555**), and fruit with achenes confined to upper part. Stem up to 20cm, with short thread-like stolons; leaflets with appressed hairs or hairless on upper surface. Flowers creamy-white. May–Jun. Meadows, rocks, woods. B, DK, SF, F, D, N, S.

558 Lady's Mantle *Alchemilla vulgaris*
Ascending or spreading perennial to 45cm, with thick woody rootstock, and leaves mostly basal. Leaves rounded or kidney-shaped in outline, lobed to $\frac{1}{2}$ or less into 7–11 broad toothed lobes with teeth with a tuft of hairs; leaf-stalks long; stipules brownish, papery. Flowers greenish, 3–4mm across, in a branched inflorescence in dense or lax clusters. Sepals usually 4. About 24 micro-species have been included in this aggregate species. May–Sep. Damp grasslands, open woods, rock-ledges in mountains. B, GB, DK, F, D, IRL, NL, N, S; int SF. **198**

559 Alpine Lady's Mantle *Alchemilla alpina*
Distinguished by its rounded leaves which are divided to the base, or almost so, into 5–7 lanceolate lobes, toothed at apex, silvery-hairy beneath. Flowering stems 5–20cm, with stem leaves few, sometimes 3-lobed. Flowers yellowish-green, c. 3mm across, in dense clusters in a terminal inflorescence. Jun–Aug. Mountain grasslands, rocks, screes. GB, SF, F, D, IRL, IS, N, S.

560 559

560 Parsley-piert *Aphanes arvensis*
Small prostrate or spreading, greyish-green annual, with leafy stems up to 30cm, but usually smaller. Leaves deeply 3-lobed, the lobes further divided into 3–5 oblong segments; leaf-stalk short, fused with lobed stipules. Flowers greenish, less than 2mm, in stalkless axillary clusters surrounded by the triangular lobes of the stipules. Stamen 1. Fruit bottle-shaped, with spreading sepals. Apr–Jul. Cultivated fields, bare ground in grassland. Throughout area covered, except SF, IS, N.

561 Slender Parsley-piert *Aphanes microcarpa*
Like **560** but a more slender not greyish annual, and lobes of stipules surrounding flower clusters oblong, twice as long as broad, and nearly as long as the entire basal part (stipules triangular-ovate, little longer than broad and half as long as entire basal part in **560**). Fruit ovoid, with sepals converging. Apr–Jul. Bare ground or poor grassland on sandy soils. B, GB, DK, F, D, IRL, NL, S.

560

PEA FAMILY

Leguminosae

Annual and perennial herbs, or shrubs. Leaves often compound and ending in a tendril. Stipules present. Flowers 5-merous, with distinctive bilaterally symmetrical structure (standard, wings, keel). Stamens 10; ovary a single carpel. Fruit 2-valved, dehiscent, or jointed and indehiscent. Root nodules, containing bacteria, fix atmospheric nitrogen. Important constituent of grasslands, and widely cultivated for food (peas, beans), green fertilizer and fodder.

562 Broom *Cytisus scoparius*
Usually a much-branched shrub 1–3m, but sometimes more or less prostrate (by the sea), with green 5-angled stems, and leaves with 3 leaflets, except on young twigs. Leaflets 6–20mm, narrowly lanceolate to obovate. Flowers golden-yellow, 1·6–2cm long, solitary or paired in axils of leaves, in irregular spike-like cluster. Pod 2·5–4cm, oblong–flattened, with marginal hairs, black when ripe. Apr–Jun. Heaths, open woods, coastal shingle. Throughout area covered, except SF, IS. **212**

563 Dyer's Greenweed *Genista tinctoria*
Spreading or erect spineless shrub, usually less than 1m, with many erect branches with variable narrowly lanceolate pointed, hairless or densely silvery-haired leaves. Flowers bright yellow, 0·8–1·5cm, hairless, in short dense terminal clusters. Calyx hairless, with unequal teeth. Pod 2·5–3cm flat, hairless. A very variable species. Jun–Sep. Dry pastures. B, GB, DK, F, D, NL, N, S.

564 Hairy Greenweed *Genista pilosa*
Spreading or ascending shrub up to 1·5m, with leaves usually oblanceolate, silvery-hairy beneath. Flowers solitary of paired in axils of bracts, in lax clusters on ascending branches. Flowers c. 1cm, upper petal broadly ovate with silvery adpressed hairs, calyx about half as long. May–Jun. Heaths, cliffs. B, GB, DK, F, D, NL. **212**

565 Petty Whin *Genista anglica*
Spiny spreading branched shrub up to 50cm or more, with small lanceolate to elliptic entire hairless leaves. Flowers pale yellow, 6–8mm long, in lax clusters; calyx hairless, with more or less equal teeth. Pod 1·2–1·5cm, sickle-shaped, hairless. May–Jun. Heaths, moors. B, GB, DK, F, D, NL, S. **228**

566 German Greenweed *Genista germanica*
Erect shrub up to 60cm, with spines. Leaves elliptic to lanceolate, with long spreading hairs on lower surface.

566

Flowers yellow, in lax clusters; upper petal ovate acute 8mm, ⅔ as long as keel. Calyx silky-haired. May–Sep. Screes, grassy places, heaths. B, DK, F, D, NL, S.

567 Winged Broom *Chamaespartium sagittale*
Spreading woody perennial forming mats, usually with erect herbaceous stems 10–50cm, with distinctive wings and without spines. Leaves elliptic, hairless above, hairy beneath. Flowers yellow, 1–1·2cm, in dense terminal elongated clusters. Calyx tubular 2-lipped, upper lip 2-lobed, lower with 3 teeth, silvery-hairy; upper petal broadly ovate. Pod narrow, hairy, 1·4–2cm. May–Sep. Woods, hills, dry pastures. B, F, D. **214**

568 Gorse *Ulex europaeus*
Dense very spiny shrub, 0·5–3m, with stout, rigid deeply furrowed spines up to 2·5cm. Leaves with 3 leaflets on young plant, but reduced to scales or spines on mature plants. Flowers yellow, 1·5–2cm, with wings longer than the keel. Calyx ⅔ length of petals, with spreading hairs. Pod 1–2cm, black, hairy. Mar–Dec. Rough grassy places, heaths, cliffs. GB, F, D, IRL, NL; int B, DK, N, S. **214**

569 Western Gorse *Ulex gallii*
Differs from **568** in having spines which are faintly furrowed, and bracteoles to 0·6mm (bracteoles 3–5mm in **568**). Dense spiny shrub up to 2m. Flowers deep golden-yellow, smaller 1–1·2cm; calyx at least 10mm, with teeth converging (teeth spreading in **568**). Pod c. 1cm. Jul–Sep. Heaths, cliffs, sandy grasslands. GB, F, IRL.

570 Dwarf Gorse *Ulex minor*
Spreading shrub with spiny branches, up to 1m, and hairy twigs with reddish-brown hairs. Spines slender, not rigid. Flowers yellow, like **569** but calyx less than 10mm, and teeth spreading. Wings and keel equal, as long as calyx (wings curved, longer than keel in **569**). Pod c. 8mm, with shaggy hairs. Jul–Sep. Dry heaths. GB, F. **214**

571 Sweet Lupin *Lupinus luteus*
Hairy annual up to 80cm, with long terminal spike of bright yellow flowers. Leaves digitate, with 3–5 obovate–oblong leaflets. Flowers in whorls, scented; calyx 2-lipped; petals 13–16mm black, densely hairy. Jun–Sep. Widely cultivated and naturalized. Int B, F, D, NL.

572 Tree Lupin *Lupinus arboreus*
Branched shrub 1–3m with leaves with 5–12 oblong–ovate, rough-hairy leaflets. Flowers yellow or sometimes white, 14–17mm, scented, in lax whorled clusters. Calyx 2-lipped. Pod 4–8cm, brown, with stiff adpressed hairs. May–Aug. Dry banks, sand-dunes. Native of California. Int GB, IRL. **214**

571

115

573 Garden Lupin *Lupinus polyphyllus*
Stout usually unbranched perennial up to 1·5m with blue-purple, pink or white flowers. Leaves with 9–17 ovate–lanceolate, nearly hairless leaflets. Flower spikes rather dense, to 60cm; flowers in clusters. Calyx with entire, not lobed lip; petals 12–14mm. Pod 2·5–4cm, brown, sparsely hairy. Jun–Aug. Native of north-western America. Cultivated for fodder, widely naturalized. Int DK, SF, F, D, NL, N, S.

574 Wild Lupin *Lupinus nootkatensis*
Distinguished by its long terminal spike of blue, purple, pink or white flowers. Rather stout hairy perennial, with leaves with 6–8 oblanceolate leaflets. Flowers 1·5–2cm. May–Jul. River-shingle, moors. Native of north-western N. America. Int GB, N.

575 Goat's Rue *Galega officinalis*
Erect nearly hairless perennial 0·5–1·5m, with pinnate leaves with 4–8 pairs of oblong to lanceolate leaflets and a terminal leaflet. Flowers white to pale purplish-blue, 1–1·5cm; calyx with bristle-like teeth about as long as the tube. Pod 2–5cm, cylindrical. Jul–Sep. Waste ground. F, D; int B, GB. **241**

ASTRAGALUS
FLOWERS YELLOW OR WHITE

576 Wild Liquorice *Astragalus glycyphyllos*
Stout erect or spreading perennial up to 1m or more, with pinnate leaves with usually 4–6 pairs of ovate leaflets; stipules lanceolate. Flowers cream to pale yellow, in dense axillary clusters, much shorter than the leaves. Petals 1–1·5cm, upper petal notched. Calyx with short teeth, hairless or with black hairs. Pod 3–4cm, hairless. Jul–Aug. Grassy and bushy places. Throughout area covered, except IS. **198**

577 Wild Lentil *Astragalus cicer*
Robust perennial up to 60cm or more, pinnate leaves with 10–15 pairs of lanceolate leaflets, with short adpressed hairs. Flowers yellow, many in dense axillary clusters borne on stems more than half as long as the subtending leaves. Flowers 1·4–1·6cm; calyx-teeth half as long as tube. Pod 1–1·5cm, inflated, with black and white hairs. Jun–Jul. Grassy places. B, F, D. **228**

578 Yellow Alpine Milk-vetch *Astragalus frigidus*
Erect, hairless, unbranched perennial up to 35cm, with pinnate leaves with 3–8 pairs of ovate to broadly elliptic leaflets. Flowers yellowish-white, in elongated clusters 2–5cm, borne on stems as long or longer than the subtending leaves. Flowers 1·2–1·4cm, upper petal notched; calyx with short triangular teeth. Pod 2–3cm, densely

PEA
FAMILY

black or white hairy, becoming nearly hairless. Jul–Aug.
Mountain grasslands. F, D, N, S. **198**

579 *Astragalus penduliflorus*
Differs from **578** in having leaflets less than 7mm wide,
and pod up to 1cm wide (leaflets more than 7mm wide
and pod less than 1cm wide in **578**). Flowers yellow,
1–1·2cm; calyx-tube green. Stout erect usually branched
perennial to 50cm with leaves with 7–15 pairs of elliptic
leaflets. Jul–Aug. Meadows, screes. F, D, S.

ASTRAGALUS
FLOWERS BLUE, PURPLE OR VIOLET

580 Purple Milk-vetch *Astragalus danicus*
Slender ascending perennial up to 30cm. Leaves pinnate
with 6–13 pairs of oblong blunt or notched, sparsely hairy
leaflets. Flowers purplish, numerous in rounded or
oblong clusters on stems longer than the subtending
leaves. Petals 1·5–1·8cm; calyx with teeth up to half as
long as tube. Pod ovoid, 7–8mm, white-hairy. May–Jul.
Grasslands, sand-dunes. GB, DK, F, D, IRL, S.

581 Alpine Milk-vetch *Astragalus alpinus*
Slender spreading or ascending perennial up to 30cm,
with pinnate leaves with 7–12 pairs of elliptic leaflets;
stipules sometimes fused round stem. Flowers 1–1·4cm,
either whitish with bluish-violet keel (subsp. *alpina*) or
purplish-violet (subsp. *arcticus*), in lax clusters on stems
longer than the subtending leaf. Pod 8–15mm, at first
with blackish hairs. Jul–Aug. Grassy places in
mountains. GB, SF, F, D, N, S.

580

582 *Astragalus norvegicus*
Stout, erect, usually hairless perennial up to 40cm;
pinnate leaves with usually 6–7 pairs of oblong–ovate
notched leaflets, hairless when mature. Flowers pale
violet, 1–1·2cm, in dense oblong clusters with up to 30
flowers on stems longer than subtending leaf. Pod ovoid,
c. 1cm, with blackish hairs when young. Jul. Arctic part of
area covered, and in mountains. N, S.

583

583 *Astragalus arenarius*
Slender spreading or ascending perennial up to 30cm.
Pinnate leaves with 2–9 pairs of lanceolate to linear
leaflets, with adpressed hairs; stipules fused at base.
Flowers purplish to lilac, rarely white or yellowish, in lax
oblong clusters on stems shorter than subtending leaves.
Petals 1·3–1·7cm. Pod 1·2–2cm, oblong, usually with
adpressed hairs. Jun–Jul. Sandy ground. D, S; int SF.

584 Yellow Oxytropis *Oxytropis campestris*
Compact perennial; pinnate leaves with 10–15 pairs of

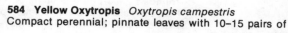

117

elliptic or lanceolate leaflets; stipules fused at base and
to leaf-stalk. Flowers yellow, white, or pale violet,
1·5–2cm, in ovoid clusters on stem to 20cm arising from
the base; keel with terminal tooth. Pod ovoid–oblong
1·4–1·8cm, hairy. Jul–Sep. Mountain pastures, rocks,
screes. GB, SF, F, N, S.

585 Purple Oxytropis *Oxytropis halleri*
Differs from **584** in having flowering stems longer than
the leaves, and flowers bluish-purple. Softly hairy
perennial, with stout rootstock. Leaves with 10–14 pairs
of elliptic to lanceolate leaflets. Flowers 1·5–2cm, in
clusters of 5–15. Pod ovoid, up to 2cm, densely hairy.
Jun–Aug. Mountain cliffs, dry grasslands. GB, F.

586 Northern Milk-vetch *Oxytropis lapponica*
Stems up to 10cm, pinnate leaves with 8–14 pairs of
lanceolate to oblong–lanceolate leaflets, with adpressed
hairs; stipules fused to $\frac{1}{2}$-way and to leaf-stalk. Flowers
blue-violet, in globular clusters; petals 8–12mm. Pod
narrowly oblong, 8–15mm, pendulous, with adpressed
hairs. Jul. Mountains. SF, F, N, S. **274**

585

587 *Oxytropis deflexa*
Like **586** but leaves with 11–16 pairs of leaflets; stipules
not fused together at base. Flowers white, in oblong
clusters. Jul–Aug. N.

588 Hairy Milk-vetch *Oxytropis pilosa*
Stems up to 50cm; pinnate leaves with 9–13 pairs of
oblong to linear–oblong leaflets, adpressed hairs, and
leaf-stalks with spreading hairs; stipules not fused.
Flowers pale yellow, hairy, in oblong clusters; petals
1·2–1·4cm. Pod 1·5–2cm, ovoid to narrowly cylindrical,
with dense hairs. Jun–Aug. Rocks, gravels. F, D, S.

588

VICIA
FLOWER CLUSTERS STALKED; FLOWERS AT LEAST 9MM LONG

589 Wood Bitter-vetch *Vicia orobus*
Hairy perennial up to 60cm, distinguished by its white
flowers with purple veins, and the absence of tendrils on
the leaves. Leaflets numerous, oblong to elliptic,
fine-pointed. Flowers 1·2–1·5cm, in clusters of 6–20,
long-stalked. Calyx teeth unequal, shorter than
calyx-tube. Pod 2–3cm, yellow, hairless. Jun–Sep. Rocky
woods. B, GB, DK, F, D, IRL, N. **241**

590 *Vicia pisiformis*
Hairless perennial to 2m; leaves with 3–4 pairs of ovate to
rounded fine-pointed leaflets; tendrils branched.
Flowers yellow, 8–30 in cluster; petals 1·3–2cm. Pod
2·5–4cm, pale brown, hairless. May–Aug. F, D, N, S.

591 Tufted Vetch *Vicia cracca*
Scrambling perennial up to 2m, with variably hairy pinnate leaves; with 6–15 pairs of linear to ovate–oblong leaflets; tendrils branched. Flowers blue-violet, 8–12mm, in dense clusters; calyx teeth very unequal, the upper minute. Pod 1–2·5cm with fruit-stalk shorter than calyx. May–Aug. Grassy and bushy places. Throughout area covered. **274**

592 Fine-leaved Vetch *Vicia tenuifolia*
Differs from **591** in having narrow linear–lanceolate leaflets, and larger purple to bluish-lilac flowers usually 1·2–1·8cm in dense clusters. Limb of standard petal longer than basal 'claw'. Pod 2–3·5cm. Jun–Aug. Grassy places, cultivated fields. B, DK, F, D, S; int GB, NL.

592

593 Danzig Vetch *Vicia cassubica*
Hairy or nearly hairless perennial up to 60cm or more. Leaves with 5–16 pairs of linear–lanceolate to elliptic leaflets. Flowers purple or blue, with wings and beak whitish; calyx teeth unequal, shorter than calyx-tube. Pod oblong 1·5–3cm, yellow, hairless. Jun–Jul. Open woods. DK, SF, F, D, N, S.

594 Wood Vetch *Vicia sylvatica*
Slender, usually hairless, much-branched trailing perennial up to 2m. Leaves with 5–12 pairs of oblong leaflets; stipules deeply toothed; tendrils branched. Flowers white with purple veins in long-stalked clusters; calyx-teeth unequal, bristle-like, shorter than calyx-tube. Pod 2·5–3cm, black, hairless. Jun–Jul. Shady places, coastal shingle and cliffs. GB, DK, SF, F, D, IRL, N, S.

595 *Vicia dumetorum*
Nearly hairless perennial up to 1·5m or more, with leaves with 3–5 pairs of ovate leaflets; stipules moon-shaped, toothed. Flowers blue or purple, 1·2–2cm, in clusters of 2–14. Calyx-teeth unequal. Pod 2·5–6cm, brown, hairless. Jun–Aug. Open woods, hedges. DK, F, D, S.

594

596 Fodder Vetch *Vicia villosa*
Annual up to 2m; leaves with 4–12 pairs of linear to elliptic leaflets; stipules not toothed. Flowers violet, purple or blue, sometimes with white or yellow wings, 1–2cm; calyx strongly swollen at base, teeth unequal. Pod 2–4cm, brown, stalked. Jun–Nov. Bare and waste ground. F, D; int B, GB, DK, SF, NL, N, S.

VICIA
FLOWER CLUSTERS STALKED; FLOWERS LESS THAN 9MM LONG

597 Hairy Tare *Vicia hirsuta*
Slender, rather weak hairy annual, with climbing stems 20–70cm. Leaves with 4–10 pairs of linear to oblong–

119

ovate leaflets; tendrils usually branched. Flowers white and purplish-tinged, 2–5mm, in long-stalked clusters of 1–8 almost equalling the leaves in length. Pod 6–11mm, black, usually hairy. May–Aug. Cultivated fields, grassland. Throughout area covered; int IS.

598 Slender Tare Vicia tenuissima
Slender almost hairless annual, with weak branched climbing stems up to 60cm. Leaves with 2–5 pairs of linear pointed leaflets; stipules entire. Flowers pale purple, 6–9mm long, in clusters of 2–5, on stalks longer than the subtending leaf; calyx-teeth unequal. Pod 1·2–1·7cm, brown, hairy or hairless. Jun–Aug. Hedgerows, cultivated fields. B, GB, F, NL.

599 Smooth Tare Vicia tetrasperma
Differs from 598 in having usually 1 or 2 flowers on stalks about as long as the leaves (stalks longer than leaves in 598). Flowers pale purple, 4–8mm. Pod 9–16mm, brown, usually hairless. Jun–Aug. Grassland, cultivated fields. Throughout area covered except IS.

597

VICIA
FLOWER CLUSTERS STALKLESS, OR ON VERY SHORT STALKS

600 Bush Vetch Vicia sepium
Usually hairy climbing or trailing perennial up to 1m. Leaves with 3–9 pairs of ovate–oblong fine-pointed leaflets; stipules elliptical, nearly entire, spotted; tendrils 1–3. Flowers dull bluish-purple, 2–6 on very short stalks; petals 1·2–1·5cm; calyx with unequal teeth. Pod 2–3·5cm, black, hairless. Apr–Nov. Hedgerows, bushy places. Throughout area covered.

601 Vicia pannonica
Hairy annual up to 60cm, with purple or yellow flowers and upper petal hairy on the upper side. Leaves with 4–10 narrow–oblong fine-pointed leaflets; stipules entire, spotted. Flowers 2–4 in each cluster; petals 1·4–2·2cm; calyx-teeth nearly equal. Pod 2–3·5cm, yellow, finely hairy. Apr–Jun. Fields, roadsides, lawns. F; int D, NL.

600

602 Common Vetch Vicia sativa
Trailing or climbing, hairy annual up to 80cm. Leaves with 3–8 pairs of linear to heart-shaped leaflets; stipules toothed, usually with a dark spot. Flowers pink to purple, usually 1–2 in leaf-axils; petals 1–3cm; calyx-teeth equal, longer or shorter than calyx-tube. Pod 2·5–7cm, yellow-brown to black, hairy or hairless. A very variable species. Apr–Sep. Borders of fields, grassy places, cultivated ground. Throughout area covered. 259

603 Spring Vetch *Vicia lathyroides*
Spreading downy annual 5–20cm, with many stems and tiny solitary lilac flowers. Leaves with 2–4 pairs of obovate to linear leaflets, with unbranched tendrils or tendrils absent; stipules entire. Flowers 5–8mm; calyx-teeth equal. Pod 1·3–3cm, with a short curved beak, black, hairless. Apr–May. Sandy ground near sea. Throughout area covered; except IS.

604 Yellow Vetch *Vicia lutea*
Slender hairy or hairless perennial with spreading stems up to 60cm, and leaves with 3–10 pairs of linear to oblong leaflets; stipules entire or toothed. Flowers pale yellow often purple-tinged, 1–3 in leaf axils. Petals 2–3·5cm; calyx with unequal teeth. Pod 2–4cm, usually with dense white hairs with swollen bases. May–Jul. Coastal shingle, grassy places near sea. GB, F; int D. **198**

605 Bithynian Vetch *Vicia bithynica*
Hairless or hairy annual up to 60cm; leaves with 2–3 pairs of oblong–lanceolate to ovate leaflets; stipules toothed. Flowers with purple upper petal and white wings and keel; petals 1·6–2cm; calyx-teeth unequal, longer than calyx-tube. Pod 2·5–5cm, brown or yellow, softly hairy. May–Jun. Fields, hedges, bushy cliffs. GB, F.

606 *Vicia narbonensis*
Differs from **605** in having dark purple flowers 1–3cm, and lower leaves without tendrils, Leaves with 1–3 pairs of ovate to elliptic entire or toothed leaflets; stipules entire or toothed. Flowers 1–6 in each cluster; calyx with unequal teeth, the lower longer than the calyx-tube. Pod 3–7cm, brown or black, with toothed hairy margin, otherwise hairless. May–Jun. Damp fields, ditches, woods. F; int D. **267**

605

607 Broad Bean *Vicia faba*
Erect robust annual with 4-angled stems, and leaves without tendrils, but otherwise similar to **606**. Flowers fragrant, usually white with black wings. Pod 8–20cm, with few large seeds, densely hairy when young. May–Jul. Cultivated throughout Europe, and sometimes locally naturalized.

LATHYRUS
LEAVES WITHOUT LEAFLETS

608 Yellow Vetchling *Lathyrus aphaca*
Rather weak hairless, climbing annual up to 1m, with distinctive broadly arrow-shaped leaf-like stipules, each with a long unbranched tendril in axil. Flowers yellow, usually solitary, on long slender stalks; petals 6–18mm; calyx-teeth 2–3 times as long as calyx-tube. Pod 2–3·5cm,

brown, hairless. May–Aug. Fields, dry places on sands, gravel or limestone. F; int B, GB, D, NL. **214**

609 Grass Vetchling *Lathyrus nissolia*
Readily distinguished by its linear grass-like leaves, and its 1–2 crimson flowers on long slender stalks. Erect nearly hairless annual to 90cm; tendrils absent. Flowers 8–18mm; calyx-teeth unequal, much shorter than calyx-tube. Pod 3–6cm. May–Jul. Grassy places, roadsides, uncultivated ground. B, GB, F, D, NL. **259**

LATHYRUS
LEAVES WITH ONLY ONE PAIR OF LEAFLETS; STEMS WINGED

610

610 Narrow-leaved Everlasting Pea
Lathyrus sylvestris
Stout climbing perennial with conspicuously winged stems, 1–2m. Leaflets 2, linear–lanceolate; tendrils branched; stipules linear to half arrow-shaped. Flowers pink-purple, 1·3–2cm, 3–12 in long-stalked clusters longer than the subtending leaves. Calyx-teeth unequal. Pod 4–7cm, brown, hairless. Jul–Aug. Woods, hedges, field-margins. B, GB, DK, SF, F, D, NL, N, S.

611 Broad-leaved Everlasting Pea *Lathyrus latifolius*
Differs from **610** in having larger pink-purple flowers 2–3cm, and stipules at least half as wide as stem (stipules less than half as wide as stem in **610**). Stout climbing perennial 1–3m. Flowers in axillary clusters of 5–15 on stalks longer than the leaves. Pod 5–11cm. Jul–Sep. Hedges, railway embankments. F; nat B, GB, D. **259**

612 Hairy Vetchling *Lathyrus hirsutus*
Spreading much-branched annual up to 120cm, with winged stem. Leaflets 2, linear to oblong; stipules linear with basal lobes. Flowers red with pale blue wings, 7–15mm, 1–3 in each cluster. Pod 2–5cm, brown with projections, hairy. Jun–Jul. Cultivated ground, hedges, roadsides. B, F, D; int GB.

LATHYRUS
STEMS WITH ONLY ONE PAIR OF LEAFLETS; STEMS NOT WINGED

613 Meadow Vetchling *Lathyrus pratensis*
Clambering perennial with angled stems up to 1·2m, leaves having 1 pair of leaflets, with a terminal tendril; stipules large leaf-like, arrow-shaped. Flowers yellow, 5–12, in long-stalked clusters much longer than the leaves; petals 1–1·6cm. Pod black. A very variable species. May–Aug. Grasslands, scrub. Throughout area covered. **214**

614 Tuberous Pea *Lathyrus tuberosus*
Distinguished from **615** by its slightly larger brigh

PEA FAMILY

red-purple flowers up to 2cm, in clusters of 2–7. Perennial with angled stems, to 120cm; leaves with one pair of elliptic to oblong leaflets. Pod brown, hairless. Jun–Jul. Grassy places, cultivated ground. B, F, D, NL; int GB, DK, S. **259**

615 *Lathyrus sphaericus*
Nearly hairless annual up to 50cm, with leaves with 1 pair of narrowly lanceolate to linear leaflets 2–6cm; stipules linear, half arrow-shaped. Flowers orange-red, solitary, on small stalks with slender point. Pod 3–7cm, brown, hairless and with prominent longitudinal veins. Apr–Jul. Cultivated ground, roadsides, grassy places, open ground. DK, F, S.

LATHYRUS
SOME LEAVES WITH 2 OR MORE PAIRS OF LEAFLETS; STEMS WINGED

616 *Lathyrus heterophyllus*
Like **611** but upper leaves usually with 2–3 pairs of leaflets. Flowers pink-purple, smaller, 1·2–2·2cm. Jul–Aug. F, D, S.

617 Bitter Vetch *Lathyrus montanus*
Slender hairless or nearly hairless perennial with winged stem, up to 50cm. Leaves with usually 2–4 pairs of ovate leaflets, without tendrils; stipules narrowly lanceolate. Flowers crimson becoming bluish, 1–1·6cm, 2–6 in each cluster. Calyx-teeth unequal. Pod 2·5–4·5cm, red-brown, hairless. May–Jul. Open woods, heaths, pastures. Throughout area covered; except IS. **259**

618

618 Marsh Pea *Lathyrus palustris*
Slightly downy, weak climbing perennial, up to 120cm, with narrow-winged stems. Leaves with 3–5 pairs of linear to lanceolate leaflets, and a terminal tendril; stipules 1–2cm, lanceolate or ovate, half arrow-shaped. Flowers purple or bluish, in clusters of 2–8, each 12–20mm. Pod 2·5–6cm, brown, hairless. Jun–Aug. Marshes, fens. Throughout area covered.

LATHYRUS
STEMS ANGLED, NOT WINGED; UPPER LEAVES WITH TENDRILS

619 Sea Pea *Lathyrus japonicus*
Stout, somewhat blue-green spreading perennial, with 4-angled stems up to 90cm. Leaves with 2–5 pairs of elliptic, pinnately-veined leaflets 2–4cm, usually with tendrils; stipules large triangular to spear-shaped. Flowers purple becoming blue, 1·4–2·2cm, on stems usually shorter than leaves. Pod 3–5cm, brown, becoming hairless. Jun–Jul. Coastal sands and shingle. GB, DK, SF, D, IRL, IS, N, S. **274**

LATHYRUS
LEAVES WITHOUT TENDRILS

620 *Lathyrus pannonicus*
Hairless or sparsely hairy perennial up to 50cm, with stem not winged or narrowly winged, and roots fleshy and tuberous. Leaves with 1–4 pairs of linear to oblong–elliptic leaflets. Flowers pale cream, reddish- or purple-tinged, 3–9 in each cluster, borne on stems longer than the subtending leaves; petals 1·2–2cm. Pod 3–6·5cm, pale brown, hairless. A very variable species. May–Jul. Damp fields, woods. F, D.

621 Spring Pea *Lathyrus vernus*
Perennial up to 40cm, with unwinged stems, and distinctive leaves with 2–4 pairs of ovate to lanceolate leaflets with long acute points. Stipules large, usually ovate–lanceolate and semi-arrow-shaped. Flowers reddish-purple becoming blue, in long-stalked axillary clusters of 3–10. Petals 1·3–2cm; calyx-teeth unequal. Pod 4–6cm, brown, hairless. Apr–Jun. Woods. DK, SF, F, D, N, S; int B, NL. **259**

622 Black Pea *Lathyrus niger*
Differs from **621** in having leaflets blunt or slightly acute and shorter stipules 4–10mm (stipules 1–2·5cm in **621**). Leaflets usually 3–6 pairs. Flowers purple becoming blue, 1–1·5cm. Pod 3·5–6cm, black, hairless. May–Jul. Open woods. B, GB, DK, SF, F, D, NL, N, S.

ONONIS
FLOWERS PINK, PURPLE OR WHITE

623

623 Small Restharrow *Ononis reclinata*
Low spreading annual, with glandular-sticky, hairy stems up to 15cm. Leaves with 3 oblong–lanceolate to nearly rounded toothed leaflets to 8mm. Flowers pink or purple, to 1cm, solitary in axils of leaves; petals about equalling calyx which has narrow acute teeth longer than the calyx-tube. Pod 8–14mm, hairy, deflexed when ripe. May–Jun. Cliffs by sea, sandy grassy places. GB, F.

624

624 Common Restharrow *Ononis repens*
Usually a spreading shrubby perennial up to 70cm, often rooting at the nodes, and without stiff spines. Leaves with 1–3 ovate leaflets. Flowers pink or purple, 1·5–2cm, usually one at each node, in lax leafy spike-like clusters; calyx usually shorter than petals, densely hairy. Pod 5–7mm. Jun–Sep. Poor dry soils. Throughout area covered, except IS; int SF.

625 Spiny Restharrow *Ononis spinosa*
Dwarf shrub with erect or spreading, usually robust spiny branches, up to 80cm. Leaves mostly with 3 blunt leaflets,

variable in shape, toothed. Flowers pink or purple, 6–20mm, usually borne singly at each node and forming a lax cluster. Calyx-teeth linear, glandular-hairy, petals usually much longer. Pod up to 1cm long. Apr–Sep. Poor pastures, roadsides. Throughout area covered, except SF, IRL, IS. **241**

626 *Ononis arvensis*
Hairy shrubby perennial with erect stems up to 1m, and leaves with 3 elliptic to ovate leaflets. Flowers pink, 1–2cm, borne in pairs from each node and forming a dense terminal cluster. Pod about as long as calyx. A very variable species. Apr–Sep. Fields, dry grasslands, roadsides. DK, SF, D, N, S.

ONONIS
FLOWERS YELLOW

627 Large Yellow Restharrow *Ononis natrix*
Erect much-branched dwarf shrub up to 60cm, densely glandular-hairy, with usually 3 variable ovate to linear leaflets 12–20mm. Flowers yellow, often red- or violet-veined, 1·2–2cm, in lax leafy clusters. Pod 1·2–2·5cm. Very variable species. May–Aug. Dry open places, arid slopes. F, D. **215**

628 *Ononis pusilla*
Differs from **627** in having smaller yellow flowers, 5–12mm, with petals about equalling the calyx, and with conspicuous leaf-like bracts larger than the flowers. Perennial up to 25cm, with woody base, and long-stalked leaves with 3 elliptic to nearly rounded leaflets. Pod 6–8mm. Jun–Aug. Uncultivated ground. F; int B.

MELILOTUS
FLOWERS WHITE

629 White Melilot *Melilotus alba*
Readily distinguished by its slender terminal and axillary long-stalked lax spikes of tiny white flowers. Erect branched annual or biennial up to 1·5m, with leaves with 3 narrow–oblong to nearly rounded toothed leaflets. Flowers 4–5mm; upper petal (standard) longer than wings and keel. Pod 3–5mm, net-veined. Jul–Oct. Open ground. DK, SF, F, D, NL, N, S; nat B, GB. **172**

MELILOTUS
FLOWERS YELLOW, SMALL 2–3·5MM

630 Small Melilot *Melilotus indica*
Erect or ascending annual up to 50cm, distinguished by its dense terminal and axillary stalked clusters of many tiny pale yellow flowers, each 2–3mm. Leaves with 3

630

lanceolate–oblong, toothed leaflets. Upper petal longer than wings and keel. Pod rounded, strongly net-veined. May–Jun. Fields, damp sands, waysides. F; int B, GB, D, NL.

631 Melilotus dentata

Erect branched annual up to 1·5m, with clusters of bright yellow flowers, each flower 3–3·5mm long. Differs from **630** in having stipules of middle leaves toothed (stipules entire in **630**). Flowers with wings shorter than upper petal and longer than keel. Pod obovoid, slightly net-veined. Jul–Aug. Saline meadows, river-banks. DK, D, S.

MELITOTUS
FLOWERS YELLOW, 3–9MM

632

632 Ribbed Melilot Melilotus officinalis

Erect or spreading branched biennial up to 2·5m, with slender lax many-flowered spikes of yellow flowers. Leaflets 3, ovate to obovate, upper leaves with narrower leaflets, all toothed. Flowers 4–7mm long, with wings and upper petal equal and longer than the keel. Pod 3–5mm, strongly transversely wrinkled, hairless, brown when ripe. May–Sep. Fields, waste places. B, F, D, NL; int GB, DK, SF, IRL, N, S.

633 Tall Melilot Melilotus altissima

Differs from **632** in having hairy pods, net-veined, and black when ripe. Flowers yellow, 5–7mm, with upper petal, wings and keel all equal. Stem up to 1·5m; leaves with 3 oblong–ovate to wedge-shaped, toothed leaflets. May–Sep. Damp salt-rich places, fields, waysides. B, DK, F, D, NL, N, S; int GB, IRL. **215**

634 Star-fruited Fenugreek Trigonella monspeliaca

Annual up to 35cm, with densely adpressed hairs on stems. Leaves with 3 wedge-shaped, entire or toothed leaflets. Flowers yellow, c. 4mm, in almost stalkless umbel-like clusters. Calyx-teeth slightly longer than calyx-tube. Pods pendent linear, 7–17mm, slightly curved, and spreading in a star. Mar–Jun. Rocks, dry ground. B, F.

635 Classical Fenugreek Trigonella foenum-graecum

Distinguished by its solitary or paired yellowish-white flowers tinged with violet at base, each 12–18mm. Sparsely hairy annual up to 50cm; leaves with 3 obovate to oblong, toothed leaflets, 2–5cm. Pod 6–11cm, with a beak 2–3cm long. Widely cultivated for fodder. Apr–May. Waste ground. Native of S-W. Asia. Int B, F, D. **199**

MEDICAGO
FRUIT SICKLE-SHAPED OR BEAN-SHAPED

636 Black Medick *Medicago lupulina*
Low, often spreading, downy annual or perennial, up to 60cm. Leaves with 3 rounded oblong, usually fine-pointed, toothed leaflets; stipules lanceolate to ovate. Flowers yellow, tiny 2–3mm, 10–50 in dense rounded clusters on long stalks from leaf-axils. Pod kidney-shaped, black when ripe and obscurely net-veined. May–Oct. Grassy places, waste ground, dry banks, walls. Throughout area covered. **215**

637 Lucerne *Medicago sativa*
Somewhat hairy perennial up to 80cm, with leaves with 3 obovate to almost linear leaflets. Flowers blue to purple, in lax terminal and axillary clusters. Petals 5–11mm; calyx bell-shaped, with 5 nearly equal teeth. Pod spiral with 1½–3½ turns, with 10–20 seeds. A very variable species. Jun–Oct. Grassy places, waste ground, roadsides. Native of S-W. Asia. Int throughout area covered, except IS. **274**

637a Sickle Medick ssp. *falcata*, up to 60cm, often spreading. Flowers yellow, pod straight to sickle-shaped, with 2–5 seeds. Dry, grassy places; the wild variant of this species forms intermediate populations in some areas. **215**

MEDICAGO
FRUIT IN A SPIRAL OF ONE OR MORE TURNS (see also **637**)

638 Spotted Medick *Medicago arabica*
Spreading nearly hairless annual 20–50cm; leaves with 3 heart-shaped toothed leaflets with wedge-shaped base, and usually central dark spot; stipules toothed. Flowers bright yellow, c. 5–7mm, usually in short-stalked clusters of 1–4. Pod globular, in a lax spiral of 4–7 turns, usually with spines half to three-quarters as long as the diameter of the pod. Apr–Sep. Grasslands, bare ground, roadsides, often near the sea. B, GB, F, D, NL; int IRL, S.

639 Toothed Medick *Medicago polymorpha*
Smaller, more hairy annual than **638**, with leaflets without a dark spot; stipules more deeply toothed. Leaflets obovate to obcordate, with wedge-shaped base, toothed only near apex. Flowers yellow, 3–4·5mm, in clusters of 1–8. Pod disk-like or shortly cylindrical in a lax spiral of 1½–6 turns, either spineless or with spines longer than the pod and deeply grooved. May–Jul. Sandy and gravelly places near the sea. GB, F, D; int B, NL.

640 Bur Medick *Medicago minima*
Shaggy-hairy annual up to 40cm, with obovate to obcordate leaflets, toothed near apex. Flowers yellow,

638

4–4·5mm in axillary clusters of 1–6. Pod more or less globular, in a lax spiral of 3–5 turns, sparsely hairy, somewhat glandular, usually spiny. Mar–Jun. Sandy heaths and fields. B, GB, DK, F, D, NL, S.

TRIFOLIUM
FLOWERS YELLOW OR BROWNISH-YELLOW

641 Hop Trefoil *Trifolium campestre*
Much-branched ascending hairy annual up to 30cm or more. Leaves short-stalked, with 3 obovate notched and toothed leaflets, the middle leaflet stalked; stipules half-ovate, dilated and rounded at base. Flowers yellow, 4–5mm, numerous in dense globular heads to 1·5cm, on stalks longer than the subtending leaves; calyx with very unequal teeth. May–Sep. Dry grassy places. Throughout area covered, except IS; int SF.

642 Large Trefoil *Trifolium aureum*
Like **641** but flowers golden-yellow, 6–7mm, with heart-shaped upper petal, and leaflets all almost stalkless or equally short-stalked. Robust with many erect stems up to 30cm, with oblong–obovate or rhombic leaflets; stipules not dilated below. Flower-heads to 1·6cm across. Jun–Aug. Fields, waste places. B, DK, SF, F, D, NL, N, S; casual in GB.

641

643 Lesser Trefoil *Trifolium dubium*
Distinguished from **641** by its smaller yellow flowers 3–3·5mm, in heads 8–9mm across (flower-heads up to 15mm across in **641**), which turn yellowish-brown after flowering. Upper petal narrowly oblong. Spreading or ascending annual up to 25cm or more; leaves with mid-leaflet stalked; stipules broadly ovate. May–Oct. Dry grassy places. Throughout area covered, except IS; int SF.

644 *Trifolium spadiceum*
Annual or biennial with erect little-branched, nearly hairless stems up to 40cm. Uppermost leaves almost opposite, with oblong stalkless leaflets; stipules oblong–lanceolate. Flowers golden-yellow, c. 6mm, becoming dark brown after fertilization. Fruiting heads up to 2·5cm across. Jun. Grassy places. SF, F, D, N, S.

645 Slender Trefoil *Trifolium micranthum*
Spreading or ascending much branched annual up to 10cm, with tiny obovate to heart-shaped toothed leaflets usually to 5mm long. Flower-stalks very slender. Flowers 1–6, in heads c. 4mm across, deep yellow, becoming yellowish-brown after fertilization. May–Aug. Grassy places, lawns. B, GB, DK, F, D, IRL, NL, N.

644

646 Sulphur Clover *Trifolium ochroleucon*
Matted perennial, with ascending hairy stems 10–50cm.
Leaflets oblong–elliptic or lanceolate 1·5–3cm, with
marginal hairs. Flowers yellowish-white, rarely pink, in
globular or oblong, short-stalked heads, 2–4cm. Petals
1·5–2cm, twice as long as calyx which has lowest tooth
longer than upper 4, which is recurved in fruit. Jun–Aug.
Dry grasslands, hedge-banks, roadsides. B, GB, F, D. **199**

TRIFOLIUM
FLOWERS PURPLE, PINK, RED, WHITE OR CREAM; FLOWER-HEADS ELONGATE,
AT LEAST TWICE AS LONG AS BROAD

647 Hare's-foot Clover *Trifolium arvense*
Erect or spreading branched annual or biennial up to
40cm, usually softly whitish- or reddish-hairy. Upper
leaves stalkless, with 3 linear–oblong leaflets.
Flower-heads oblong, stalked, to 2cm, with numerous
tiny whitish or pinkish flowers. Petals c. 4mm, shorter
than calyx. Calyx-tube globular in fruit, densely hairy,
with longer reddish bristle-like teeth. Jun–Aug. Dry and
sandy places. Throughout area covered, except IS. **241**

648 Crimson Clover *Trifolium incarnatum*
Rather robust erect or ascending annual up to 50cm, with
conspicuous elongate–cylindrical flower-head with
numerous crimson flowers. Leaflets rounded to obovate,
toothed towards apex; stipules ovate, often leafy.
Flower-heads 1–4cm long, long-stalked; petals 1–1·2cm;
calyx with spreading teeth in fruit. May–Jul. Cultivated
for fodder; nat B, GB, DK, SF, F, D, NL, N, S.
Long-headed Clover ssp. *molineri* up to 25cm, spreading
or ascending; flowers pink or pale cream. Native on
coastal cliffs in F and GB (Cornwall). **234**

649 Knotted Clover *Trifolium striatum*
Low spreading, downy annual 5–50cm or more. Leaves
with 3 obovate leaflets; stipules ovate, with spiny tip.
Flowers pink, in oblong to globular stalkless axillary
heads 1–1·5cm. Petals 4–5mm, the upper petal equal or
longer than upper calyx tooth; calyx with ovoid hairy tube
and fine-pointed teeth, becoming swollen in fruit.
May–Jul. Dry grassy places. Throughout area covered,
except SF, IS, N.

TRIFOLIUM
FLOWERS PURPLE, PINK, RED, WHITE OR CREAM; FLOWER-HEADS GLOBULAR,
OR LESS THAN TWICE AS LONG AS WIDE. FLOWER-HEADS STALKLESS, OR
SHORT-STALKED FROM LEAF-AXILS

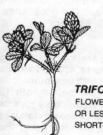

650 Twin-headed Clover *Trifolium bocconei*
Slender spreading or erect hairy-stemmed annual

5–25cm, distinguished by its stalkless purplish flower-heads, the upper usually in unequal pairs. Leaflets of upper leaves narrowly wedge-shaped, finely toothed. Flower-heads 9–15mm, conical or cylindrical; flowers numerous, c. 5mm, equalling calyx. Calyx-tube cylindrical, hairy, teeth unequal. Jun–Jul. Dry places, banks. GB, F; int D.

651 Fenugreek *Trifolium ornithopodioides*
Prostrate, spreading, hairless, dwarf annual 2–20cm or more, with flower-head short-stalked, with usually 2–4 white or pale pink flowers. Leaves with 3 obovate to wedge-shaped, toothed, shortly stalked leaflets; leaves long-stalked, longer than flower-heads. Flowers 6–8mm, with narrowly oblong upper petal; calyx with nearly equal teeth longer than calyx-tube. Pod longer than calyx. May–Jul. Dry bare or trampled ground. GB, F, D, IRL, NL.

652 Clustered Clover *Trifolium glomeratum*
Hairless annual with many spreading or ascending stems up to 20cm, and with stalkless globular, pink flower-heads 8–12mm, in axils of much longer leaves. Leaflets obovate, toothed. Flowers 4–5mm, petals little longer than calyx, which has a 10-veined hairless calyx-tube with reflexed teeth. May–Jul. Dry places, waysides, fields. GB, F, IRL.

653 Suffocated Clover *Trifolium suffocatum*
Hairless, prostrate spreading annual with stems 1–5cm. Leaves long-stalked, leaflets ovate to wedge-shaped, notched. Flower-heads globular, 5–6mm, stalkless; petals white, shorter than calyx which has pointed recurved teeth as long as the calyx-tube. Mar–Jun. Dry bare ground, usually near the sea. GB, F.

654 Rough Clover *Trifolium scabrum*
Rather stout spreading or ascending hairy annual, with many stems up to 25cm. Leaflets ovate, leathery, finely toothed. Flower-heads numerous, globular or ovoid, whitish or rarely pink, 5–12mm. Petals usually shorter than calyx which persists in fruit, with rigid spreading spiny slightly recurved teeth. May–Jul. Dry grasslands, sandy and rocky ground. B, GB, F, D, IRL, NL.

655 *Trifolium alpestre*
Perennial with rhizomes, and with erect or ascending usually unbranched hairy stems up to 40cm. Leaflets lanceolate to narrow elliptic, 2–5cm, with very numerous curved veins; stipules fused for half their length to leaf-stalk, usually papery. Flowers purple, rarely pink or white, c. 1·5cm, in globular stalkless or nearly stalkless heads to 2·5cm across. Calyx-teeth slender, hairy, the lowest much longer. Very variable species. Jun–Aug. Open woods, scrub, pastures. B, DK, F, D.

656

656 Sea Clover *Trifolium squamosum*
Erect or spreading branched hairy annual up to 40cm; leaflets oblong to lanceolate with hairy margins. Flowers pale pink, in ovoid or conical heads 1·2cm, on short stalks. Flowers 5mm, twice as long as calyx. Fruiting calyx with tough bell-shaped calyx-tube, 10-veined, and lanceolate pointed spreading leafy teeth, the lowest 3-veined. May–Jul. Damp grassy places near sea. GB, F.

TRIFOLIUM
FLOWER-HEADS DISTINCTLY STALKED WITH STALKS 2CM OR MORE; FLOWER-HEAD WITH 2 LEAVES, CLOSE BELOW FLOWER-HEAD

657 Red Clover *Trifolium pratense*
Erect or spreading branched tufted perennial up to 1m; leaves with obovate to nearly rounded leaflets hairy below. Flowers pink or reddish-purple, in dense ovate heads 2–4cm long, solitary or paired, and with two trifoliate leaves surrounding the base of each head. Flowers 12–15mm, rarely cream or white, usually twice as long as calyx. Calyx 10-veined and with triangular slender pointed teeth, hairy. Very variable species. May–Sep. Grasslands; widely cultivated for fodder. Throughout area covered. 241

658 Zigzag Clover *Trifolium medium*
Differs from 657 in stipules of middle leaves with free part awl-shaped (stipules with free part triangular, bristly-pointed in 657), and flower-heads, ultimately short-stalked. Flower-heads red-purple, globular or ovoid 2·5–3·5cm, usually solitary. Calyx usually hairless; corolla 1·2–2cm. Ascending often branched perennial to 50cm, or more. May–Sep. Dry pastures, hedgerows, woods, vineyards. Throughout area covered, except IS. 241

659 Subterranean Clover *Trifolium subterraneum*
Spreading, hairy branched annual to 30cm, with usually long-stalked leaves with inverse heart-shaped, spotted leaflets and stipules semi-ovate entire. Flowers whitish, pink-veined, in heads of usually 2–5 fertile flowers 8–14mm and numerous sterile flowers which develop after flowering into down-curved calyx. Fruiting heads globular, long-stalked, pressed to soil or buried. A very variable species. Apr–Sep. Grassy places on sandy soils. B, GB, F, IRL, NL. 172

660

660 Upright Clover *Trifolium strictum*
Erect or ascending branched hairless annual up to 15cm. Leaflets linear to elliptic, the upper often lanceolate, with veins ending in stalked glands; stipules conspicuous, ovate or rhombic, with glandular teeth. Flower-heads pink, spherical, 7–10mm, borne on stalks 1–2 times as long as leaves; petals 5–6mm, upper petal slightly longer

131

than hairless calyx-teeth. May–Jun. Grassy and rocky places. GB, F; int D.

661 *Trifolium montanum*
Perennial with woody rootstock and several erect hairy stems up to 60cm. Stem-leaves with elliptic to oblong leaflets to 4cm, hairless above, silvery-hairy beneath. Flower-heads white or yellowish, rarely pink, becoming yellowish-brown, in long-stalked heads. Petals 7–9mm, upper petal recurved; calyx hairy. May–Jul. Poor dry grasslands, open woods. B, SF, F, D, N, S. **199**

662 White Clover *Trifolium repens*
Creeping perennial rooting at the nodes, with long-stalked globular heads of scented white flowers. Leaves long-stalked, with obovate to elliptic leaflets, usually with bright green or light or dark marks along the veins. Flowers fragrant 8–13mm, with upper petal 2–2½ times as long as the calyx, which has two upper teeth longer than the others. Upper petal entire. A very variable species. May–Oct. Grassy places. Throughout area covered; often cultivated for fodder.

662

663 Western Clover *Trifolium occidentale*
Like **662** but usually more compact; leaflets almost rounded, with blunt or notched apex, blue-green above and without white or dark markings, and upper calyx-teeth triangular (upper calyx-teeth narrowly lanceolate in **662**). Stipules reddish. Flower-heads white or pale pink, slightly scented. Petals 8–9mm; upper petal notched. Mar–Jun. Sand-dunes, low coastal cliffs, dry grassy places by sea. GB, F, IRL.

664 Alsike Clover *Trifolium hybridum*
Distinguished from **662** by its long-pointed calyx-teeth which are nearly equal and separated by a broad blunt space between the teeth. (Calyx teeth lanceolate, unequal and separated by a narrow acute space between the teeth in **662**.) Erect perennial up to 1m, rarely prostrate. Flower-heads purplish or white, becoming pink and then brown, globular, c. 2·5cm, long-stalked. Jun–Sep. Waste places, roadsides, margins of fields. F; int B, GB, DK, SF, D, IRL, NL, N, S. **242**

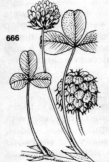

666

665 *Trifolium michelianum*
Annual with thick hollow branched stems often constricted at the nodes, up to 65cm. Leaves long-stalked; leaflets oblong to obovate, toothed. Flower-heads pink, in lax globular heads 2–2·5cm wide; petals 8–11mm; calyx with long nearly equal teeth 3–4 times as long as calyx-tube. Flowers deflexed after flowering. Jun–Jul. Wet meadows, marshes. F.

666 Strawberry Clover *Trifolium fragiferum*
Creeping perennial up to 30cm, with short erect

flowering stem and pale pink flowers. Leaves with elliptic to inverse heart-shaped leaflets; stipules papery. Flower-heads hemispherical, 1–2·2cm or more across, long-stalked, becoming more or less globular or cylindrical in fruit and surrounded by bracts forming a deeply dissected involucre. Petals 6–7mm; upper lip of calyx greatly inflated in fruit. May–Sep. Damp grassy places, saline meadows, waysides. Throughout area covered, except IS.

667 Reversed Clover *Trifolium resupinatum*
Hairless spreading or erect annual up to 30cm, or more, with leaves with obovate leaflets up to 2cm. Flowers pink, 2–8mm, twisted through 180° with keel above upper petal in globular stalked heads. Fruiting heads globular, to 2cm or more across; calyx pear-shaped with 2 spreading upper teeth. A very variable species. Apr–Jun. Damp grassy places, disturbed ground. B, F; int B, GB, D, NL.

668 Common Birdsfoot Trefoil *Lotus corniculatus*
Perennial with spreading, ascending stems or erect up to 50cm, and leaves with 5 lanceolate to nearly rounded leaflets. Flowers yellow, often flushed with red, 1–1·6cm, in heads of 2–7 flowers, borne on stout stems up to c. 8cm. Calyx-teeth triangular, equal, shorter to slightly longer than calyx-tube. Pod 1·5–3cm. A very variable species. May–Sep. Grassy places, sand-dunes, cliffs. Throughout area covered; int IS. **228**

669 Narrow-leaved Birdsfoot Trefoil *Lotus tenuis*
Like **668** but leaflets of upper leaves linear to narrowly lanceolate, at least 4 times as long as wide. Flowers yellow, 6–12mm, in heads of usually 1–4; calyx-teeth shorter than calyx-tube. Stems slender up to 90cm. Jun–Aug. Dry pastures, waysides. B, GB, DK, F, D, NL, S; int SF, N.

669

670 Greater Birdsfoot Trefoil *Lotus uliginosus*
Erect or ascending hairy perennial with hollow stems, up to 1m. Leaves with obovate leaflets, to 2·5cm, blue-green beneath. Flowers yellow often red-tinged, in long-stalked heads of usually 5–12 flowers. Petals 1–1·8cm; calyx-teeth spreading in bud, about as long as calyx-tube. Pod 1·5–3·5cm. Jun–Aug. Marshes, damp grasslands. B, GB, DK, F, D, IRL, NL, S; int SF, N. **228**

671 Hairy Birdsfoot Trefoil *Lotus subbiflorus*
Spreading hairy annual 5–60cm, with leaves with 5 oblong to lanceolate entire leaflets. Flowers yellow veined with orange, 2–4, on stems much longer than the leaves. Petals 5–10mm, with keel long-beaked; calyx-teeth longer than calyx-tube. Pod 6–16mm, straight, up to 3 times as long as calyx. Apr–Sep. Grassy sandy places, fields and rocks near the sea. GB, F, IRL.

671

133

672 Slender Birdsfoot Trefoil *Lotus angustissimus*
Like **661**, but keel with a short beak and with right-angle on lower edge (keel bluntly angled on lower edge in **671**). Flowers yellow, sometimes purple-veined, 5–12mm, in clusters of 1–3, on stalks shorter or longer than the leaves. Pod 1·5–3cm, 4–7 times as long as calyx. Apr–Aug. Grassy places, roadsides, sands. GB, F.

672

673 Kidney Vetch *Anthyllis vulneraria*
Annual to perennial; stems 5–50cm, spreading or ascending, sometimes erect, with pinnate leaves; lower leaves with unequal ovate to elliptic leaflets, the upper leaves with linear–oblong equal, subequal or sometimes unequal leaflets. Flowers usually yellow, but (especially on coast) also cream, pink, or orange in dense globular clusters to 4cm across, with 2 deeply divided bracts beneath the usually paired heads. Petals 12–15mm; calyx inflated and constricted at apex and with 5 unequal teeth. Pod ovoid, netted. Very variable species, with some 20 subspecies identified. Apr–Sep. Dry grasslands, cliffs, roadsides. Throughout area covered. **215**

674 Birdsfoot *Ornithopus perpusillus*
Hairy annual with spreading stems up to 30cm, and leaves with 7–13 pairs of small elliptic to oblong leaflets. Flowers white or pink, 3–5mm, in heads of 3–8 flowers, and with bracts below the flower-head longer than the flowers and with 5–9 lobes. Calyx-teeth not more than half as long as calyx-tube. Pod 1–1·8cm, constricted between segments, and with straight or hooked beak. May–Oct. Sandy and gravelly places. B, GB, DK, F, D, IRL, NL, S. **242**

674

675 Orange Birdsfoot *Ornithopus pinnatus*
Distinguished from **674** by its orange-yellow flowers without leafy bracts below the flower-heads. Nearly hairless annual to 50cm, with leaves with 3–7 pairs of narrow linear to oblanceolate leaflets. Flowers 6–8mm, in heads of 1–5. Pod 2–3·5cm, not constricted between segments. Apr–Jul. Sandy fields, heaths. GB, F.

676 Scorpion Senna *Coronilla emerus*
Small shrub up to 1m or more, with leaves with 2–4 pairs of obovate blue-green leaflets. Flowers pale yellow, often red-tipped, 1·4–2cm, in axillary heads of 1–5 flowers, borne on stems about as long as the leaves. Basal stalk (claw) of upper petal 2–3 times as long as calyx. Pod 5–11cm, with 3–12 segments. Apr–Jun. Rocks, old walls, wood verges. F, D, N, S; int DK. **215**

677 *Coronilla minima*
Small shrub up to 30cm or more, with leaves with 2–6 pairs of elliptic to obovate stalkless leaflets with papery margins. Flowers yellow, usually 5–8mm, or more, and usually in heads of up to 10 flowers. Pod 1–3·5cm,

with 1–7 oblong 4-angled segments. Apr–Jun. Grassy places. F.

678 Small Scorpion-vetch *Coronilla vaginalis*
Differs from **677** in having shortly stalked leaflets, and stipules 3–8mm, leafy with papery tips and soon falling (stipules c. 1mm, papery, persistent in **677**). Small shrub up to 50cm. Flowers yellow, 6–10mm, in heads of 4–10. Pod 1·5–3·5cm, with 3–8, 6-angled segments, with 4 of the angles winged. Jun–Aug. Rocks. F, D.

679 Scorpion-vetch *Coronilla coronata*
Herbaceous perennial with ascending stems up to 70cm. Leaves with 3–7 pairs of elliptic to obovate, stalked leaflets; stipules papery, fused. Flowers yellow, 7–11mm, in heads of 12–20 flowers. Pod 1·5–3cm, with usually 1–5 bluntly 4-angled segments. May–Jul. Dry woods, scrub, grasslands. F, D.

680 Crown Vetch *Coronilla varia*
Stout much-branched sprawling perennial up to 120cm. Leaves with usually 7–12 pairs of oblong or elliptic leaflets; stipules not fused, papery. Flowers white, pink or purple, 1–1·5cm, in dense globular heads of usually 10–20 flowers. Pod 2–6cm, with 3–8 oblong, 4-angled segments. May–Aug. Bushy places, river banks. F, D, NL; int B, GB, DK, N, S. **242**

681 Horseshoe Vetch *Hippocrepis comosa*
Spreading or erect perennial with flowering stems 10–40cm. Leaves with 3–8 pairs of obovate to linear, densely hairy or nearly hairless leaflets. Flowers yellow, in lax heads of 5–12 flowers, borne on stem much longer than the leaves. Petals 6–10mm, with stalk of upper petal usually longer than the calyx. Pod 1·5–3cm, with horseshoe-shaped segments, and ornamented with red-brown warts. May–Jun. Grassy places, rocks, hills. B, GB, F, D, NL. **216**

682 Sainfoin *Onobrychis viciifolia*
Stout erect perennial up to 80cm; leaves with 6–14 pairs of ovate to oblong leaflets. Flowers pink with purple veins, in elongated clusters of up to 9cm. Petals 10–14mm; calyx hairy, with teeth 2–3 times as long as calyx-tube. Pod rounded, 5–8mm across, flattened, with conspicuous net of veins, often toothed on veins and margin. May–Aug. Calcareous pastures; widely cultivated for fodder. Int B, GB, DK, F, S.

682

WOOD SORREL FAMILY

Oxalidaceae

Annual and perennial herbs, often with fleshy roots. Leaves compound. Stamens 10. Fruit a capsule.

OXALIS
FLOWERS WHITE, RED, VIOLET OR PURPLE

683 Wood Sorrel *Oxalis acetosella*
Slender perennial with creeping rhizome with fleshy tooth-like remains of leaf-bases, and long-stalked leaves with 3 heart-shaped, notched hairless leaflets. Flowers white with pale lilac veins, to pale purple or violet, bell-shaped, 8–15mm, solitary on long stalks; sepals oblong–lanceolate. Pod ovoid, angled. Apr–May. Woods, shady places. Throughout area covered. **242**

684 Pink Sorrel *Oxalis articulata*
Distinguished by its terminal cluster of pink flowers, borne on leafless stems to 35cm. Leaves in rosettes, each leaf with 3 heart-shaped, notched leaflets covered with orange or brown swellings. Petals 1·2–2cm; sepals lanceolate, with 2 apical swellings. May–Sep. Cultivated in gardens; established in waste places. Native of S. America. Int GB, F, IRL.

OXALIS
FLOWERS YELLOW

685 Procumbent Yellow Sorrel *Oxalis corniculata*
Low creeping perennial, with spreading stems up to 50cm, rooting at the nodes. Leaves with 3 heart-shaped, deeply notched leaflets, 5–18mm. Flowers yellow, 1–7 in a terminal umbel-like cluster; petals 4–7mm; sepals lanceolate. Pods hoary, 1–2·5cm, on deflexed stalks. May–Oct. Dry open places, cultivated ground. Probably native of S. Europe, but now worldwide. F; int B, GB, SF, D, IRL, NL, N, S.

686 Upright Yellow Sorrel *Oxalis europaea*
Like **685** but stems with branched hairs, not rooting at the nodes, and leaves nearly opposite; stipules absent (leaves alternate, stipules oblong, fused to leaf-stalk in **685**). Flowers yellow, in flat-topped clusters. Pods not hoary, without deflexed stalks. Jun–Oct. Cultivated ground, wood-margins, waysides. Native of N. America and E. Asia. Int throughout area covered, except IS.

687 *Oxalis stricta*
Like **685** with yellow flowers in umbel-like clusters, and

685

WOOD SORREL
FAMILY

fruiting stalks deflexed, but a tufted perennial with
ascending stems up to 20cm, not rooting at the nodes.
Leaves nearly opposite, or in groups; stipules oblong,
inconspicuous. Jul–Oct. Cultivated ground. Native of N.
America. Int GB, DK, F, D.

688 Bermuda Buttercup *Oxalis pes-caprae*
Tufted perennial with underground stem bearing bulbils,
and basal rosette of leaves. Leaflets 3, heart-shaped,
deeply notched. Flowers yellow, with petals 2–3cm, in
terminal umbel-like cluster, borne on long stalk longer
than the leaves. Mar–Jun. Cultivated ground, open
places near the coast. Native of S. Africa. Int GB, F. **216**

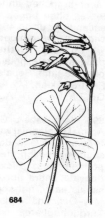

684

GERANIUM FAMILY

Geraniaceae

Annual, biennial or perennial herbs, frequently aromatic on bruising. Leaves compound or lobed. Flowers regular, 5-merous. Fruit beaked, splitting at maturity.

GERANIUM
ANNUALS OR BIENNIALS; PETALS WITH A DISTINCT STALK (CLAW); SEPALS ERECT DURING FLOWERING

689 Shining Cranesbill *Geranium lucidum*
Much-branched annual, with smooth shining rounded leaves often tinged red, and flowering stems erect or ascending, up to 40cm. Leaves divided to nearly ⅔ the width of the rounded blade into 5 wedge-shaped lobes which are further shortly 3-lobed. Flowers pinkish-purple; petals 8–10mm with claw longer than the obovate limb. Sepals with fine points, strongly keeled. Fruit wrinkled. May–Aug. Hedge-banks, shady rocks. B, GB, DK, SF, F, D, IRL, N, S. **260**

690 Herb Robert *Geranium robertianum*
Annual or biennial with spreading or ascending stems up to 50cm. Leaves 3–8cm wide, very deeply divided into 3–5 segments which are further twice divided into oblong pointed lobes. Flowers bright pink; petals 9–13mm, obovate, entire, abruptly contracted into a narrow claw; sepals hairy, not keeled. Fruit with network of ridges. May–Oct. Shady places, rocks, walls, coastal shingle. Throughout area covered, except IS. **242**

691 Little Robin *Geranium purpureum*
Like **690**, but flowers smaller, with purplish-pink petals 5–9mm, and with limb of petal broader than long. Pollen yellow (pollen orange or purple in **690**). Fruit with numerous ridges. Jun–Sep. Hedgebanks, walls, coastal shingle. GB, F, IRL.

691

GERANIUM
ANNUALS OR BIENNIALS; PETALS WITHOUT A DISTINCT STALK (CLAW); SEPALS SPREADING DURING FLOWERING

692 Round-leaved Cranesbill
Geranium rotundifolium
Glandular-hairy annual, with erect or ascending stems up to 40cm. Leaves with rounded blades, with 5–7 shallow wedge-shaped, rounded-toothed lobes, the upper leaves more deeply lobed with more acute lobes. Petals pink, entire or slightly notched 5–7mm; sepals

with short point. Fruit hairy, without ridges. May–Aug.
Waste places, walls. B, GB, F, D, IRL.

693 Long-stalked Cranesbill *Geranium columbinum*
Annual with ascending or erect stems up to 60cm, with
short reflexed hairs. Leaves divided almost to base into
5–7 rhombic, deeply pinnately-cut lobes with
linear–oblong segments. Flowers pinkish-purple on
flower-stalks longer than the subtending leaves; petals
7–10mm; sepals awned, spreading hairy, nearly hairless,
without ridges. Jun–Jul. Dry grassy places. Throughout
area covered, except IS.

694 Cut-leaved Cranesbill *Geranium dissectum*
Differs from **693** in having flower-stalks shorter than
subtending leaves. Hairy annual with ascending
branched stems up to 60cm. Leaves divided to base into 7
narrow, toothed lobes. Flowers pinkish or purple; petals
c. 5mm; sepals 5–6mm, densely hairy, with short tip. Fruit
hairy. May–Sep. Cultivated land, bare ground, grassy
places. Throughout area covered, except IS.

695 Dove's-foot Cranesbill *Geranium molle*
Much branched, densely hairy greyish-green annual,
with several spreading or ascending stems up to 40cm.
Basal leaves divided to $\frac{2}{3}$ into 5–7 ovate lobes with 3 short
terminal segments, uppermost leaves stalkless, all softly
hairy. Flowers pinkish-purple; petals deeply notched at
apex, 3–7mm; sepals with short point, 4–5mm. Fruit
hairless, usually with transverse ridges. Apr–Sep. Waste
places, bare grassy places, sand-dunes. Throughout
area covered, except IS.

696 Small-flowered Cranesbill *Geranium pusillum*
Like **695** but flowers smaller, with pale lilac petals
2–4mm, and sepals c. 4mm; 3–5 stamens sterile, without
anthers. Fruit hairy, without transverse ridges. May–Sep.
Waste places. Throughout area covered, except IS.

697 *Geranium bohemicum*
Hairy stems up to 60cm. Leaves with blades 2–6cm
across divided to $\frac{3}{4}$ into 5–7 obovate or rhombic,
irregularly pinnately-cut lobes, with oblong segments.
Flowers bright blue-violet with darker veins, on stalks
longer than subtending leaves. Petals 8–9mm; sepals
longer, fine-pointed. Fruit hairy, without transverse
ridges. Jul–Sep. Coniferous forests. SF, F, D, N, S.

GERANIUM
PERENNIALS

698 Bloody Cranesbill *Geranium sanguineum*
Erect or spreading branched perennial up to 40cm,
stems with long white hairs and stalkless glands;

694

695

139

699

rhizome stout creeping. Leaves divided to $\frac{4}{5}$ of width into 5–7 narrow lobes, each lobe with 1–3 pairs of oblong–acute segments. Flowers bright reddish-purple, usually solitary; petals obovate–notched, 1·5–2cm. Fruit somewhat hairy, without ridges. Jun–Aug. Rocky and sandy ground, usually on limestone. Throughout area covered, except NL, IS. **260**

699 Meadow Cranesbill *Geranium pratense*
Stout perennial up to 80cm, with many stems, and with thick rootstock. Leaves lobed almost to base, into 5–7 ovate and pinnately-lobed oblong acute segments. Flowers large, bright blue-violet, in rather compact terminal clusters; petals obovate, entire, 1·5–2cm; sepals 1·1–1·5cm. Flower-stalks down-curved after flowering, erect in ripe fruit. Fruit hairy, without ridges. Jun–Sep. Grassy places. B, GB, SF, F, D, IRL, NL, N, S; int DK.

700 Wood Cranesbill *Geranium sylvaticum*
Differs from **699** in having flower-stalks erect as fruit matures, and sepals smaller, 6–12mm. Perennial up to 60cm, with leaves less deeply divided (c. $\frac{3}{4}$) into 5–7 ovate toothed or pinnately-cut lobes. Petals mauve to purple, obovate, 6–18mm. Jun–Aug. Woods, in mountains. Throughout area covered; int NL. **260**

701 Dusky Cranesbill *Geranium phaeum*
Distinguished by its dark blackish- or brownish-purple flowers, and petals spreading horizontally or curved downwards, with protruding stamens and style. Perennial with erect stems up to 70cm, with short glandular and long non-glandular hairs. Leaves divided to $\frac{2}{3}$, into 7 broadly oblong, weakly pinnately-cut lobes. Flowers many, in lax terminal or axiliary clusters; flower-stalks erect after flowering. Petals 8–10mm, rounded, entire or with a fine point. May–Aug. Damp shady places, meadows. F, D; int B, GB, DK, IRL, NL, S. **267**

702 Marsh Cranesbill *Geranium palustre*
Perennial with stems up to 60cm, and with fibrous roots arising from a short rhizome. Leaves divided up to $\frac{4}{5}$ into 5–7 obovate toothed lobes. Flowers purple or lilac, in a lax cluster, with flower-stalks deflexed after flowering, densely hairy. Petals 1·2–1·8cm, entire or slightly notched, hairy at base; sepals with fine points, with adpressed hairs on veins. Fruit hairy, without ridges. Jul–Aug. Damp grassy places. B, DK, SF, F, D, S. **260**

703 Hedgerow Cranesbill *Geranium pyrenaicum*
Perennial with erect stems 30–70cm, with short glandular hairs and long non-glandular hairs. Leaves divided, to $\frac{2}{3}$, into 5–7 wedge-shaped cut-off lobes with rounded terminal teeth or blunt segments; upper leaves more deeply divided. Flower purple or lilac; petals deeply notched, 7–10mm; sepals 4–5mm, with a short point.

Fruit with adpressed hairs. May–Sep. Grassy places, open woods. GB, F, IRL; int B, DK, SF, D, NL, N, S. **275**

704 French Cranesbill *Geranium endressii*
Perennial with erect hairy stems up to 80cm, and long slender creeping rhizome. Leaves divided to ⅔ into 5 ovate–rhombic, irregularly toothed lobes. Flowers pink, not darker veined, long-stalked, rather few in lax cluster. Petals obovate, up to c. 16mm; sepals shorter. Jun–Aug. Damp and shady places, marshes. F; int B, GB.

705 Pencilled Cranesbill *Geranium versicolor*
Differs from **704** by the white or pale lilac petals with violet veins; petals deeply notched. Flower-stalks with sparser long hairs (flower-stalks densely hairy in **704**). Jun–Sep. Garden escape from S-E. Europe. Int GB, F, IRL.

706 Knotted Cranesbill *Geranium nodosum*
Distinguished by its stems which are usually swollen at the nodes, and its bright pink or violet flowers with darker veins. Perennial with erect stems up to 50cm, and slender creeping rhizome. Leaves with 3–5 ovate–elliptic toothed lobes. Petals 12–17mm, deeply notched; sepals 8–9mm, with adpressed hairs. Fruit hairy, with a transverse ridge. May–Aug. Mountain woods. F; int B, GB, D, NL. **242**

705

707 Common Storksbill *Erodium cicutarium*
Annual; stems spreading 5–60cm, often fetid. Leaves pinnate, leaflets pinnate or pinnately-lobed. Flowers pinkish-purple, lilac or white, in umbels of up to 12 flowers; bracts brownish. Petals 4–11mm, the upper 2 often with blackish basal patch; sepals 5–7mm. Fruit with spirally-twisted beak 1–7cm. Apr–Sep. Bare, grassy places, sandy soils, often by sea. Throughout area covered, except IS. **260**

708 Sea Storksbill *Erodium maritimum*
Small spreading downy annual or biennial, with branched hairy stems 2–20cm. Leaves mostly basal, to 2·5cm long, ovate, rounded-toothed or lobed. Flowers pale pink or white, usually solitary; petals c. 3mm, but often absent; sepals longer, to 4·5mm. Fruit with short beak up to 1cm. Apr–Jul. Dry places, bare or trampled ground, sparse grassland, usually near the sea. GB, F, IRL.

708

709 Musk Storksbill *Erodium moschatum*
Annual or biennial, smelling strongly of musk, with stout branched spreading or ascending stems up to 60cm, densely hairy above. Leaves oblong–lanceolate in outline, pinnate, with ovate toothed or lobed leaflets. Flowers violet or purple, in long-stalked umbels of 5–12 flowers; petals c. 1·5cm, often fallen by midday; sepals 6–9mm. Fruit with brown or white hairs; beak to 4·5cm. Apr–Sep. Cultivated ground, waste places, usually near the sea. GB, F, IRL, NL; int B, D. **260**

141

FLAX FAMILY

Linaceae

Annual, biennial or perennial herbs. Leaves small, simple. Petals delicate, soon falling. Fruit 10-valved, dehiscent. Mostly species of grassland.

LINUM
FLOWERS YELLOW, WHITE OR PINK

710 Fairy Flax *Linum catharticum*
Small slender hairless annual 3–15cm, with ovate-lanceolate lower leaves and opposite lanceolate upper leaves. Flowers white, in lax clusters on slender stalks, nodding in bud; petals narrowly obovate, 4–6mm, twice as long as lanceolate glandular-hairy sepals. Capsule globular. Jun–Sep. Grasslands, damp ground. Throughout area covered.

711 *Linum flavum*
Robust erect hairless perennial up to 60cm, with yellow flowers, many in branched clusters. Lower leaves spoon-shaped, the upper lanceolate. Petals c. 2cm, with ovate limb and short stalk; sepals lanceolate pointed, up to 8mm. May–Aug. Dry grassy places. D. **216**

712 *Linum tenuifolium*
Distinguished by its pink or almost white flowers, with petals 2–2½ times as long as the lanceolate pointed, finely toothed, glandular-hairy sepals. Hairless perennial up to 45cm; leaves linear 1-veined and with minutely toothed rough margins. May–Jul. Dry hills. B, F, D.

713 *Linum suffruticosum*
Differs from **712** in having white petals with violet or pink stalks 3–4 times as long as sepals. Stems 5–40cm, spreading or ascending, much-branched below with many short non-flowering shoots; leaves linear with strongly inrolled margins. Sepals 4–6mm, 3-veined. May–Jul. Grassy places, hills. F.

LINUM
FLOWERS BLUE OR LILAC

714 Perennial Flax *Linum perenne*
Hairless perennial, very variable, with several slender erect or spreading leafy stems, branched above, up to 60cm. Leaves linear entire, 1–3-veined. Flowers blue, c. 2cm across, many in a terminal cluster; petals 3–4 times as long as unequal sepals. Fruit globular. Jun–Jul. Dry grasslands, bare ground, waste places. GB, F, D.

710

715 Pale Flax *Linum bienne*
Biennial or perennial, rarely annual, with branched slender stems 6–60cm. Leaves linear or narrowly lanceolate, fine-pointed, with 1–3 veins. Flowers blue, with petals 2–3 times as long as sepals. Sepals ovate pointed, the inner with papery hairy margins. Stigmas linear. May–Sep. Dry grasslands, often near the sea. GB, F, IRL.

716 Flax *Linum usitatissimum*
Like **715** but always annual, with more robust single stem. Flowers blue, 1·7–2cm across; sepals 6–9mm (sepals 4–5·5cm in **715**). Jun–Oct. Widely cultivated, although now less frequently. Casual throughout area covered. **283**

717

717 Allseed *Radiola linoides*
Tiny hairless annual, with slender branching stems usually less than 5cm. Leaves up to 3mm, opposite, elliptic, 1-veined. Flowers white, numerous in branched clusters; petals 4, c. 1mm, equalling the 3-toothed sepals. Capsule globular. May–Aug. Damp sandy and peaty ground. B, GB, DK, F, D, IRL, NL, N, S.

SPURGE FAMILY

Euphorbiaceae

Annual, biennial or perennial herbs, containing latex. Leaves alternate, simple. Flowers green or yellowish, grouped within an involucre in characteristic inflorescence (cyathium), or in axillary clusters; male and female flowers separate. Fruit a capsule.

718 Dog's Mercury *Mercurialis perennis*
Hairy perennial with erect unbranched leafy stems up to 50cm, and with underground rhizome. Leaves opposite, narrowly to broadly elliptic, toothed stalked, crowded on upper part of stem; lowest leaves scale-like. Flowers green, 4–5mm across, one-sexed on different plants. Male flowers in long axillary spikes, with 3 calyx-lobes; female flowers 1–3 in long-stalked axillary clusters, elongating in fruit. Fruit 2-lobed, hairy. Feb–May. Woods, particularly of oak and beech, shady places. Throughout area covered, except IS. **189**

719 Annual Mercury *Mercurialis annua*
Pale green usually hairless annual, with branched stem up to 50cm. Leaves opposite, ovate to broadly lanceolate, toothed. Flowers green; male flowers in long-stalked clusters; female flowers few, almost stalkless, with 3 broadly triangular calyx-lobes; both male and female flowers usually on same plant. Fruit 2-lobed, usually with bristly hairs. May–Nov. Cultivated ground, waste land. B, GB, DK, F, D, NL; int SF, IRL, N, S.

EUPHORBIA
GLANDS OF INVOLUCRE ROUNDED OR OVAL; ANNUALS OR BIENNIALS

720 Purple Spurge *Euphorbia peplis*
Small spreading somewhat fleshy annual, usually with 4 branched reddish stems up to 40cm. Leaves sickle-shaped to oblong, blunt or notched, short-stalked. Inflorescence branched, with flower-clusters in the axils of each branch. Glands roundish, reddish-brown, with small paler appendages to involucre. Fruit deeply grooved, smooth, purplish. Jul–Sep. Sandy sea-shores, shingle. GB, F.

721 Broad-leaved Spurge *Euphorbia platyphyllos*
Hairless or hairy annual up to 80cm or more, with numerous axillary rays. Leaves obovate to oblong–lanceolate with heart-shaped base, finely toothed. Leaves of primary rays elliptic–oblong, of secondary rays triangular. Fruit covered with rounded swellings. Jul–Sep. Waste places, cultivated ground. B, GB, F, D, NL.

720

144

722 Upright Spurge *Euphorbia serrulata*
Like 721 but a smaller more slender, always hairless, annual. Umbel with 2–5 rays, and secondary rays with leaves narrowing downwards and passing gradually into primary ray-leaves. Fruit covered with cylindrical swellings. Jun–Sep. Cultivated ground, roadsides, ditches. B, GB, F, D, NL.

723 Sun Spurge *Euphorbia helioscopia*
Hairless annual with usually simple stems 10–50cm. Leaves obovate blunt, toothed in upper half. Leaves of primary and secondary rays similar to stem leaves but smaller, often yellowish. Flowers in a broad umbel, with 5 primary and 3 secondary rays. Fruit smooth. Apr–Oct. Disturbed ground. Throughout area covered, except IS.

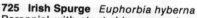

EUPHORBIA
GLANDS OF INVOLUCRE ROUNDED OR OVAL; PERENNIALS

724 Marsh Spurge *Euphorbia palustris*
Robust tufted hairless blue-green perennial, with erect stems up to 1·5m, from a creeping rhizome. Leaves lanceolate to oblong–lanceolate, turning reddish-purple in autumn. Primary rays more than 5, with ovate leaves, secondary rays with rounded yellowish leaves. Fruit covered with small rounded swellings. Apr–Jul. Marshes, river valleys. SF, F, D, NL, N, S; int B.

725 Irish Spurge *Euphorbia hyberna*
Perennial with stout rhizome, and stems up to 60cm, usually with axillary rays. Leaves oblong to oblanceolate blunt or notched, not toothed, hairless above and sparsely hairy beneath, and turning pinkish-red. Primary rays usually 5 with leaves like lower leaves. Flowers c. 4mm; glands ovate. Fruit hairless, with short and long slender swellings, stalked. May–Jun. Woods, shady places. GB, F, IRL.

725

726 Hairy Spurge *Euphorbia villosa*
Stout hairy or hairless perennial up to 1·2m, with numerous stems bearing non-flowering and flowering branches. Leaves oblong to elliptic, blunt or acute, entire or finely toothed near apex. Leaves of primary rays ovate, fine-pointed, of secondary rays smaller but as wide, yellowish. Rays usually 5, 3-times branched. Glands of involucre ovate. Fruit hairless, or densely hairy, with minute swellings. Jun–Aug. Damp places. F, D.

727 Sweet Spurge *Euphorbia dulcis*
Distinguished by its long fleshy swollen, jointed rhizome. Stems slender up to 50cm, each with 4–8 axillary rays; leaves elliptic to oblong. Primary rays usually 5, slender, with leaves like the lower leaves but wider; secondary ray-leaves heart-shaped, finely toothed. Glands oval,

dark purple after flowering. Fruit hairy or hairless, deeply grooved, irregularly covered with cylindrical and hemispherical swellings. Apr–Jul. Shady places, woods. B, F, D, NL; int GB, DK.

728 *Euphorbia brittingeri*
Downy perennial with woody rootstock, and many slender stems up to 45cm. Leaves oblong–elliptic to obovate, finely toothed. Primary ray-leaves ovate to broadly elliptic, secondary ray-leaves yellowish at flowering. Primary rays usually 5. Fruit with crowded swellings. May–Jul. Fields, damp woods, uncultivated ground. B, F, D.

729 *Euphorbia seguierana*
Hairless, blue-green, somewhat tufted perennial up to 60cm, branched or not from the base and with many axillary rays. Leaves linear to elliptic–oblong, somewhat leathery. Primary ray-leaves broader, or ovate, secondary ray-leaves rhombic to kidney-shaped. Primary rays 5–30, branched up to 4 times. Glands of involucre ovate. Capsule smooth, except for weak swellings on the keels. Apr–Jul. Dry places. B, F, D, NL.

EUPHORBIA
GLANDS OF INVOLUCRE SICKLE-SHAPED OR WITH HORNS;
ANNUALS OR BIENNIALS

730 Caper Spurge *Euphorbia lathyris*
Greyish hairless biennial 0·5–1·5m, with linear to lanceolate, entire opposite leaves, in two ranks. Primary rays with broader leaves, secondary rays with triangular–ovate acute, paler leaves. Primary rays 2–4, branched several times. Glands with 2 club-shaped horns. Fruit c. 12mm, smooth with spongy wall. Jun–Aug. Woods. F; int B, GB, D, NL. **189**

731 Dwarf Spurge *Euphorbia exigua*
Low slender greyish hairless annual 5–35cm, branched from the base, with linear to oblong entire leaves. Leaves of primary rays smaller, stalkless, of secondary rays triangular–ovate to lanceolate. Primary rays 3–5, much branched. Glands horned. Fruit smooth but glandular on keels. May–Sep. Cultivated ground, waste places. Throughout area covered, except SF, IS.

732 Petty Spurge *Euphorbia peplus*
Small often branched, hairless annual up to 40cm. Leaves ovate to rounded, entire, stalked. Primary ray-leaves with shorter stalks, secondary ray-leaves, smaller, obliquely ovate. Primary rays 3, much branched above, in lax inflorescence. Glands with 2 slender horns. Fruit smooth, each valve with 2 dorsal ridges. Jun–Oct. Cultivated ground. Throughout area covered, except IS.

731

733

733 Portland Spurge *Euphorbia portlandica*
Hairless blue-green perennial, much-branched from the
base, with stems 5–40cm. Leaves obovate to narrowly
oblanceolate, blunt, entire. Primary ray-leaves similar,
secondary ray-leaves rhombic, blunt and with a fine
point. Primary rays usually 4–5, branched above. Glands
with 2 horns, yellowish. Fruit deeply grooved, mealy on
keels. Apr–Sep. Coastal sands and cliffs. GB, F, IRL.

734 Sea Spurge *Euphorbia paralias*
Stout hairless, somewhat fleshy, blue-green perennial
with several woody, leafy stems up to 70cm. Leaves
fleshy, the lowest obovate–oblong, middle leaves
narrower, the upper ovate, all entire and overlapping.
Primary rays 3–6, branched above, secondary rays with
rounded to kidney-shaped concave leaves. Glands
moon-shaped with short horns. Fruit deeply grooved,
with swellings on keels, hairless. Jun–Sep. Sea-shores
and sand-dunes. B, GB, F, IRL, NL. **189**

735

735 Leafy Spurge *Euphorbia esula*
Hairy or hairless perennial up to 120cm, with stems with
many non-flowering axillary branches, and up to 20
axillary flowering rays. Leaves linear to broadly ovate,
pinnately veined, entire. Leaves of primary rays shorter
and wider, of secondary rays rhombic to kidney-shaped.
Primary rays 5–17, once or twice branched. Glands
short-horned. Fruit deeply grooved, mealy on keels.
Jun–Jul. Grassy waste places. B, F, D, NL; int GB, DK, SF,
N, S.

736 Cypress Spurge *Euphorbia cyparissias*
Hairless perennial 20–50cm, usually branched from
base, but with non-flowering shoots and up to 7
flowering axillary shoots. Leaves linear entire. Primary
ray leaves linear to oblong, secondary ray-leaves
kidney-shaped to rounded. Primary rays usually 9–18,
once or twice branched. Glands horned. Fruit deeply
grooved, with tiny swellings. May–Aug. Grasslands,
scrub. B, F, D, NL; int GB, DK, SF, N, S. **228**

737 Wood Spurge *Euphorbia amygdaloides*
Hairy tufted perennial with stems 40–90cm, without
non-flowering branches, and up to 30 axillary flowering
rays. Leaves oblanceolate to spoon-shaped, entire.
Leaves of primary rays broadly ovate, of secondary rays
partially or wholly fused, greenish-yellow. Primary rays
usually 5–11, branched up to 4 times. Glands with curved
horns. Fruit deeply grooved, pitted. Apr–Jun. Damp
woods. B, GB, F, D, IRL, NL. **189**

MILKWORT FAMILY

Polygalaceae

Perennial herbs or small shrubs. Flowers bilaterally symmetrical, often in terminal clusters. Fruit a capsule.

POLYGALA
SHRUBLETS WITH LEATHERY LEAVES

738 Shrubby Milkwort *Polygala chamaebuxus*
More or less spreading evergreen shrublet up to 15cm, with ovate to narrowly lanceolate, rather leathery leaves. Flowers yellow to white and tipped with purple or red, and keel bright yellow becoming purple or brownish-red; flowers solitary or paired in axils of leaves. Sepals unequal, the outer spreading; petals 1–1·4cm; keel with lobed crest. Jun–Sep. Woods and grassy places in mountains. F, D. **228**

POLYGALA
PERENNIALS WITH SOFT LEAVES; LOWER LEAVES FORMING A ROSETTE AND LARGER THAN UPPER LEAVES

739 Common Milkwort *Polygala vulgaris*
Slender perennial with spreading stems up to 35cm with woody stock. Leaves obovate to elliptic, the upper linear–lanceolate and longer. Flowers blue, pink or white, in long conical terminal clusters; bracts about as long as flower-stalks. Flowers 4–7mm; sepals unequal, the inner much longer than outer sepals. Fruit about as long as outer sepals. Very variable species. May–Aug. Grasslands. Throughout area covered, except IS.

740 Heath Milkwort *Polygala serpyllifolia*
Differs from **739** in having lower leaves opposite (leaves all alternate in **739**). Flowers usually blue, in clusters of 3–10 (clusters 10–40 in **739**). Fruit shorter and wider than inner sepals. Slender spreading or ascending perennial up to 25cm, with elliptic to obovate leaves, the upper linear–lanceolate. May–Aug. Heaths, grassy places. B, GB, DK, F, D, IRL, NL, N.

741 Tufted Milkwort *Polygala comosa*
Differs from **739** in having bracts longer than the flower-stalks at flowering. Flowers usually lilac-pink, in dense conical or cylindrical clusters of 15–50 flowers. Bracts longer than flower buds. Petals about as long as sepal wings which are 4–6mm. Capsule shorter than wings and about as wide. May–Aug. Dry meadows, hills, open woods. B, SF, F, D, NL, S.

POLYGALA

PERENNIALS WITH SOFT LEAVES; LOWER LEAVES FORMING A ROSETTE AND
LARGER THAN UPPER LEAVES

742 Chalk Milkwort *Polygala calcarea*
Spreading perennial with leafless stolons terminating in
rosettes of leaves from which arise several erect
flowering stems up to 20cm. Rosette-leaves
spoon-shaped to obovate; stem-leaves linear–lanceolate
blunt. Flowers blue or white 6–7mm, in a spike-like
cluster of 6–20. Petals longer than sepal-wings. May–Jul.
Calcareous pastures. B, GB, F, D. **283**

743 Dwarf Milkwort *Polygala amarella*
Small perennial with rosette of basal leaves and simple
flowering stems up to 10cm. Lower leaves elliptic to
obovate; stem leaves widest towards apex. Flowers
usually blue, or violet, pink or white, 2–4mm; sepal
wings elliptic, longer and narrower than capsule. May–Aug.
Grasslands. B, GB, DK, SF, F, D, N, S.

743

BALSAM FAMILY

Balsaminaceae

Rather stout annual herbs. Leaves simple. Sepals 3, the
lowest large and spurred; petals 5. Fruit a fleshy capsule
with many seeds, dehiscing explosively. Plants of wet
and shady places, often by streams.

744 Indian Balsam *Impatiens glandulifera*
Hairless stout-stemmed annual 1–2m, with leaves
opposite, or in whorls of threes. Leaves lanceolate to
broadly elliptic, pointed, with glandular teeth. Flowers
large, pinkish-purple, rarely white, 2·5–4cm, with large
sepal-sac with a thin abruptly curved spur. Petals 5, the
lower 4 fused into 2 pairs. Jul–Oct. River-banks, damp
waste places. Native of Himalaya. Int throughout area
covered, except IS. **243**

745 Touch-me-not Balsam *Impatiens noli-tangere*
Flowers yellow, up to 3·5cm, with small brownish spots
and sepal-sac gradually contracted into a spur curved a
right angles to the sac. Hairless annual up to 1·8m, with
alternate, ovate to oblong toothed and stalked leaves
Flowers in axillary clusters, of 3–6. Jul–Sep. Damp shady
places, by streams. B, GB, DK, SF, F, D, NL, N, S. **199**

746 Orange Balsam *Impatiens capensis*
Like **745** but distinguished by its orange flowers with
large reddish-brown blotches, and sepal-sac abruptly
contracted into a curved spur lying parallel to the sac
Jul–Sep. Riversides, canals. Native of N. America. Int GB
F. **229**

747 Small Balsam *Impatiens parviflora*
Distinguished from **745** by its much smaller pale yellow
flowers 6–18mm, and sepal-sac gradually contracted
into a straight or slightly curved spur. A slender hairless
annual up to 1m. Jun–Sep. Shady and damp places
Native of C. Asia. Int B, GB, DK, SF, F, D, N, S.

MALLOW FAMILY

Malvaceae

Annual or perennial herbs. Leaves alternate, often palmately lobed. Flowers regular, 5-merous. Stamens many, united into a tube. Fruit disc-shaped, splitting into 1-seeded nutlets.

MALVA
EPICALYX-SEGMENTS OVATE, NOT MORE THAN 3 TIMES AS LONG AS WIDE

748 Large-flowered Mallow *Malva alcea*
Erect perennial up to 125cm, with stems with star-shaped hairs above. Lower leaves heart-shaped/rounded, less deeply lobed than upper leaves which are divided almost to the base into usually 5 toothed or pinnately-lobed segments. Flowers bright pink; petals 2–3·5cm, deeply notched. Epicalyx-segments 3, ovate–triangular, densely hairy. Fruit smooth or faintly ribbed. Very variable species. Jun–Sep. Sunny slopes, banks, woods, fields. B, DK, F, D, NL, S; int SF, N. **243**

749 Common Mallow *Malva sylvestris*
Biennial or perennial up to 1·5m, with erect or spreading stem with simple or star-shaped hairs. Leaves kidney-shaped to heart-shaped/rounded, with 3–7 rounded to oblong toothed lobes. Flowers pink or purple with darker veins; petals deeply notched, 1·2–3cm. Epicalyx-segments lanceolate to elliptic. Fruit hairy or hairless, strongly netted, not winged. A variable species. Jun–Aug. Waste places, dry ground, hedges. Throughout area covered, except IS. **243**

MALVA
EPICALYX-SEGMENTS LINEAR TO NARROWLY EGG-SHAPED, AT LEAST 3 TIMES AS LONG AS WIDE

750 Musk Mallow *Malva moschata*
Erect perennial with hairy stems up to 80cm, like **748**. Lower leaves rounded in outline, with 5–7 deep lobes, the upper leaves twice pinnately cut with narrow strap-shaped lobes. Flowers pale pink or white, with notched petals 2–4cm. Epicalyx-segments linear to narrowly elliptic, hairless or sparsely hairy. Fruit with long white hairs. Jun–Sep. Poor grasslands, meadows, hedge-banks. B, GB, F, D, IRL, NL; int DK, SF, N, S. **243**

751 Dwarf Mallow *Malva neglecta*
Annual up to 60cm, with spreading or ascending stems. Leaves kidney-shaped to rounded, with 5–7 shallow,

toothed lobes, densely white-hairy with star-shaped
hairs. Flowers pale lilac to whitish, with petals 9–13mm
deeply lobed, at least twice as long as sepals.
Epicalyx-segments linear to oblong, shorter than sepals.
Fruit hairy, smooth. Jun–Sep. Margins of fields, walls,
disturbed ground, by paths. Throughout area covered
except IS; casual in SF.

752 Chinese Mallow Malva verticillata
Differs from 751 in having flowers in dense whorls and
flowers with smaller petals c. 7mm, not more than twice
as long as sepals. Calyx strongly enlarging in fruit.
Stamen-tube almost hairless (hairy in 751). Fruit weakly
ridged (smooth in 751). Jun–Sep. Cultivated as a salad
plant. Native of S-E. Asia. Int GB, F, D, NL.

753 Least Mallow Malva parviflora
Annual with erect branched stem up to 50cm. Leaves
heart-shaped to rounded, with 5–7 triangular toothed
lobes, long-stalked. Flowers pale blue-lilac, usually in
clusters of 2–4. Sepals strongly enlarging in fruit,
becoming spreading and papery. Fruit hairy or hairless,
strongly net-veined, with slightly winged angles.
Apr–Jun. Cultivated land, waste ground. F; int GB.

754 Small Mallow Malva pusilla
Differs from 753 in being usually prostrate, and having
pale pink flowers in clusters of up to 10. Sepals with long
hairs, scarcely enlarging in fruit. Fruit without winged
angles. Petals 3–4mm, about as long as calyx. Jun–Sep.
Waste places, paths, vineyards. B, DK, D, NL, N, S; int GB,
SF, F.

753

755 Tree Mallow Lavatera arborea
Robust erect, softly-hairy biennial 1–3m, with large
rounded and shallowly 5–7-lobed leaves. Flowers lilac
with purple veins at base, in clusters of 2–7, in a long
spike-like inflorescence. Petals 1·5–2cm. Epicalyx-
segments rounded to oblong, blunt, longer than sepals,
strongly enlarging and spreading in fruit. Fruit ridged
and calyx curved over fruit. Apr–Sep. Sandy shores,
rocks and waste places by sea. GB, F, IRL. 261

756 Small Tree Mallow Lavatera cretica
Differs from 755 in having epicalyx-segments shorter
than sepals, and stems herbaceous (stems woody in
lower part in 755). Flowers lilac, in clusters of 2–8; sepals
only slightly enlarging in fruit. Fruit smooth or slightly
ridged. Apr–Jul. Bare and waste places. GB, F. 243

757 Lavatera thuringiaca
Perennial with woolly-haired stems up to 2m, with leaves
heart-shaped/rounded and usually 5-lobed. Flowers
solitary, large, pinkish-purple, in leaf-axils. Petals usually

2–4·5cm; sepals triangular-pointed and longer than the epicalyx-segments which are united to about half-way. Fruit keeled. Jul–Sep. D; int SF, F, S.

758 Marsh Mallow *Althaea officinalis*
Densely grey-hairy erect perennial up to 2m, with star-shaped hairs. Leaves triangular–ovate, toothed, undivided or palmately-lobed. Flowers usually pale lilac-pink, in terminal and axillary clusters. Petals 1·5–2cm. Epicalyx-segments 7–9, linear–lanceolate, shorter than sepals, curved in fruit. Fruit densely hairy, smooth. Jun–Sep. Damp places, ditches. B, GB, DK, F, D, IRL, NL. **243**

759 Rough Marsh Mallow *Althaea hirsuta*
Annual with rough-hairy stems up to 60cm. Leaves heart-shaped to rounded, toothed, undivided or palmately-lobed. Upper leaves more deeply lobed with 3–5 linear toothed lobes. Flowers pinkish-lilac, with petals little longer than the lanceolate to ovate long-pointed sepals. Epicalyx-segments lanceolate pointed, nearly as long as sepals. Fruit hairless. May–Jul. Cultivated ground. F, D; int B, GB.

760 Hollyhock *Alcea rosea*
Tall erect perennial 1–3m, with large rounded to weakly 3–5-lobed, rough-hairy leaves. Flowers in a long terminal spike-like cluster, pink, or sometimes white or violet. Petals 3–5cm; epicalyx-segments as long as sepals. Fruit winged, with deep narrow furrows. Jul–Sep. Waste places; widely cultivated. Garden origin. Int GB, F, D. **268**

759

DAPHNE FAMILY

Thymelaeaceae

Small shrubs or rarely annual herbs. Leaves alternate, simple. Flowers regular, 4-merous, tubular. Fruit a 1-seeded fleshy berry or a dry nut.

761 Spurge Laurel *Daphne laureola*
Low evergreen shrub up to 1m, with greenish hairless young shoots. Leaves obovate to oblanceolate, shining, leathery and hairless. Flowers yellowish-green, 8–12mm across, in short axillary clusters from previous years growth. Corolla tubular, with 4 much shorter spreading lobes. Fruit ovoid, black, fleshy. Feb–Apr. Woods, hedges. B, GB, F, D; int DK, IRL. **190**

762 Mezereon *Daphne mezereum*
Deciduous shrub up to 2m, with hairy young shoots. Leaves oblong–lanceolate and narrowed to a short stalk. Flowers pinkish-purple, 1–1·4cm across, fragrant, in axillary clusters of 2–4 in a lax spike, appearing before or with the leaves. Fruit bright red. Feb–Apr. Woods, scrub. B, GB, SF, F, D, NL, N, S; int DK. **244**

763 Annual Thymelaea *Thymelaea passerina*
Erect branched annual up to 50cm, with linear-lanceolate acute leaves. Flowers greenish, hairy, 2–3mm long, solitary or 2–3 in a cluster, arising from a tuft of silky hairs and subtended by 2 lanceolate bracts. Fruit hairy. Jul–Oct. Dry waste ground. B, F, D.

763

ST JOHN'S WORT FAMILY

Guttiferae

Perennial herbs or small shrubs, often with black glands. Leaves opposite, simple, with translucent glands. Flowers regular; petals yellow (sometimes reddish) contorted in bud. Stamens many, in bundles. Fruit a capsule or a fleshy berry.

HYPERICUM
LOW SHRUBS OR PERENNIALS WITH WOODY BASE

764 Tutsan *Hypericum androsaemum*
Half-evergreen undershrub up to 70cm, with stems 2-winged and often reddish. Leaves broadly ovate, stalkless and sometimes clasping stem. Flowers yellow, c. 2cm across, and with unequal ovate sepals which enlarge in fruit and become deflexed. Petals obovate; stamens numerous, shorter than petals. Fruit rounded, fleshy, reddish then black. Jun–Aug. Damp shady places. B, GB, F, IRL. **229**

765 Rose of Sharon *Hypericum calycinum*
Distinguished from **764** by its stems, 4-angled, rising from a creeping rhizome. Flowers yellow, solitary, 7–8cm across. Sepals unequal. Anthers reddish. Fruit dry, ovoid, down-curved. Shrub up to 60cm. Jun–Oct. Shrubberies, banks. Native of N. Anatolia. Int GB, F, IRL. **216**

766 Stinking Tutsan *Hypericum hircinum*
Shrub up to 1m, with erect 2-lined or 4-angled stems with lanceolate to ovate leaves. Flowers yellow, 3cm across. Petals broadly oblanceolate, 11–18mm; stamens longer than petals. Sepals deciduous in fruit. Fruit elliptic, 3-lobed, leathery. May–Aug. Damp places, riversides. Native of Mediterranean. Int GB, F, IRL.

767 Tall Tutsan *Hypericum inodorum*
Intermediate between **764** and **766**, but a taller shrub up to 2m, and with yellow flowers with petals 7–15mm, and stamens longer. Leaves ovate to lanceolate, not smelling when crushed (as in **766**). Sepals 5–8mm, unequal, ovate, persistent until fruit ripens. Fruit, ellipsoid, reddish, succulent. Native of Madeira. Int GB, F.

HYPERICUM
HERBACEOUS PERENNIALS OR ANNUALS; HAIRY PLANTS, AT LEAST ON LOWER SURFACE OF LEAVES

768 Hairy St John's Wort *Hypericum hirsutum*
Erect perennial up to 1m or more, with densely hairy

ST JOHN'S WORT FAMILY

768

stems and leaves. Leaves oblong to elliptic or lanceolate, without glands. Flowers yellow, to 1·5cm across, in a cylindrical cluster. Sepals with marginal stalked black glands; petals sometimes red-veined; anthers yellow. Jun–Aug. Woodlands, river banks, damp grasslands. Throughout area covered, except IS.

769 Marsh St John's Wort *Hypericum elodes*
Greyish hairy perennial with creeping rooting stems, and erect stems up to 30cm, growing in shallow water or on damp mud. Leaves rounded to broadly elliptic, glandular-hairy. Flowers pale yellow, appearing tubular; petals without glands; sepals ovate erect, with red glandular hairs. Jun–Sep. Wet places on sandy or peaty soils. B, GB, F, D, IRL, NL. **216**

HYPERICUM
PERENNIALS; HAIRLESS PLANTS. STEMS ROUNDED

770

770 Slender St John's Wort *Hypericum pulchrum*
Slender perennial with erect hairless stems 20–90cm. Leaves ovate with heart-shaped clasping base on main stems, leaves narrower and stalked on axillary shoots. Flowers yellow tinged red, c. 1·5cm across, in narrow pyramidal or cylindrical inflorescence. Sepals and petals with marginal black glands. Anthers orange to reddish. Jul–Aug. Woods, heaths, cliffs. B, GB, DK, F, D, IRL, NL, N, S.

771 Pale St John's Wort *Hypericum montanum*
Distinguished by its black glands on leaf margins, sepals and anthers. Erect hairless perennial up to 80cm, with ovate to elliptic stalkless leaves. Flowers pale yellow, 1·5cm across, in flat-topped or shortly cylindrical cluster. Jun–Aug. Woods, hedges, shrubby places. B, GB, DK, SF, F, D, NL, N, S.

772 Flax-leaved St John's Wort
Hypericum linarifolium
Erect or spreading hairless perennial up to 65cm, with distinctive narrowly oblong to linear leaves. Flowers yellow, to 2cm across, with petals 2–4 times as long as sepals. Black glands present on leaves, sepals and petals. Capsule about twice as long as sepals. Jun–Jul. Rocky places. GB, F.

773

773 Trailing St John's Wort *Hypericum humifusum*
Slender spreading perennial up to 30cm, with oblong to lanceolate upper leaves with translucent glands. Flowers pale yellow, to 1cm across. Petals 1–2 times as long as unequal sepals, which usually have black marginal glands. Capsule equalling sepals. Jun–Oct. Open woods, heaths, sandy fields, by paths. B, GB, DK, F, D, IRL, NL, S.

HYPERICUM

PERENNIALS; HAIRLESS PLANTS. STEMS 4-ANGLED

774 Square-stalked St John's Wort
Hypericum tetrapterum
Distinguished by its narrowly 4-winged hollow stem. Erect or spreading perennial up to 1m. Leaves rounded to broadly oblong, stalkless, with translucent dots. Flowers pale yellow, 1·5–2cm across, in a dense flat-topped cluster. Sepals lanceolate to narrowly oblong pointed, usually without black glands. Jun–Sep. Damp places. Throughout area covered, except SF, IS, N.

775 Wavy St John's Wort *Hypericum undulatum*
Differs from **774** in having larger petals more than 7·5mm usually tinged with red (petals to 7mm in **774**), and leaves with wavy margins. Erect perennial up to 1m, with narrowly 4-winged stem. Petals usually 8–10mm, with or without a few black glands. Sepals with 3–14 black dots (sepals with 1–2 black dots in **774**). Jun–Jul. Damp places. GB, F.

776 Imperforate St John's Wort
Hypericum maculatum
Distinguished from **775** by its blunt sepals and stems which are 4-lined, not winged. Perennial up to 1m, with ovate to elliptic leaves with a dense network of veins and without translucent dots, or a few in the upper leaves. Flowers golden-yellow; sepals with rounded or toothed apex, with or without a few black dots; petals with numerous black dots or streaks. Jun–Jul. Grasslands, damp woods, hedges. Throughout area covered, except IS.

HYPERICUM

ANNUALS OR PERENNIALS; STEMS WITH 2 LINES

777 Perforate St John's Wort *Hypericum perforatum*
Distinguished by its rounded stem with 2 lines. Erect perennial up to 1m, with ovate to linear stalkless leaves, with numerous large translucent dots. Flowers golden-yellow, 1–1·5cm long, with petals with few marginal black dots. Sepals lanceolate to linear acute, with or without black dots. Jul–Aug. Grasslands, wood margins, bushy places, dry waste ground. Throughout area covered, except IS. **216**

778 *Hypericum mutilum*
Distinguished by its ovate to lanceolate leaves with rounded or broadly wedge-shaped base and blade with 3–5 veins. Annual or perennial up to 40cm, branched above. Flowers yellow; sepals 1·5–3mm. Capsule 2·5–4mm. Marshes. Native of N. America. Int F, D.

ST JOHN'S WORT FAMILY

779 *Hypericum majus*
Distinguished by its lanceolate to oblong leaves with rounded to broadly wedge-shaped bases, and usually with 5–7 veins. Annual or perennial up to 35cm. Petals yellow; sepals 5–7mm. Capsule 5·5–7·5mm. Margins of ponds and streams. Native of N. America. Int F, D.

780 Irish St John's Wort *Hypericum canadense*
Distinguished by its linear to oblanceolate leaves, with narrow wedge-shaped bases, and usually 1–3-veined. Petals yellow; sepals 2–4·5mm. Capsule 4–6mm. Jul–Aug. Wet heaths. F, IRL, NL.

VIOLET FAMILY

Violaceae

Annual or perennial herbs. Leaves alternate. Stipules present. Flowers solitary, 5-merous, bilaterally symmetrical, spurred. Fruit a 3-valved capsule.

VIOLA
'VIOLET'-LIKE FLOWERS WITH PETALS ALL EQUAL, 2 UPPER ERECT, 2 LATERAL SPREADING AND 1 BASAL PETAL; FLOWERING STEMS ARISING DIRECTLY FROM ROOTSTOCK

781 Sweet Violet *Viola odorata*
Perennial up to 15cm, with long spreading rooting stolons, and leaves in a rosette. Leaves rounded to kidney-shaped with deeply heart-shaped base, long-stalked. Flowers violet, pinkish or white, fragrant, c 1·5cm, with spur c. 6mm and longer than calyx-lobes. Mar–May; Aug–Sep. Woods, scrub, hedge-banks. Throughout area covered, except SF, IS. **275**

782 White Violet *Viola alba*
Perennial with stems 5–15cm. Flowers white or violet, fragrant, 1·5–2cm, lateral petals bearded, and spur violet. Stolons long, slender; stipules linear–lanceolate with long hairs. Mountain grassland. Mar–Apr. Valleys in open woods. F, D, S.

783 *Viola suavis*
Flowers violet with a white throat, fragrant, 1·5–2cm. Stolons stout, short; stipules lanceolate, fringed with long hairs. F; int D.

784 Hairy Violet *Viola hirta*
Differs from **781** in having no stolons, hairy narrower leaves, and unscented flowers. Spring leaves heart-shaped, summer leaves oblong–ovate with deep

780

158

heart-shaped base. Bracts below middle of flower-stalk. Flowers violet, c. 1·5cm, with spur dark violet and longer than calyx-lobes. Mar–Jun. Calcareous grassland, open scrub. B, GB, DK, F, D, IRL, NL, N, S; int SF. **275**

785 *Viola collina*
Like **784** but flowers pale blue and spur whitish, fragrant. Bracts placed below middle of flower-stalk. Stipules linear to oblong–lanceolate, more hairy and with long marginal bristles (marginal bristles short in **784**). Mar–Apr. Woods. B, SF, F, D, N, S.

787

786 *Viola uliginosa*
Perennial with long creeping rhizomes and short shoots bearing rosettes of heart-shaped leaves with ovate–lanceolate entire stipules. Flowers violet, 2–3cm, arising from base of rosette; spur stout, violet. Sepals ovate–lanceolate, to 6mm. Jun. Moorlands, marshes. DK, SF, D, S.

787 Marsh Violet *Viola palustris*
Perennial to 10cm, with slender creeping rhizome, and 3–4 kidney-shaped, hairless, shining leaves wider than long, in a rosette. Flowers pale lilac 1–1·5cm, with blunt pale lilac spur, not fragrant. Sepals ovate blunt. Stipules ovate–lanceolate, entire or finely toothed, not fused. Apr–Jul. Bogs, marshes. Throughout area covered.

788 *Viola epipsila*
Like **787** but larger in all its parts. Leaves always paired, slightly longer than wide, with scattered hairs beneath. Flowers pale lilac, 1·5–2cm; bracts borne on upper third of flower-stalks. Jun. Marshes. DK, SF, D, IS, N, S.

789 *Viola selkirkii*
Stemless perennial with slender rhizome, and leaves in basal rosette, broadly ovate with deep heart-shaped base, toothed, with only a few scattered hairs; leaf-stalk up to twice as long as blade. Stipules ovate–lanceolate, remotely fringed. Flowers pale violet, c. 1·5cm, with stout blunt spur to 7mm; sepals acute. May. Coniferous woods, damp places. SF, N, S.

VIOLA
VIOLET-LIKE FLOWERS; FLOWERS ARISING FROM SHORT, LATERAL, LEAFY AERIAL STEMS, NOT ON STEMS DIRECTLY FROM ROOTSTOCK

790 Teesdale Violet *Viola rupestris*
Perennial with a basal rosette of leaves and flowering stems up to 10cm. Leaves heart-shaped to kidney-shaped, usually hairy; stipules ovate–lanceolate. Flowers reddish-violet, pale blue or white, 1–1·5cm; spur c. 3mm, pale violet; lower petals usually notched.

May–Jun. Calcareous grassland, pine woods, sandy soils. B, GB, SF, F, D, NL, N, S.

791 Early Dog Violet *Viola reichenbachiana*
Perennial with erect stems up to 15cm, and basal rosette of leaves. Leaves heart-shaped, about as long as wide; stipules of stem leaves narrowly lanceolate, widely fringed. Flowers violet, 1·2–1·8cm, with narrow petals and slender straight dark violet spur to 6mm. Mar–May. Woods, hedges, sandy places. B, GB, DK, F, D, IRL, NL, S.

792 Common Dog Violet *Viola riviniana*
Differs from **791** by lobes of calyx 2–3mm (lobes of calyx 1mm or less in **791**), and stout pale spur often curved upwards and notched at tip (spur slender straight, not notched, deep violet in **791**). Flowers larger, 1·4–2·5cm, with wider blue-violet petals. Perennial, variable in size, with heart-shaped leaves. Mar–Apr. Woods, heaths, mountains. Throughout area covered. **275**

793 *Viola mirabilis*
Like **792** but distinguished by its stems with a line of hairs, and its entire stipules which turn brown. Open flowers up to 2cm, arising from the base of the rosette of leaves; aerial stems with flowers which do not open. Flowers pale violet, fragrant; spur whitish, 6–8mm. May. Woodlands. B, DK, SF, F, D, N, S.

794 Heath Dog Violet *Viola canina*

Very variable perennial with spreading to erect stems up to 40cm, without basal rosette of leaves. Leaves ovate to lanceolate, usually with heart-shaped base; stipules toothed or almost entire, up to half as long as leaf-stalk. Flowers blue or white, 1·5–2·5cm, with white or greenish-yellow spur to 3 times as long as rather conspicuous sepal-lobes. Apr–Jun. Heaths, open woods, fens, sand-dunes. Throughout area covered. **244**

795 Pale Dog Violet *Viola lactea*
Like **794** but flowers pale bluish-white, with a short greenish spur longer than calyx-lobes. Petals 3 times as long as wide. Perennial with ascending stems up to 15cm, with lanceolate to ovate–lanceolate leaves with rounded or wedge-shaped base, often purplish-tinged. May–Jun. Heaths. GB, F, IRL.

795

796 Fen Violet *Viola persicifolia*
Erect perennial with stolons, and stems up to 25cm, with triangular–lanceolate leaves with cut-off or shallow heart-shaped base, not in rosettes. Flowers white with violet veins, appearing circular in front view. Petals obovate to rounded, scarcely longer than wide; spur greenish, as wide as long and slightly longer than calyx-lobes. Jun–Jul. Marshes, fens. Throughout area covered, except IS.

33 Alpine Bistort

107 Spring Beauty

119 Spring Sandwort

125 Wood Stitchwort

126 Common Chickweed

127 Greater Chickweed

130 Greater Stitchwort

132 Lesser Stitchwort

141 Alpine Mouse-ear

143 Field Mouse-ear

146 Sticky Mouse-ear

148 Dwarf Mouse-ear

150 Water Chickweed

161 Strapwort

165 Coral Necklace

167 Corn Spurrey

178 Italian Catchfly

185 Bladder Campion

163

187 Rock Catchfly

190 White Campion

197 Fastigiate Gypsophila

212 Superb Pink

213 White Water-lily

235 Wood Anemone

245 Erect Clematis

249 Glacier Crowfoot

255 Ranunculus pseudofluitans

254 Pond Water-crowfoot

259 River Water-crowfoot

260 Fan-Leaved Water-crowfoot

306 Climbing Corydalis

370 Garlic Mustard

363 Dame's Violet

377 Alpine Rock-cress

166

381 Water-cress

386 Large Bitter-cress

410 Hoary Alison

411 Horse-radish

423 Common Whitlow-grass

412 Sweet Alison

424 Common Scurvy-grass

430 Shepherd's-purse

434 Field Penny-cress

438 Wild Candytuft

452 Hoary Cress

168

456 Sea Kale

461 Corn Mignonette

486 *Saxifraga paniculata*

478 White Stonecrop

489 Meadow Saxifrage

490 Drooping Saxifrage

496 Starry Saxifrage

494 Kidney Saxifrage

500 Tufted Saxifrage

508 Grass of Parnassus

515 Bramble

520 Field Rose

516 Dewberry

531 Barren Strawberry

526 Mountain Avens

532 *Potentilla montana*

536 Rock Cinquefoil

555 Wild Strawberry

629 White Melilot

659 Subterranean Clover

820 Enchanter's Nightshade

854 Sanicle

860 Golden Chervil

862 Cow Parsley

866 Sweet Cicely

871 Pignut

874 Ground Elder

875 Greater Water Parsnip

883 Hemlock Water Dropwort

173

893 Hemlock

902 Fool's Water-cress

914 Scots Lovage

924 Milk Parsley

927 Hogweed

928 Giant Hogweed

937 *Orlaya grandiflora*

175

938 Wild Carrot

939 Diapensia

959 Labrador Tea

957 Cassiope

999 Chickweed Wintergreen

972 Cowberry

1005 Brookweed

1048 Squinancywort

1049 Dyer's Woodruff

1051 Cleavers

1056 Northern Bedstraw

1057 Woodruff

177

1060 Common Marsh Bedstraw

1144 White Horehound

1065 Hedge Bedstraw

1082 Heliotrope

1157 White Dead-nettle

1188 Gipsywort

1206 Black Nightshade

1212 Gratiola

1151 Downy Hemp-nettle

1326 Ribwort Plantain

1338 Common Valerian

179

1345 *Dipsacus laciniatus*

1376 Water Lobelia

1383 Daisy

1411 Mountain Everlasting

1412 *Antennaria alpina*

1437 Yarrow

1435 Stinking Chamomile

1438 Sneezewort

1439 Chamomile

1440 Sea Mayweed

1447 Feverfew

1449 Ox-eye Daisy

182

1573 *Sagittaria natans*

1627 St Bernard's Lily

1628 *Anthericum ramosum*

1583 Frogbit

1584 Water Soldier

1643 Common Star of Bethlehem

1663 Three-cornered Leek

1670 Ramsons

1672 Lily of the Valley

1675 Solomon's Seal

1676 Angular Solomon's Seal

1681 Summer Snowflake

184

1682 Spring Snowflake

1683 Snowdrop

1685 Poet's Narcissus

1709 Ivy-leaved Duckweed

1737 Autumn Lady's Tresses

1743 Greater Butterfly Orchid

1742 Lesser Butterfly Orchid

186

11 Dwarf Birch

12 Hop

14 Common Nettle

16 Roman Nettle

15 Small Nettle

62 Wood Dock

187

73 Red Goosefoot

82 Fat Hen

69 Sea Beet

99 Annual Sea-Blite

101 Prickly Saltwort

220 Stinking Hellebore

188

221 Green Hellebore

454 Lesser Swine-cress

718 Dog's Mercury

730 Caper Spurge

734 Sea Spurge

737 Wood Spurge

761 Spurge Laurel

853 Marsh Pennywort

817 White Bryony

868 Alexanders

851 Marestail

917 Garden Angelica

1124 Common Water-starwort

1323 Greater Plantain

1332 Moschatel

1443 Pineappleweed

1591 Sea Arrowgrass

1593 Broad-leaved Pondweed

1594 Bog Pondweed

1703 Bog Arum

1705 Italian Lords and Ladies

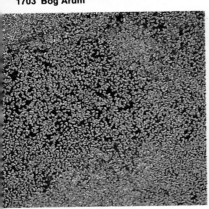

1707 Common Duckweed

1711 Branched Bur-reed

192

1735 Common Twayblade

1741 Musk Orchid

1702 Sweet Flag

13 Hemp

24 Mistletoe

91 Sea Purslane

100 Shrubby Sea-Blite

124 Sea Sandwort

159 Annual Knawal

160 Perennial Knawal

179 White Sticky Catchfly

184 Spanish Catchfly

231 Wolfsbane

285 Mousetail

195

287 Common Meadow-rue

303 Yellow Horned Poppy

379 Tower Cress

400 Gold of Pleasure

458 Weld

459 White Mignonette

460 Wild Mignonette

468 Navelwort

509 Goat's-beard Spiraea

510 Dropwort

511 Meadowsweet

518 Burnet Rose

521 Agrimony

525 Salad Burnet

576 Wild Liquorice

558 Lady's Mantle

578 Yellow Alpine Milk-vetch

604 Yellow Vetch

198

635 Classical Fenugreek

646 Sulphur Clover

661 *Trifolium montanum*

745 Touch-me-not Balsam

877 Rock Samphire

945 Serrated Wintergreen

199

1046 Vincetoxicum

1072 Wild Madder

1083 Common Gromwell

1095 Tuberous Comfrey

1097 Creeping Comfrey

1136 Wood Sage

200

1169 Annual Woundwort

1176 Cut-leaved Selfheal

1210 Small Tobacco Plant

1204 Henbane

1224 White Mullein

1225 Dark Mullein

1247 Large Yellow Foxglove

1248 Small Yellow Foxglove

1288 Leafy Lousewort

1291 *Pedicularis lapponica*

1325 Sea Plantain

1350 Yellow Scabious

1405 Highland Cudweed

1451 Mugwort

1461 White Butterbur

1487 Carline Thistle

1501 Cabbage Thistle

1539 Smooth Sow-thistle

1624 German Asphodel

1626 False Helleborine

1644 Spiked Star of Bethlehem

1712 Unbranched Bur-reed

1734 Birdsnest Orchid

1740 Creeping Lady's Tresses

204

26 Birthwort

216 Yellow Water-lily

222 Winter Aconite

225 Globeflower

228 Marsh Marigold

248 Yellow Pheasant's Eye

206

264 Lesser Spearwort

262 Lesser Celandine

267 Greater Spearwort

268 Creeping Buttercup

271 Meadow Buttercup

275 Bulbous Buttercup

305 Greater Celandine

308 Yellow Corydalis

325 London Rocket

329 *Sisymbrium austriacum*

334 Treacle Mustard

336 Winter-cress

339 American Winter-cress **342 Great Yellow-cress**

344 *Rorippa pyrenaica* **349 Rape**

353 White Mustard **354 Charlock**

209

357 Wallflower Cabbage

395 Woad

397 *Bunias erucago*

420 Yellow Whitlow-grass

472 Reflexed Stonecrop

474 Biting Stonecrop

210

477 Annual Stonecrop

488 Yellow Saxifrage

505 Opposite-leaved Golden Saxifrage

527 Wood Avens

544 *Potentilla collina*

547 Alpine Cinquefoil

211

549 Sulphur Cinquefoil

550 Spring Cinquefoil

552 Shrubby Cinquefoil

553 Silverweed

562 Broom

564 Hairy Greenweed

529 Alpine Avens

567 Winged Broom

568 Gorse

570 Dwarf Gorse

572 Tree Lupin

608 Yellow Vetchling

613 Meadow Vetchling

214

627 Large Yellow Restharrow

633 Tall Melilot

636 Black Medick

637a Sickle Medick

673 Kidney Vetch

676 Scorpion Senna

215

681 Horseshoe Vetch

688 Bermuda Buttercup

711 *Linum flavum*

765 Rose of Sharon

769 Marsh St John's Wort

777 Perforate St John's Wort

799 Two-flowered Violet

806 Common Rock-rose

808 Hoary Rock-rose

810 Common Fumana

869 Biennial Alexanders

926 Wild Parsnip

976 Primrose

977 Cowslip

978 Oxlip

993 Creeping Jenny

994 Yellow Loosestrife

995 Dotted Loosestrife

996 Tufted Loosestrife

1015 Yellow-wort

1021 Great Yellow Gentian

1043 Fringed Water-lily

1063 Lady's Bedstraw

1071 Crosswort

1134 Ground Pine

1148 Large-flowered Hemp-nettle

1159 Yellow Archangel

1215 Musk

1220 Great Mullein

1236 Common Toadflax

220

1286 Yellow Bartsia

1295 Yellow Rattle

1379 Goldenrod

1417 Elecampane

1419 *Inula britannica*

1421 *Inula ensifolia*

221

1444 Cottonweed

1423 Common Fleabane

1426 Trifid Bur-marigold

1436 Yellow Chamomile

1445 Corn Marigold

1446 Tansy

222

1459 Coltsfoot

1467 Arnica

1469 Leopardsbane

1471 Groundsel

1480 Common Ragwort

1481 Marsh Ragwort

223

1483 Oxford Ragwort

1485 Marigold

1484 Spring Groundsel

1526 Catsear

1527 Spotted Catsear

1529 Rough Hawkbit

224

1531 Hawkweed Oxtongue

1535 Goatsbeard

1538 Prickly Sow-thistle

1541 Marsh Sow-thistle

1554 Common Dandelion

1556 Nipplewort

1558 Beaked Hawksbeard

1564 Smooth Hawksbeard

1569 Leafy Hawkweed

1570 Mouse-eared Hawkweed

1571 Alpine Hawkweed

1625 Bog Asphodel

226

1632 Yellow Star of Bethlehem

1638 Wild Tulip

1693 Yellow Iris

1752 Elder-flowered Orchid

1769 Man Orchid

227

565 Petty Whin

668 Common Birdsfoot Trefoil

736 Cypress Spurge

670 Greater Birdsfoot Trefoil

738 Shrubby Milkwort

577 Wild Lentil

746 Orange Balsam

764 Tutsan

1001 Scarlet Pimpernel

1022 Spotted Gentian

1168 Yellow Woundwort

1214 Monkey Flower

1237 Prostrate Toadflax

1280 *Melampyrum nemorosum*

1397 Common Cudweed

1415 Ploughman's Spikenard

1425 Nodding Bur-marigold

1532 Bristly Oxtongue

230

1418 Irish Fleabane

8 Net-leaved Willow

52 Sheep's Sorrel

60 Curled Dock

61 Clustered Dock

65 Broad-leaved Dock

70 Good King Henry

294 Corn Poppy

295 Long-headed Poppy

304 Red Horned Poppy

464 Oblong-leaved Sundew

512 Cloudberry

513 Arctic Bramble

969 Cranberry

974 Bilberry

648 Crimson Clover

234

075 Dodder

304 Thyme Broomrape

1310 Ivy Broomrape

641 *Lilium bulbiferum*

1686 Black Bryony

235

18 *Parietaria officinalis*

28 Sea Knotgrass

30 Amphibious Bistort

39 Water-pepper

43 Pale Persicaria

44 Redshank

236

49 Buckwheat

55 Common Sorrel

108 Pink Purslane

169 Greater Sea Spurrey

170 Rock Sea Spurrey

174 Ragged Robin

237

180 Nottingham Catchfly

194 Small-flowered Catchfly

199 Soapwort

201 Proliferous Pink

288 Great Meadow-rue

297 Prickly Poppy

309 *Corydalis solida*

311 Bulbous Corydalis

313 White Ramping Fumitory

368 Sea Rocket

383 Cuckoo Flower

389 Hairy Bitter-cress

239

391 Coralroot

408 Perennial Honesty

426 Danish Scurvy-grass

469 House Leek

483 *Sedum hispanicum*

528 Water Avens

240

575 Goat's Rue

589 Wood Bitter-vetch

625 Spiny Restharrow

647 Hare's-foot Clover

657 Red Clover

658 Zigzag Clover

664 Alsike Clover

674 Birdsfoot

680 Crown Vetch

683 Wood Sorrel

690 Herb Robert

706 Knotted Cranesbill

744 Indian Balsam

748 Large-flowered Mallow

749 Common Mallow

750 Musk Mallow

756 Small Tree Mallow

758 Marsh Mallow

243

762 Mezereon

794 Heath Dog Violet

829 Rosebay Willowherb

833 Broad-leaved Willowherb

835 Spear-leaved Willowherb

846 American Willowherb

855 Astrantia

910 Caraway

954 Cornish Heath

960 Trailing Azalea

961 Blue Heath

963 Bearberry

989 Water Violet

990 Sowbread

1000 Sea Milkwort

1006 Thrift

1016 Common Centaury

1034 Field Gentian

246

1040 Marsh Felwort

1042 Bogbean

1077 Sea Bindweed

1079 Great Bindweed

1081 Field Bindweed

1096 White Comfrey

1135 Cut-leaved Germander

1145 Bastard Balm

1146 Common Hemp-nettle

1153 Red Dead-nettle

1156 Henbit Dead-nettle

1158 Spotted Dead-nettle

1160 Motherwort

1165 Limestone Woundwort

1167 Marsh Woundwort

1171 Catmint

1181 Lesser Calamint

1184 Marjoram

1194 Water Mint

1243 Ivy-leaved Toadflax

1282 Red Bartsia

1300 Purple Toothwort

1301 Globularia

1309 Bedstraw Broomrape

1324 Hoary Plantain

251

1331 Twinflower

1378 Hemp Agrimony

1388 Alpine Aster

1390 Blue Fleabane

1460 Butterbur

1466 Purple Coltsfoot

1488 Stemless Carline Thistle

1500 Slender Thistle

1504 Meadow Thistle

1511 Sawwort

1513 Red Star-thistle

1537 Salsify

253

1582 Flowering Rush

1630 Meadow Saffron

1647 Autumn Squill

1667 Babington's Leek

1640 Martagon Lily

254

1665 Rosy Garlic

1747 Fragrant Orchid

1753 Early Marsh Orchid

1756 Heath Spotted Orchid

1757 Common Spotted Orchid

1763 Bug Orchid

1766 Monkey Orchid

1770 Lizard Orchid

255

175 Alpine Catchfly

176 Sticky Catchfly

177 Corncockle

186 Moss Campion

188 Sweet William Catchfly

191 Red Campion

204 Deptford Pink

205 Sweet William

206 Carthusian Pink

209 Maiden Pink

409 Honesty

439 Garden Candytuft

602 Common Vetch

609 Grass Vetchling

611 Broad-leaved Everlasting Pea

614 Tuberous Pea

617 Bitter Vetch

621 Spring Pea

259

689 Shining Cranesbill

698 Bloody Cranesbill

700 Wood Cranesbill

702 Marsh Cranesbill

707 Common Storksbill

709 Musk Storksbill

260

755 Tree Mallow

818 Purple Loosestrife

819 Grass Poly

831 Great Hairy Willowherb

955 Heather

949 Cross-leaved Heath

950 Dorset Heath

952 Bell Heather

962 St Dabeoc's Heath

979 Birdseye Primrose

991 Cyclamen

1035 Autumn Gentian

1087 **Purple Viper's Bugloss**

1089 *Pulmonaria officinalis*

1138 **Wall Germander**

1150 **Red Hemp-nettle**

1162 **Black Horehound**

263

1182 Wild Basil

1185 Breckland Thyme

1223 Hoary Mullein

1240 Purple Toadflax

1246 Foxglove

1277 Field Cow-wheat

1292 Marsh Lousewort

1293 Lousewort

1340 Red Valerian

1502 Spear Thistle

1505 Tuberous Thistle

1506 Dwarf Thistle

1516 Greater Knapweed

265

1517 Common Knapweed

1658 Round-headed Leek

1656 Chives

1701 Wild Gladiolus

1761 Loose-flowered Orchid

1771 Pyramidal Orchid

322 Common Fumitory

515 Bramble

524 Great Burnet

534 Marsh Cinquefoil

606 *Vicia narbonensis*

701 Dusky Cranesbill

760 Hollyhock

975 Crowberry

1023 Purple Gentian

1119 Houndstongue

1166 Hedge Woundwort

1201 Whorled Clary

268

1203 Deadly Nightshade

1226 French Figwort

1287 Moor King

1639 Fritillary

1230 Water Figwort

1660 Keeled Garlic

1666 Sand Leek

1719 Lady's Slipper

1750 Black Vanilla Orchid

1765 Burnt Orchid

1728 Dark Red Helleborine

1751 Frog Orchid

1772 Fly Orchid

1773 Early Spider Orchid

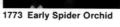

1775 Bee Orchid

229 Common Monk's-hood

98 Glasswort

230 Northern Wolfsbane

232 Forking Larkspur

239 Hepatica

241 Small Pasque Flower

244 Alpine Clematis

286 Columbine

293 Opium Poppy

586 Northern Milk-vetch

591 Tufted Vetch

619 Sea Pea

637 Lucerne

703 Hedgerow Cranesbill

781 Sweet Violet

784 Hairy Violet

792 Common Dog Violet

800 Mountain Pansy

802 Wild Pansy

988 Alpine Snowbell

1002 Blue Pimpernel

1007 Common Sea-lavender

1027 *Gentiana clusii*

1025 Willow Gentian

276

1044 Lesser Periwinkle

1045 Greater Periwinkle

1047 Field Madder

1050 Blue Woodruff

1073 Jacob's Ladder

1085 Purple Gromwell

1086 Viper's Bugloss

1092 Common Comfrey

1094 Russian Comfrey

1099 Large Blue Alkanet

1102 Borage

1121 Vervain

1140 Skullcap

1141 Spear-leaved Skullcap

1172 *Glechoma hederacea*

1175 Selfheal

1177 Large Selfheal

1183 Hyssop

1189 Pennyroyal

1199 Meadow Clary

1200 Wild Clary

1205 Bittersweet

1251 Blue Water Speedwell

1315 Large-flowered Butterwort

279

1346 Devilsbit Scabious

1354 Clustered Bellflower

1361 Creeping Bellflower

1364 Peach-leaved Bellflower

1365 Giant Bellflower

1366 Nettle-leaved Bellflower

1368 Venus's Looking Glass

1369 Large Venus's Looking Glass

1384 Sea Aster

1496 Musk Thistle

1509 Creeping Thistle

1514 Cornflower

1515 Perennial Cornflower

1542 Blue Lettuce

1548 Alpine Sow-thistle

1651 Tassel Hyacinth

1652 Small Grape Hyacinth

1689 Flag Iris

1692 Stinking Iris

1697 Autumn Crocus

1759 Early Purple Orchid

1767 Military Orchid

282

223 Love-in-a-mist

224 *Nigella arvensis*

716 Flax

742 Chalk Milkwort

856 Sea Holly

1026 Marsh Gentian

1028 Spring Gentian

1030 Bladder Gentian

1098 Alkanet

1103 Oysterplant

1106 Water Forget-me-not

1111 Wood Forget-me-not

1117 Blue-eyed Mary

1131 Bugle

1132 Blue Bugle

1255 Germander Speedwell

1263 Ivy-leaved Speedwell

1272 Slender Speedwell

1273 Spiked Speedwell

1353 Bearded Bellflower

1370 Spiked Rampion

1372 Round-headed Rampion

1523 Chicory

1653 Grape Hyacinth

1495 Alpine Sawwort

1646 Spring Squill

1648 Alpine Squill

1649 Bluebell

288

VIOLET FAMILY

797 Meadow Violet *Viola pumila*
Hairless perennial with erect or ascending stems up to
15cm. Leaves lanceolate and usually with wedge-shaped
base, blade usually longer than leaf-stalk; stipules large,
entire or coarsely toothed. Flowers pale blue, c. 1·5cm;
spur short, only slightly longer than calyx-lobes. Jun–Jul.
Damp meadows, woods, grasslands. F, D, S.

798 *Viola elatior*
Like **797** but a larger, shorter haired, perennial up to
50cm. Flowers pale blue, 2–2·5cm, with short spur.
Stipules conspicuous, 2–5cm, entire or coarsely toothed
at base, equalling or longer than leaf-stalks. May–Jun.
Damp grasslands and scrub. F, D, S; int B.

VIOLA
'PANSY'-LIKE FLOWERS WITH PETALS UNEQUAL IN SIZE, WITH 2 ERECT PETALS,
2 LATERAL PETALS DIRECTED UPWARDS, AND THE BROADER BASAL PETAL
OFTEN MULTICOLOURED

799

799 Two-flowered Violet *Viola biflora*
Distinguished by its bright yellow flowers with the 4
upper petals directed upwards. Perennial with slender
creeping rhizome and basal rosette of leaves, and leafy
flowering stems up to 20cm. Leaves kidney-shaped to
heart-shaped, toothed. Flowers 1·5cm, with short spur,
not fragrant. Jun–Aug. Damp shady places, mainly in
mountains. SF, F, D, N, S. **217**

800 Mountain Pansy *Viola lutea*
Perennial with slender rhizome and flowering stems up
to 20cm. Leaves ovate to lanceolate, hairless or hairy;
stipules divided into 3–5 lobes. Flowers yellow, violet or
yellow-violet, 1·5–3cm; lower petals with a dense
network of veins; spur slender, twice as long as
calyx-lobes. Very variable species. May–Aug. Mountain
grasslands, lead mine spoil, coastal cliffs and sands. B,
GB, F, D, IRL, NL. **275**

801 *Viola hispida*
Distinguished by the spreading hairs covering the whole
plant. Lower leaves rounded, upper ovate or oblong, all
toothed. Flowers violet or yellowish, c. 2cm; spur c. 4mm,
little longer than calyx-lobes. May–Oct. Calcareous
cliffs. F.

802 Wild Pansy *Viola tricolor*
Usually annual, with more or less erect stems up to 25cm
or more. Lower leaves heart-shaped to ovate, toothed;
upper leaves ovate to lanceolate with wedge-shaped
base, toothed. Stipules deeply pinnately lobed, the
terminal lobe larger and usually leaf-like. Flowers violet,
yellow or violet-yellow 1–2·5cm or more; petals longer
than calyx; spur variable in length. Apr–Nov. Sandy

289

places, cultivated fields. Throughout area covered.
Ssp. *curtisii* is a low-growing perennial with narrower
fleshy leaves. Sand-dunes; rarely inland. **275**

803 Field Pansy *Viola arvensis*
Distinguished from **802** by its smaller flowers, 1–1·5cm
with petals as long or shorter than sepals. Lower petal
cream to yellow, the upper cream to bluish-violet. Annual
up to 40cm, with ascending stem with deflexed hairs.
Leaves oblong/spoon-shaped, acute or obtuse, toothed;
stipules pinnately lobed. Apr–Oct. Fields, waste places,
waysides. Throughout area covered, except IS.

804 Dwarf Pansy *Viola kitaibeliana*
Densely hairy annual 2–10cm. Lower leaves rounded,
upper oblong/spoon-shaped with rounded forward-
pointing lobes and with a larger shortly stalked terminal
lobe. Flowers tiny, violet or cream to yellow, 4–8mm.
Mar–Jul. Dry open places, sand-dunes. GB, F; int D.

803

ROCK-ROSE FAMILY

Cistaceae

805

Small shrubs or rarely annual herbs. Leaves simple, small. Flowers regular; petals free, delicate, yellow, contorted in bud. Stamens numerous. Fruit a capsule.

805 Spotted Rock-rose *Tuberaria guttata*
Hairy annual 5–30cm, with basal rosette of elliptic to obovate leaves. Upper leaves linear–lanceolate, all leaves with star-shaped hairs. Flowers yellow, 1–2cm across, with petals usually dark-spotted at base, in long-stalked terminal cluster; sepals unequal. May–Aug. Sands, open woods, heaths, cliffs. GB, F, D, IRL, NL.

HELIANTHEMUM
ALL LEAVES WITH STIPULES

806 Common Rock-rose
Helianthemum nummularium
Much-branched, woody-based, spreading perennial up to 50cm, with grey or white-woolly lanceolate leaves and with lanceolate leaf-like stipules at base. Flowers usually yellow; petals 6–12mm. Capsule ovoid, about as long as the prominently veined sepals. Variable species. Jun–Aug. Grassy and rocky places on calcareous soils. Throughout area covered, except IS, N. **217**

807 White Rock-rose *Helianthemum apenninum*
Differs from **806** in having smaller linear stipules, and white flowers with petals with yellow stalks. Lax spreading, much-branched woody-based perennial up to 50cm. Leaves linear, green, grey or white, woolly-haired or nearly hairless above, but densely so on underside. Flowers c. 2cm across, in terminal cluster; sepals hairy over whole outer surface. May–Jul. Sunny slopes, rocks, open woods. B, GB, F, D.

HELIANTHEMUM
LOWER LEAVES WITHOUT STIPULES

808 Hoary Rock-rose *Helianthemum canum*
Small spreading woody undershrub, with spreading and ascending stems up to 20cm, or more. Leaves elliptic to linear, green or grey-woolly above, grey-woolly beneath. Flowers yellow, with petals 4–8mm, in a lax or dense cluster. Very variable species. May–Jul. Limestone cliffs, dry pastures. GB, F, D, IRL, S. **217**

809 *Helianthemum oelandicum*
Lax or densely tufted dwarf shrub, to 20cm. Leaves elliptic

to narrowly lanceolate, green on both sides, and all leaves without stipules. Flowers pale yellow in simple or branched clusters; petals 5–10mm. May–Jul. Rocks, dry pastures. F, D, S.

810 Common Fumana *Fumana procumbens*
Spreading dwarf shrub up to 40cm, with linear fine-pointed alternate leaves and with spreading marginal hairs; stipules absent. Flowers yellow, 1·5–2cm across, solitary in axils of leaves and not forming a cluster. Flower-stalks about as long as adjacent leaves, recurved from the base. May–Jul. Dry calcareous grassland, stony slopes. B, F, D, S. **217**

HEATH FAMILY

Frankeniaceae

811

Small shrubs or perennial herbs. Leaves opposite, small. Flowers regular. Mostly plants of saline habitats.

811 Sea-heath *Frankenia laevis*
Perennial with spreading much-branched, mat-forming branches up to 40cm. Leaves linear, with inrolled margins, opposite, sometimes with a white crust. Flowers purplish to whitish, solitary or clustered on the upper part of the stems and branches. Calyx tubular with 4–5 teeth, nearly hairless or shortly hairy; petals 4–5, obovate blunt, 4–6mm. Jul–Sep. Maritime sands and shingle, dry saltmarshes. GB, F.

WATERWORT FAMILY

Elatinaceae

Small, aquatic, annual or perennial herbs. Leaves simple, opposite or whorled. Flowers 3- to 4-merous.

812 Waterwort *Elatine alsinastrum*
Annual or perennial 2–80cm, growing in shallow water or on wet mud or sand. Underwater leaves linear, in whorls of up to 18 leaves, land-leaves lanceolate to ovate in whorls of 3. Flowers green, pinkish or whitish, 2·5mm across, solitary in axils of leaves. Sepals and petals 4, ovate, stamens 8. Carpels 4. Jun–Sep. Pools and lakes. SF, F.

813 Eight-stamened Waterwort *Elatine hydropiper*
Differs from **812** in having opposite leaves, and sepals

815

shorter than the mature capsule. Creeping tufted annual 2–16cm, with stalkless pink flowers in leaf-axils; petals as long or longer than sepals. Jun–Sep. Pools, sandy shores. Throughout area covered, except IS.

814 *Elatine triandra*
Annual differing from **812** and **813** in having 3 sepals, petals and stamens. Flowers white or red; petals longer than sepals; carpels 3. Jun–Oct. Lake mud. B, SF, F, D, NL, N, S.

815 Six-stamened Waterwort *Elatine hexandra*
Annual or short-lived perennial 2–20cm, with opposite leaves. Flowers stalked; petals 3, white with pink veins, longer than the 3 sepals. Stamens 6; carpels 3. Jul–Sep. Pools, lakes, ditches, sandy shores. B, GB, DK, F, D, IRL, NL, N, S.

GOURD FAMILY

Cucurbitaceae

Annual or perennial climbing herbs. Flowers 5- (to 6-)merous. Fruit a fleshy berry.

816 *Bryonia alba*
Rough hairy climbing perennial with branched stems, to 4m. Leaves 5-angled or 5-lobed with lobes ovate to triangular, sharply toothed, the central lobe much longer; tendrils unbranched. Flowers greenish-white, in stalked axillary clusters. Calyx bell-shaped, 5-toothed; corolla with 5 spreading lobes. Stamens 3. Fruit a fleshy black berry. Jun–Aug. Hedges. D; int B, DK, SF, F, N, S.

817 White Bryony *Bryonia cretica*
Differs from **816** in having male and female flowers on different plants (on same plants in **816**). Stigma with small hairy projections (stigma hairless in **816**). Leaves with central lobe not markedly longer than lateral lobes. Fruit a red berry, to 1cm across. Jun–Aug. Hedges. B, GB, F, D, NL; int DK, IRL, N, S. **190**

LOOSESTRIFE FAMILY

Lythraceae

Annual or perennial herbs. Leaves opposite or in whorls. Flowers regular. Petals free, pink or purple. Fruit a capsule, with many small seeds. Plants of wet habitats.

818 Purple Loosestrife *Lythrum salicaria*
Erect, usually densely grey-hairy perennial up to 1·5m, with stem with 4 more or less raised lines. Leaves ovate to lanceolate, with cut-off or rounded base, stalkless, opposite or in whorls of 3. Flowers reddish-purple, in whorls in the axils of small bracts, forming a long terminal spike. Petals 6, 1cm; stamens 12. Jun–Aug. Fens, riversides, damp places. Throughout area covered, except IS. **261**

819 Grass Poly *Lythrum hyssopifolia*
Low nearly hairless annual with erect or ascending branches, up to 30cm. Leaves linear to oblong, alternate. Flowers pale pink, axillary; petals 2–3mm. Stamens 4–6. Calyx with epicalyx-segments twice as long as sepals. Jul–Sep. Disturbed or seasonally flooded ground. B, GB, F, D; int N, S. **261**

WILLOWHERB FAMILY
Onagraceae

Annual or perennial herbs. Leaves simple. Flowers regular, or weakly bilaterally symmetrical, usually 4-merous. Fruit an elongate capsule, or dry and indehiscent. Often species of damp or shady habitats; many are weeds of waste and cultivated land.

820 Enchanter's Nightshade *Circaea lutetiana*
Perennial up to 60cm, with opposite ovate acute leaves with cut-off or heart-shaped base, sparsely toothed, hairy. Flowers white or pinkish, 4–8mm; sepals, petals and stamens 2. Petals 2–4mm, deeply notched. Inflorescence elongating before petals have fallen. Fruit 2-lobed, with hooked bristles. Jun–Sep. Woods, shady places. Throughout area covered, except SF, IS. **172**

821 Alpine Enchanter's Nightshade *Circaea alpina*
Differs from **820** in inflorescence not elongating until petals have fallen, the open flowers clustered at apex. Fruit with 1 fertile lobe, densely covered with often straight bristles. Perennial up to 30cm; leaves heart-shaped, toothed, hairless. Petals pink, 0·6–1·5mm, shallowly notched. Jul–Aug. Mountain woods. B, GB, DK, SF, F, D, NL, N, S.

821

822 Upland Enchanter's Nightshade
Circaea ×intermedia
Like **820** with inflorescence elongating before petals have fallen, but plants all sterile. Petals 1·4–4mm, pink, deeply notched. Grows with **820** and **821**. Jul–Aug. Woods, shady places. B, GB, DK, F, D, IRL, NL, N, S.

823

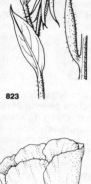

827

823 Common Evening Primrose *Oenothera biennis*
Erect annual or biennial with hairy stem 100–150cm, without red spots. Leaves broadly lanceolate. Flowers yellow, with saucer-shaped petals 2·5–3cm long; inflorescence long, erect. Calyx-tube long, to 4·5cm. Jun–Aug. Sandy places, waste ground, dry banks. Native of Eurasia. Nat throughout area covered, except SF, IS.

824 Large-flowered Evening Primrose
Oenothera erythrosepala
Like **823** but stem and ovaries with red spots, and calyx red-striped or red. Petals 4–6cm; calyx-tube 3–5cm long. Jun–Sep. Waste places, sand-dunes. Native of N. America. Int B, GB, DK, F, D, IRL, NL.

825 Small-flowered Evening Primrose
Oenothera parviflora
Stem erect or spreading, 100–200cm, hairy and with inflorescence slightly nodding at flowering. Leaves nearly hairless. Flowers yellow, with petals c. 11mm, in a stout rather dense inflorescence. Sepal apices short, forming U-shaped pairs. Jun–Aug. Waste places. Native of N. America. Int F, D, NL, N; casual in GB.

826 *Oenothera ammophila*
Differs from **825** in having leaves white-hairy, and young capsule red-striped. Petals yellow, not more than 1·6cm; sepal-tips long-curved. Jun–Jul. Open sandy places, seashores. Native of N. America. Int DK, F, D, NL.

827 Fragrant Evening Primrose *Oenothera stricta*
Stem hairy, red-spotted, erect, 50–150cm, with basal leaves oblanceolate to linear; stem leaves narrowly lanceolate, with undulate margins, finely toothed. Petals yellow turning reddish, 2–4·5cm; calyx-tube 1·5–3cm, sepals reddish. Capsule conspicuously enlarged in upper half, hairy. Jun–Sep. Sand-dunes. Native of Chile. Int F, D, GB.

828 Hampshire Purslane *Ludwigia palustris*
Prostrate hairless perennial, with reddish stems 3–50cm. Leaves narrowly obovate, opposite, glossy, red-veined. Flowers green, tinged red, in stalkless axillary pairs; petals absent; sepals 4, to 2mm; stamens 4. Fruit a capsule, with green bands on angles. Jun–Jul. Wet places. B, GB, F, D, NL.

EPILOBIUM
LEAVES ALTERNATE; FLOWERS LARGE, SHOWY

829 Rosebay Willowherb *Epilobium angustifolium*
Stem erect up to 2·5m, with alternate lanceolate, hairless, bluish-green leaves. Flowers pink, 2–5cm across, many

in long terminal spike-like cluster, with flower-buds sharply down-turned. Sepals lanceolate, as long as the ovate/spoon-shaped short-stalked petals. Style 1–2cm, deflexed, becoming erect after flowering, with anthers deflexed; stigma 4-lobed. Fruit a long slender capsule. Jun–Sep. Woodland clearings, heaths, hedges, waste ground, sand-dunes. Throughout area covered. **244**

830 River Beauty *Epilobium latifolium*
Differs from **829** in having usually only 1–7 flowers in a leafy inflorescence. Stem 20–40cm. Leaves elliptic. Style much shorter, up to 7·5mm, deflexed throughout. Jul. River-shingle. IS.

EPILOBIUM
LEAVES OPPOSITE; STIGMA DISTINCTLY 4-LOBED

832

831 Great Hairy Willowherb *Epilobium hirsutum*
Robust erect, usually hairy, little branched perennial up to 2m. Leaves lanceolate to oblong, half-clasping stem, acutely toothed, opposite. Flowers purplish-pink, c. 2·5cm across. Petals slightly notched, mostly 1–1·5cm; sepals linear. Capsule downy, up to 8cm. Jun–Sep. Ditches, river-banks, fens, marshes. Throughout area covered, except IS; casual in SF, N. **261**

832 Lesser Hairy Willowherb *Epilobium parviflorum*
Differs from **831** in having leaves wedge-shaped at base and weakly toothed, and with smaller flowers with deeply notched pale purplish-pink petals 6–9mm. Stem robust, woolly-haired, up to 75cm. Leaves oblong to linear–lanceolate, the upper alternate. Jul–Aug. Damp places, disturbed ground. Throughout area, except IS.

833 Broad-leaved Willowherb *Epilobium montanum*
Perennial with erect stems to 80cm, with stiff adpressed hairs. Leaves ovate with shallowly toothed hairy margins, rarely entire, short-stalked. Flowers purplish-pink; petals 6–10mm, deeply notched. Plant producing stalkless rosettes in autumn. Capsule slightly downy, up to 8cm. Jul–Sep. Woods, ditches, stream-sides. Throughout area covered, except IS. **244**

834 *Epilobium collinum*
Differing from **833** in having smaller ovate leaves 1–5cm (leaves 3·5–8cm in **833**), blunt buds (buds pointed in **833**), and smaller pale purplish-pink flowers, with petals 3–6mm. Stem up to 40cm, with stiff adpressed hairs. Jun–Sep. Rocks, walls, roadsides. B, SF, F, D, IS, N, S.

835 Spear-leaved Willowherb *Epilobium lanceolatum*
Differs from **833** in having oblong blunt leaves with narrow wedge-shaped bases, and short stalk to 1cm; upper leaves alternate. Petals at first white, later

purplish-pink, 5–8·5mm. May–Jul. Open woods, rocks, waysides. B, GB, F, D, NL. **244**

EPILOBIUM
LEAVES OPPOSITE; STIGMA CLUB-SHAPED, NOT LOBED. INFLORESCENCE AND OVARY CONSPICUOUSLY HAIRY OR WITH STIFF ADPRESSED HAIRS

836 Square-stalked Willowherb
Epilobium tetragonum
Hairless perennial with squarish 4-ridged stems up to 110cm. Leaves oblong to oblong–lanceolate, finely saw-toothed, stalkless. Flowers purplish-pink in greyish hairy inflorescence. Petals usually 7–11·5mm. Capsule up to 8cm. Plant with dense rosettes of leaves in autumn. Jul–Aug. Woods, damp places. Throughout area covered, except IRL, IS; casual in N.

836

837 Short-fruited Willowherb *Epilobium obscurum*
Differs from **836** in having leafy above-ground stolons and calyx with few erect glandular hairs (stolons absent, calyx not glandular in **836**). Stems up to 90cm, with elevated sinuous lines. Leaves narrow ovate to lanceolate, finely toothed, inflorescence greyish-hairy. Petals purplish-pink, 4–7mm. Capsule up to 6cm. Jul–Aug. Wet places, moist woods. Throughout area covered, except IS.

838 Pale Willowherb *Epilobium roseum*
Perennial up to 80cm; stems with 4 narrow raised lines. Leaves lanceolate to elliptic, with narrow wedge-shaped bases, irregularly toothed, long-stalked. Flowers white, becoming pinkish-streaked; petals 3·5–7mm, in a densely grey-hairy stalked inflorescence. Capsule up to 6cm, hairy. Plant with overwintering buds. Jul–Aug. Damp places, woods, cultivated ground. Throughout area covered, except IS.

839 Marsh Willowherb *Epilobium palustre*
Perennial up to 70cm; stems with 2–4 lines of hairs above and thread-like stolons. Leaves lanceolate pointed, entire, stalkless. Flowers pale pink or white; petals 3–7mm. Jul–Sep. Wet places, marshes, bogs. Throughout area covered.

840 *Epilobium davuricum*
Low creeping perennial with glandular-hairy stems, with finely adpressed hairs above and slightly elevated lines; overwintering by rosettes. Leaves linear to elliptic, entire, stalkless, remote. Inflorescence usually nearly hairless, nodding until fruit is ripe. Petals white, rarely pink, 3–5mm. Jul–Aug. SF, N, S.

841 Alpine Willowherb *Epilobium anagallidifolium*
Creeping perennial with stems up to 10cm, with weakly

839

297

841

raised lines; stolons above ground long; leafy. Leaves ovate to elliptic, almost entire, shortly stalked. Inflorescence hairless, nodding before flowering. Petals pale purplish, 3–4·5mm; sepals red. Capsule erect, up to 3·5mm, red when ripe. Jun–Aug. Mountain bogs, wet places. GB, SF, F, D, IS, N, S.

842 *Epilobium hornemannii*
Like **841** but stolons below ground, and flowers pale violet and with larger petals 4–6mm. Stems up to 25cm; leaves ovate–elliptic, stalked. Jul. Wet places. SF, IS, N, S.

843 *Epilobium lactiflorum*
Like **842** but with short inconspicuous leafy above-ground stolons. Leaves weakly toothed. Petals 2·5–4mm, white. Jul. Wet places. SF, IS, N, S.

844 Chickweed Willowherb *Epilobium alsinifolium*
Differs from **842** in having long spreading stolons. Petals bright purplish-pink, 7–11mm. Perennial up to 25cm, with opposite ovate–lanceolate finely toothed, hairless, nearly stalkless leaves. Jul–Aug. Mountain bogs and rills. GB, SF, F, D, IRL, IS, N, S.

845 *Epilobium glandulosum*
Stem up to 80cm, with elevated bristly hairy lines; overwintering by buds. Inflorescence glandular-hairy; flowers purplish-pink; petals 5–6·5mm. Leaves rounded at base, weakly toothed, almost stalkless. Jul. Native of N. America. Int SF, N, S.

846 American Willowherb
Epilobium ciliatum (=*E. adenocaulon*)
Stems up to 140cm, with raised bristly hairy lines; overwintering by leafy rosettes. Leaves finely toothed, short-stalked. Inflorescence glandular, greyish-hairy. Flowers pinkish-purple to white; petals 2·5–6mm. Jun–Aug. Damp woods, streamsides, waste-places. Int B, GB, IRL, DK, SF, F, D, NL, N, S. **244**

847

847 New Zealand Willowherb
Epilobium brunnescens (=*E. nerterioides*)
Distinguished by its creeping matted stems which root at the nodes. Leaves tiny, c. 1cm, broadly ovate, weakly toothed, short-stalked. Flowers white, borne on erect stalks up to 7·5cm; petals 2·5–4mm. Jun–Jul. Moist stony ground, streamsides. Native of New Zealand. Int GB, IRL.

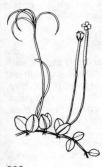

WATER-MILFOIL FAMILY

Haloragaceae

Aquatic perennial herbs. Leaves whorled. Flowers inconspicuous, regular. Fruit separating into 1-seeded nutlets.

848 Whorled Water-milfoil *Myriophyllum verticillatum*
Submerged perennial with long branched stems up to 3m, with whorls of usually 5 leaves often longer than the internodes. Leaves divided into 24–35 thread-like segments. Flowers in a spike borne above water, in whorls of 5, subtended by finely pinnately divided bracts. Flowers greenish-yellow, c. 3mm, mostly unisexual, with male flowers above and female flowers below. Petals present in male flowers, absent in female flowers. Plant perennating by club-shaped buds. Jun–Jul. Still waters, slow streams. Throughout area covered.

849 Spiked Water-milfoil *Myriophyllum spicatum*
Differs from **848** in having upper bracts below flowers simple or toothed (upper bracts pinnately-lobed in **848**). Flowering spikes usually 4cm or more long, all flowers whorled. Overwintering buds absent. Leaves usually in whorls of 4 and about as long as the internodes. Flowers in whorls of 4; female flowers with 4 small petals. Fruit with small swellings (fruit smooth in **848**). Jul–Aug. Pools, lakes, ditches. Throughout area covered.

850 Alternate Water-milfoil
Myriophyllum alterniflorum
Differs from **849** in having shorter flowering spikes not more than 3cm and apex drooping in bud, and upper flowers solitary or opposite, not in whorls; female flowers whorled at base only. Petals yellow, with red streaks. Jun–Aug. Pools, rivers. Throughout area covered.

850

MARESTAIL FAMILY

Hippuridaceae

Aquatic herb (one species only). Petals and sepals absent; stamens and ovules 1 only. Fruit a small nut.

851 Marestail *Hippuris vulgaris*
Aquatic perennial with creeping underwater rhizomes and with erect leafy unbranched stems above water up to 60cm or more. Leaves in whorls, linear–lanceolate; underwater leaves flaccid, light green; above-water leaves dark green, rigid. Flowers green, tiny, borne in leaf-axils, either male, female or hermaphrodite, the upper stalkless. Jun–Aug. Still or slow-flowing waters. Throughout area covered. **190**

DOGWOOD FAMILY

Cornaceae

Trees, shrubs or rarely herbs. Leaves simple. Flowers in clusters, 4-merous, sepals small. Fruit a drupe.

852 Dwarf Cornel *Cornus suecica*
Herbaceous perennial with erect 4-angled flowering stems up to 25cm. Leaves opposite, rounded to elliptic, pointed, stalkless. Flowers dark purple, in a ter-minal flat-topped cluster and surrounded by 4 white ovate bracts up to 16mm long. Petals 4, c. 1mm. Fruit globular, red. Jun–Aug. Moors, heaths, peaty soils. GB, DK, SF, D, NL, IS, N, S.

852

CARROT FAMILY

Umbelliferae

Annual, biennial or perennial herbs. Leaves alternate, usually pinnate or ternate, with sheathing petioles at base. Flowers grouped in a compound (rarely simple) umbel. Petals 5, frequently white. Stamens 5; ovary 2-celled. Fruit of 2 indehiscent carpels. Ripe fruit is important for identification. Many species are aromatic, and cultivated for food or flavouring.

853 Marsh Pennywort *Hydrocotyle vulgaris*
Creeping perennial, slender stems rooting at nodes; leaves long-stalked erect, rounded blades with rounded teeth, up to 4cm across. Flowers whitish, c. 1mm across, in whorls, in clusters on stem half as long as subtending leaf-stalk. Fruit rounded, ridged. Jun–Jul. Damp places, fens, shallow water. B, GB, DK, F, D, IRL, NL, N, S. **190**

854 Sanicle *Sanicula europaea*
Perennial with stout rootstock and erect stem up to 60cm. Basal leaves long-stalked, blade with 5 obovate lobes which are coarsely toothed; stem leaves smaller, almost stalkless. Flowers white or yellowish, c. 3mm, in a terminal cluster of dense globular umbels, each with 4–8 bracts. Fruit globular, covered with hooked bristles, to 5mm. Jun–Aug. Woods, damp shady places. Throughout area covered, except IS. **172**

855 Astrantia *Astrantia major*
Robust perennial up to 1m, branched above. Leaves 3–5-lobed with lanceolate to obovate toothed lobes and often further lobed. Flowers whitish, in dense flat-topped umbels, surrounded by lanceolate pointed bracteoles which are more or less fused, whitish below and pink or purplish towards apex. Calyx-teeth narrow lanceolate long-pointed. Fruit cylindrical, with inflated ridges. Jun–Aug. Woods, shady ravines, mountain meadows. F, D; int GB, DK, SF. **255**

856 Sea Holly *Eryngium maritimum*
Much branched spiny, blue-green, hairless perennial up to 60cm. Leaves usually 3-lobed, the lobes leathery, spiny toothed and wavy-margined; upper leaves clasping stem. Flowers blue, in many dense globular heads 1·5–3cm across, in a spreading cluster with ovate to lanceolate spiny bracts below; each flower-head surrounded by 3-lobed spiny bracteoles. Sepals ovate–lanceolate, spiny. Fruit elliptic, spiny. Jun–Aug. Sand-dunes, coastal shingle. B, GB, DK, F, D, IRL, NL, N, S. **283**

857 Field Eryngo *Eryngium campestre*
Much branched spiny perennial up to 70cm. Leaves

858

bluish-green, twice pinnately lobed, with spiny margins. Flowers greenish, white or purple, c. 2mm across, in dense rounded heads surrounded by much longer entire, or spiny linear–lanceolate bracts. Calyx-teeth triangular spine-tipped; petals linear. Inflorescence flat-topped, with numerous stalked flower-heads. Fruit spiny. Jun–Aug. Dry places, fallow fields. B, F, D, NL; int GB, DK.

858 Rough Chervil *Chaerophyllum temulentum*
Slender hairy branched biennial up to 1m, with purple spotted or purple bristly-hairy stems. Leaves 2–3-pinnate with apical lobes ovate blunt, dark green, with adpressed hairs above and below. Inflorescence with 6–12 primary rays without bracts; bracteoles hairy. Flowers white. Fruit cylindrical, gradually narrowed to apex, 4–7mm, hairless. May–Jul. Grassy places, hedgebanks. Throughout area covered, except SF, IS, N.

859 *Chaerophyllum hirsutum*
Robust perennial up to 120cm, with leaves 2–3-times pinnate with segments relatively broad, little divided, often overlapping. Flowers white; petals with spreading marginal hairs; style nearly erect. Bracteoles often unequal. Fruit up to 12mm, obovoid–oblong tapering gradually upwards; styles nearly erect. Jun–Aug. Woods, shady banks. F, D; int B, DK.

860 Golden Chervil *Chaerophyllum aureum*
Differs from **858** in being perennial up to 1·5m, with longer fruits 8–12mm. Leaves 3-pinnate with greenish-yellow hairs, and apical lobes long narrow, toothed. Inflorescence with 12–18 primary rays, with 1 bract, or bracts absent; bracteoles hairy. Jun–Aug. Damp meadows, hedges, shady places. F, D; int GB. **172**

861 *Chaerophyllum bulbosum*
Biennial or perennial with short rounded tuberous roots, and stems up to 2m, hairy below and often spotted or tinged purple-brown, hairless above. Leaves 2–3-pinnate, with lobes to 2mm wide. Flowers white; bracteoles ovate, hairless. Fruit 5–7mm; styles at first nearly erect, later diverging. Jun–Jul. Ditches, roadsides, cultivated ground, rocks. SF, F, D, NL, S; int B.

862 Cow Parsley *Anthriscus sylvestris*
Robust perennial 0·5–1·5m; leaves 3-pinnate with pinnately divided lobes. Umbels with 4–15 primary rays without bracts; secondary rays many, with ovate-lanceolate bracteoles. Flowers white, 3·5–4mm; petals notched with small incurved point. Fruit ovoid–oblong, 7–10mm, smooth, shining, with short beak, black or dark brown when ripe. Apr–Jun. Hedges, roadside banks, shady places. Throughout area covered, except IS. **173**

864

865

863 Garden Chervil *Anthriscus cerefolium*
Aromatic annual, with slender stems up to 70cm. Leaves 3-pinnate, lobes further pinnately-lobed. Umbels with 2–6 spreading hairy primary rays; bracts absent; bracteoles linear. Flowers white, 4mm. Fruit up to 1cm, distinctive with a long beak up to half as long as the linear fruit. May–Aug. Hedges, vineyards, wood margins. Native of E-C. and S-E. Europe, but widely cultivated. Int B, GB, DK, F, D, NL.

864 Bur Chervil *Anthriscus caucalis*
Distinguished from **863** by its ovoid fruit up to 3mm, which is usually covered with stiff spiny bristles, and its minute inconspicuous petals. Sparsely hairy annual up to 80cm, with leaves 2–3-pinnate. Flower-stalks elongating and becoming thicker than primary rays in fruit. May–Jul. Waste places, sandy soils. GB, DK, F, IRL, NL, S.

865 Shepherd's Needle *Scandix pecten-veneris*
Slender, sparsely hairy, much branched annual up to 50cm. Leaves 2–3-pinnate with linear lobes. Umbels with 1–3 primary rays with bracts usually absent; bracteoles conspicuous, longer than flower-stalks, persistent. Flowers white, petals oblong, unequal and with incurved acute apex. Fruit large, robust, 1·5–8cm, with beak 3–4 times as long as the seed-bearing part of the fruit. Apr–Jul. Cornfields, but decreasing. B, GB, DK, F, D, IRL, NL, S.

866 Sweet Cicely *Myrrhis odorata*
Strongly aromatic perennial up to 2m, branched above. Leaves 2–3-pinnate, with oblong–lanceolate deeply-toothed lobes; sheaths of leaves conspicuous. Primary rays 4–20; bracts usually absent; bracteoles several. Flowers white; petals obovate with short incurved apex. Fruit oblong, ribbed, to 2·5cm, with rough bristly hairs. May–Jun. Damp places, waysides. F, D; int B, GB, DK, SF, IRL, NL, IS, N, S. **173**

867 Coriander *Coriandrum sativum*
Hairless annual up to 50cm, foetid when crushed. Lowest leaves lobed, upper 2–3-pinnate, with linear lobes. Primary rays usually 3–5; bracts absent or 1; bracteoles usually 3, linear. Flowers white; outer petal larger, deeply lobed with apex incurved. Fruit ovoid or globular. Jun–Aug. Cultivated for its aromatic leaves and fruit. Native of N. Africa and W. Asia. Int F, D, GB.

868 Alexanders *Smyrnium olusatrum*
Hairless, pungent, stout-stemmed biennial up to 1·5m. Lower leaves divided 2–3 times into 3 rhombic–elliptic toothed lobes; stem leaves smaller and less divided, with short inflated leaf-stalks; leaves dark green, shiny. Flowers yellow, in umbels with 7–15 primary rays with few

bracts; secondary rays with few bracteoles. Petals lanceolate to obcordate with incurved apex. Fruit globular, black when ripe. Apr–Jun. Hedgebanks, waste ground, usually near sea. F; int GB, IRL, NL. **190**

869 Biennial Alexanders *Smyrnium perfoliatum*
Differs from **868** in having upper stem-leaves clasping stem and blades undivided. Stems angled and narrowly winged, up to 1·5m; leaves ovate to rounded, toothed, yellow-green. Bracts and bracteoles absent. Apr–May. Woods, rocks, uncultivated ground. F; int GB, DK, D. **217**

870 Great Pignut *Bunium bulbocastanum*
Usually erect perennial up to 1m. Leaves 2–3-pinnate; basal leaves with linear–lanceolate lobes. Primary rays usually 10–20, slender with bracts 5–10, lanceolate pointed; bracteoles similar. Flowers white; petals obcordate; sepals absent or minute. Fruit oblong-elliptic, with slender ridges, 3–5mm. Jun–Jul. Fields, uncultivated ground, mountain meadows. B, GB, F, D, NL; int DK.

870

871 Pignut *Conopodium majus*
Erect hairless perennial up to 60cm, leafless below and with globular tubers below ground. Basal leaves 2–3-pinnate, with elliptic to ovate acutely lobed lobes; stem leaves with linear lobes. Umbels with 6–12 primary rays and 0–2 bracts; bracteoles 2 or more. Flowers white, c. 5mm across; petals obcordate with incurved apex. Fruit ovoid with slender indistinct ridges; styles erect or spreading. May–Jul. Grasslands, woods, waste places. GB, F, IRL, N. **173**

872 Burnet Saxifrage *Pimpinella saxifraga*
Downy perennial up to 60cm, with rounded stem, branched above and almost leafless. Lower leaves with 3–7 pairs of ovate lobes, either simple or pinnately lobed with linear lobes. Flowers white, rarely pinkish or purplish, in an umbel with 6–25 primary rays, and with bracts and bracteoles usually absent. Fruit broadly ovoid, with inconspicuous ridges. Very variable species. Jun–Sep. Dry grasslands. B, GB, DK, F, D, IRL, NL, N, S.

873

873 Greater Burnet Saxifrage *Pimpinella major*
Differs from **872** in having stem sharply angled, and fruit with prominent whitish ridges. Larger perennial up to 1m. Lower leaves pinnate with 3–9 ovate or oblong toothed lobes; stem leaves with inflated sheath-like stalk. Flowers white to deep pink, c. 3mm across, in umbels, with 10–25 primary rays, with bracts and bracteoles usually absent. A very variable species. Jun–Aug. Grassy places. B, GB, DK, F, D, IRL, NL, N, S; int SF.

874 Ground Elder *Aegopodium podagraria*
Perennial with stems up to 1m, and long slender

rhizomes. Leaves 1–2 times divided into 3 ovate to lanceolate toothed leaflets, leaflets sometimes 3-lobed; leaf-stalk long, 3-angled; stem leaves smaller, the upper entire. Petals white, obcordate with incurved apex. Umbel with 10–20 primary rays; bracts and bracteoles absent. Fruit narrow ovoid, laterally compressed, with 5 slender ridges. Jun–Aug. Hedges, woods, cultivated ground. Throughout area covered; int GB, IRL, IS. **173**

875 Greater Water Parsnip *Sium latifolium*
Hairless aquatic perennial with much-branched ribbed stems up to 1·5m, growing in water. Submerged leaves 2–3-pinnate with linear lobes; aerial leaves pinnate with 9–15 ovate–lanceolate toothed lobes with unequal bases. Flowers white, in umbel with 20–30 primary rays and 2–6 large leaf-like bracts; bracteoles lanceolate. Petals obcordate with apex incurved. Fruit ellipsoid with thick ridges. Jul–Aug. Shallow waters. B, GB, DK, SF, F, D, IRL, NL, S; int N. **173**

876

876 Lesser Water Parsnip *Berula erecta*
Hairless aquatic perennial up to 1m, with rounded hollow stem, and with stolons. Submerged leaves 3–4-pinnate with linear lobes; lower stem leaves with usually 7–14 pairs of oblong to ovate double-toothed leaflets. Umbels borne opposite the leaves, with 10–20 primary rays with numerous bracts and bracteoles which are often leaf-like and 3-lobed or pinnately-lobed. Fruit rounded, wider than long. Jul–Aug. Shallow waters. Throughout area covered, except SF, IS.

877 Rock Samphire *Crithmum maritimum*
Distinctive blue-green, hairless, much-branched perennial up to 50cm. Leaves 1–2-pinnate with thick fleshy linear–oblanceolate segments. Flowers yellowish to greenish-white in dense umbels, with 8–36 stout primary rays; bracts and bracteoles narrow triangular to linear–lanceolate. Fruit oblong–ovoid, with prominent thick ridges. Jul–Oct. Rocks, cliffs and sands by the sea. GB, F, NL, IRL. **199**

878 Moon Carrot *Seseli libanotis*
Biennial to perennial up to 120cm, with ridged stem. Leaves 1–3-pinnate, with narrow lobes. Flowers white or pink, in umbels with 20–60 primary rays, usually with linear bracts; bracteoles linear 10–15, not fused. Sepals linear to broadly lanceolate; petals hairy on back. Fruit ovoid, up to 4mm long, with blunt ridges; styles downcurved. A variable species. Jul–Sep. Dry grasslands, rocks, wood verges. B, GB, DK, SF, F, D, N, S.

879 *Seseli annuum*
Shortly hairy or hairless biennial or perennial up to 60cm or more, with leaves 2–3-pinnate, with linear–lanceolate lobes. Flowers white or pink, in umbels with 12–40

primary rays which are finely hairy on inner side; bracts 0–1; bracteoles not fused. Fruit ovoid up to 3cm, hairless. Jun–Sep. Dry banks, roadsides, fallow fields. F, D.

OENANTHE
SOME UMBELS LEAF-OPPOSED; STALKS OF UMBELS SHORTER THAN PRIMARY RAYS

880 River Water Dropwort *Oenanthe fluviatilis*
Floating perennial with stems ascending above water; stems ridged, hollow. Basal leaves 2–3-pinnate, with ovate to rounded lobes which are shallow lobed; stem leaves 1–2-pinnate, lobes ovate shallowly lobed. Flowers white, in umbels borne opposite the leaves on short stalks, and 6–15 primary rays; petals notched with incurved apex. Fruit elliptic, with short styles. Jun–Aug. Still and slow-flowing waters. B, GB, DK, F, D, IRL.

881 Fine-leaved Water Dropwort *Oenanthe aquatica*
Distinguished from **880** by its ovoid fruit less than 4·5mm long (fruit 5mm long in **880**). Leaves mostly above water, 3-pinnate with ovate pointed lobes; submerged leaves with linear lobes. Flowers white, in umbels with 5–15 primary rays; umbel-stalk shorter than rays. Jul–Aug. Ponds, ditches. Throughout area covered, except IS.

OENANTHE
UMBELS TERMINAL. STALKS OF UMBELS LONGER THAN PRIMARY RAYS

882

882 Tubular Water Dropwort *Oenanthe fistulosa*
Slender erect perennial up to 80cm, with broad, hollow ribbed stem, constricted at the nodes. Stem leaves pinnate with linear–lanceolate pointed entire lobes; submerged leaves 2-pinnate, with slender thread-like lobes. Flowers white, in terminal umbels; primary rays 2–4, thickened in fruit. Fruit cylindrical, up to 4mm, with styles as long, in globular umbels. Jun–Sep. Ditches, marshes, still waters, damp fields. B, GB, DK, F, D, IRL, NL, S.

883 Hemlock Water Dropwort *Oenanthe crocata*
Distinguished by the lobes of the basal leaves which are ovate or rounded, blunt-toothed, and primary rays and umbel-stalks not thickened in fruit. Stout branched perennial up to 1·5m. Flowers white, in terminal umbels with 10–40 primary rays; bracts and bracteoles small. Fruit cylindrical up to 6mm, styles half as long. Jun–Sep. Ditches, edge of streams and rivers. B, GB, F, IRL. **173**

884 *Oenanthe peucedanifolia*
Differs from **883** in having lobes of basal leaves linear, and ovoid root-tubers clustered at base of stem (tubers obovoid, narrowed to attachment to stem in **883**).

CARROT FAMILY

885

Perennial up to 60cm. Jun–Aug. Wet grasslands, ditches. B, F, D, NL.

885 Parsley Water Dropwort *Oenanthe lachenalii*
Stout perennial with solid ribbed branched stem to 1m, and cylindrical to spindle-shaped root-tubers. Basal leaves 2-pinnate with linear to spoon-shaped lobes; stem leaves with linear lobes. Flowers white, in terminal umbels; primary rays 5–15, shorter than stalk of umbel. Fruit ovoid, to 3mm, with styles at least half as long. Jul–Aug. Marshes. B, GB, DK, F, D, IRL, NL, S.

OENANTHE
RAYS OF UMBELS AND STALKS THICKENED IN FRUIT

886 Corky-fruited Water Dropwort
Oenanthe pimpinelloides
Distinguished by its umbel-stalks and primary rays which have become thickened in fruit. Erect perennial up to 1m, with long-stalked ovoid root-tubers. Basal leaves 2-pinnate, with wedge-shaped or ovate lobes. Flowers white, in terminal umbels, with 6–15 primary rays. Fruit cylindrical, up to 3·5mm, with styles as long. Jul–Aug. Meadows, ditches, hedges. B, GB, F, IRL, NL.

887 Narrow-leaved Water Dropwort
Oenanthe silaifolia
Differs from **886** in having lobes of basal leaves linear–lanceolate, stem hollow, and root-tubers close to stem. Upper stem leaves 1- to 2-pinnate with linear–lanceolate lobes. Erect perennial up to 1m, with basal leaves 2- to 4-pinnate. Umbel with 4–10 primary rays, conspicuously thickened in fruit. Jun–Sep. Wet places. B, GB, F, D.

888

888 Fool's Parsley *Aethusa cynapium*
Annual 5–200cm, with ribbed stems. Leaves usually 2-pinnate, with lanceolate to ovate pinnately-lobed lobes. Flowers white; sepals absent; petals obcordate, with incurved apex, the outer larger. Umbels with 10–20 primary rays, usually without bracts; bracteoles usually 3–4, down-curved and arrow-shaped. Fruit ovoid with thick narrowly winged ridges. Variable species. Jun–Oct. Cultivated ground, waste land, woods. Throughout area covered, except IS.

889 Fennel *Foeniculum vulgare*
Tall blue-green hairless biennial or perennial up to 2·5m, smelling of aniseed, with shining ribbed stem. Leaves 3–4-pinnate, with long slender lobes. Flowers yellow, in umbels with 4–30 primary rays; petals oblong with incurved apex; bracts and bracteoles absent. Fruit oblong–ovoid to 10mm, ribbed. Jul–Sep. Rocky places, waste ground, often near the sea. GB, F, IRL; int B, D, NL.

890 Pepper Saxifrage *Silaum silaus*
Hairless perennial with ribbed stem up to 1m, from a stout cylindrical tap-root. Leaves 2–4-pinnate, with long-stalked linear to lanceolate finely toothed lobes; upper leaves 1-pinnate or reduced to an inflated leaf-stalk. Flowers yellowish; petals ovate with incurved apex. Umbels with 5–15 primary rays, with 0–3 bracts; bracteoles several, linear–lanceolate with broad papery margin. Jun–Aug. Pastures, hedgerows. B, GB, F, D, NL, S.

891 Spignel *Meum athamanticum*
Hairless, strongly aromatic, perennial 10–60cm, with base of stem surrounded by fibrous remains of leaf-stalks. Leaves mostly basal. 3–4-pinnate, with crowded thread-like lobes. Flowers white or purplish; sepals absent; petals ovate. Primary rays of umbels 3–15, with 0–2 bristly bracts; bracteoles bristly, few. Fruit oblong–ovoid, very prominently ribbed. Jun–Jul. Pastures in mountains. B, GB, F, D; int N.

892 Bladderseed *Physospermum cornubiense*
Nearly hairless perennial up to 120cm, with slender ribbed stem, and leaves 2–3 times 3-lobed, the basal leaves long-stalked. Leaf-lobes 1–3cm, pinnately-lobed with wedge-shaped base, uppermost leaves small or reduced to stalks. Flowers white; petals obovate notched with incurved apex; sepals small. Primary rays 6–20; bracts and bracteoles lanceolate–acute. Fruit ovoid, two-lobed, with slender ridges. Jun–Sep. Bushy places, woods, damp rocks. GB, F.

893 Hemlock *Conium maculatum*
Foetid, very poisonous, annual or biennial with reddish-brown spotted hollow stem up to 2·5m. Leaves 2- to 4-pinnate, soft hairless, up to 50cm long; lobes oblong–lanceolate, toothed or pinnately lobed. Flowers white, with obcordate petals with incurved apex. Umbels with primary rays 10–20, with 5–6 narrow triangular deflexed bracts with papery margins; bracteoles 3–6, fused below. Fruit glandular, laterally compressed, with prominent undulate ribs. Jun–Aug. Damp places, waste ground. Throughout area covered, except IS. **174**

BUPLEURUM
LEAVES WITH BLADE SURROUNDING STEM; BRACTS ABSENT

894 Thorow-wax *Bupleurum rotundifolium*
Erect nearly unbranched annual up to 75cm, with very distinctive elliptic to nearly rounded entire leaves clasping the stem; lower leaves shortly stalked. Flowers yellow; sepals absent. Umbels with 5–10 primary rays, bracts absent; bracteoles 5–6, oblanceolate to ovate, shortly fused at base and longer than secondary umbel,

CARROT FAMILY

yellowish-green, spreading. Fruit oblong, blackish-brown, with slender ridges. Jun–Aug. Dry open places, arable fields. B, F, D; int GB, NL.

895 False Thorow-wax *Bupleurum lancifolium*
Like **894** but leaves narrower, ovate to oblong-lanceolate. Primary rays usually 2–3, and bracteoles almost rounded with a fine point. Fruit ovoid–rounded, with conspicuous swellings. Jun–Aug. Dry open places, arable fields; spread in birdseed mixtures. F; int B, GB.

BUPLEURUM
LOWER LEAVES STALKED; BRACTS PRESENT

896 Sickle-leaved Hare's-ear *Bupleurum falcatum*
Usually slender erect perennial up to 1m, with elliptic to oblong distinctly stalked leaves with 5–7 veins; upper leaves lanceolate, often sickle-shaped, half-clasping stem. Primary rays 3–15, slender, with 2–5 very unequal lanceolate bracts; bracteoles 5, narrow lanceolate, unequal. Petals yellow. Fruit ovoid, to 6mm, with slender winged ridges. A variable species. Jul–Oct. Fields, hedgebanks, waste places. B, †GB, F, D.

897 Small Hare's-ear *Bupleurum baldense*
Small hairless greyish branched annual 2–15cm, with lower leaves stalked, the upper stalkless, all narrowly lanceolate to spoon-shaped, 3–5 veined. Primary rays usually 3–4, bracts broadly lanceolate long-pointed, blue-green, margins papery, with 3–5 veins; bracteoles lanceolate to ovate, fine-pointed, yellowish. Fruit ovate, c. 2mm, with slender ridges. Jun–Jul. Dry open places, rocky slopes by the sea. GB, F.

898 Slender Hare's-ear *Bupleurum tenuissimum*
Much-branched blue-green annual 15–75cm, with linear to linear-lanceolate leaves, the lowest shortly stalked, veins 5–7, conspicuous beneath. Primary rays 1–3, with awl-shaped fine-pointed bracts, 3-veined; bracteoles leafy, 3-veined, usually finely toothed on margin and veins. Fruit globular, with small swellings, and with slender wavy ridges. Jul–Sep. Grassy banks by the sea, dry saltmarshes. B, GB, DK, F, D, NL, S.

899 *Bupleurum gerardi*
Slender erect annual up to 75cm, with linear–lanceolate leaves half-clasping stem, veins 5–7. Primary rays 2–7, with 3–5 narrow lanceolate 3-veined bracts, one third or more as long as the rays. Bracteoles longer than flowers, narrowly lanceolate long-pointed, 1-veined. Fruit oblong–ovoid, with slender ridges. Jul–Aug. Fields, bare ground, open woods. F; int D.

898

900 Honewort *Trinia glauca*
Greyish hairless perennial up to 50cm, with angled much branched stems. Lower leaves 2–3-pinnate, with 3–5 narrow lobes. Plants either male or female; umbels without bracts and bracteoles. Petals white, with apex incurved. Fruit ovate, prominently ribbed. May–Jun. Dry grassland on limestone. GB, F, D.

900

901 Wild Celery *Apium graveolens*
Distinguished by the absence of bracteoles. Stout biennial up to 1m, strong smelling, with grooved stem. Leaves 1- to 2-pinnate, with rhombic to lanceolate, toothed or lobed segments. Flowers whitish, c. 2mm, with petals not notched. Umbels often short-stalked and leaf-opposed; primary rays 4–12; bracts and bracteoles absent. Jun–Aug. Salt-marshes, ditches especially near the sea. B, GB, DK, F, D, IRL, NL; int SF, N, S.

902 Fool's Water-cress *Apium nodiflorum*
Distinguished by its 5–7 bracteoles. Perennial up to 1m, with hollow spreading or ascending stems, rooting at the lower nodes. Leaves 1-pinnate, with 7–13 ovate to lanceolate toothed or somewhat lobed leaflets. Flowers whitish, in short-stalked or almost stalkless umbel, arising opposite the leaves. Primary rays 3–12 with bracts usually absent; bracteoles 5–7, ovate to lanceolate, with white papery margin. Jul–Aug. Ditches, margins of ponds, shallow rivers. B, GB, F, D, IRL, NL. **175**

903 Creeping Marshwort *Apium repens*
Differs from **902** in having procumbent stems rooting at each node, and stalk of umbel usually 2–3 times longer than the primary rays (shorter than primary rays in **902**). Leaflets broadly ovate to nearly rounded. Bracts 3–7. Fruit wider than long (longer than wide in **902**). Jun–Sep. Wet places. B, DK, F, D, NL.

904

904 Lesser Marshwort *Apium inundatum*
Largely submerged perennial up to 75cm, with pinnate leaves, the lower with thread-like or linear lobes, the upper with ovate often 3-lobed lobes. Flowers whitish, in umbels borne opposite the leaves. Primary rays usually 2, bracts absent; bracteoles leaf-like, lanceolate, 3–6. Fruit elliptic–oblong. Jun–Aug. Pools, ditches, marshes, streams. B, GB, DK, F, D, IRL, NL, S.

905 Garden Parsley *Petroselinum crispum*
Erect hairless biennial 20–75cm, with rounded solid stem, branched above. Leaves 3-pinnate, with wedge-shaped crisped leaflets, toothed. Umbels flat-topped, with 8–20 primary rays, and 1–3 bracts; bracteoles 5–8, oblong to ovate, fine-pointed. Petals yellowish. Fruit broadly ovoid, with slender ridges. Jun–Sep. Waste places, ruins. Origin unknown; widely cultivated. Int throughout area covered, except SF, NL, IS.

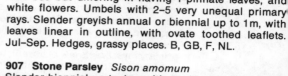

906 Corn Parsley *Petroselinum segetum*
Like **905** but differing in having 1-pinnate leaves, and white flowers. Umbels with 2–5 very unequal primary rays. Slender greyish annual or biennial up to 1 m, with leaves linear in outline, with ovate toothed leaflets. Jul–Sep. Hedges, grassy places. B, GB, F, NL.

907 Stone Parsley *Sison amomum*
Slender biennial up to 1 m, with unpleasant bituminous smell when crushed. Leaves pinnate with 7–9 pairs of oblong–ovate toothed or often lobed leaflets; upper leaves with usually 3 narrow leaflets. Flowers white, c. 3 mm; petals notched with incurved apex. Primary rays 3–6, unequal; bracts and bracteoles linear, usually 2–4. Fruit globular up to 3 mm, with very slender ridges. Jul–Aug. Hedges. GB, F.

907

908 Cowbane *Cicuta virosa*
Stout hairless branched perennial up to 120 cm, with ovoid or cylindrical rootstock. Leaves 2–3-pinnate, with linear to lanceolate lobes, acutely and deeply toothed and with asymmetrical base, and with stout leaf-stalk. Flowers white, in umbels with 10–20 primary rays; bracts absent; bracteoles 6–8 broad-linear. Petals notched, with apex incurved. Fruit globular, with wide ridges. Jul–Aug. Shallow water, damp mud. Throughout area covered, except IS.

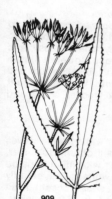

909 Longleaf *Falcaria vulgaris*
Hairless annual to perennial with rounded stems up to 90 cm, freely branched and often forming a low tangled mass. Leaves once or twice 3-lobed, with long linear–lanceolate pointed conspicuously toothed lobes. Flowers whitish, in rather open umbels, with 12–18 primary rays, with narrow pointed awl-shaped bracts and bracteoles. Petals ovate, notched with incurved apex; sepals conspicuous. Fruit oblong. Jul–Sep. Grassy and waste places. F; int B, GB, DK, NL, S.

909

910 Caraway *Carum carvi*
Hairless perennial with ridged, leafy stems up to 150 cm. Leaves 2–3-pinnate, with linear lobes. Flowers white or pinkish, in umbels with 5–16 primary rays; bracts usually absent; bracteoles absent or few. Sepals very small or absent; petals obovate, notched with incurved apex. Fruit ovoid, with prominent ridges, strong smelling when crushed. Jun–Jul. Grassy places. B, DK, SF, F, D, NL, N, S; int GB, IRL, IS. **245**

911 Whorled Caraway *Carum verticillatum*
Distinguished from **910** by its leaves with numerous whorled thread-like lobes. Erect perennial to 120 cm, with swollen roots. Flowers white. Fruit elliptic with prominent ridges. Jul–Aug. Marshes, damp meadows. B, GB, F, IRL, NL.

912 Cnidium *Cnidium dubium*
Nearly hairless biennial or perennial up to 2m, with hollow stems furrowed above. Leaves 2–3-pinnate, lobes narrow–oblong acute, finely toothed, with whitish midrib; stem leaves with purplish leaf-stalks sheathing the stem. Flowers white in umbels with 20–30 winged primary rays; bracts few or absent; bracteoles numerous, awl-shaped. Fruit globular, with wide prominent ridges. Jul–Oct. Damp woods, disturbed ground, often near sea. DK, D, S.

913 Cambridge Milk Parsley *Selinum carvifolia*
Nearly hairless perennial up to 1m, with strongly ridged, branched, leafy stem. Leaves 2–3-pinnate with linear to ovate minutely toothed, fine-pointed lobes, sometimes further lobed. Flowers white, in umbels with 5–33 primary rays; bracts absent; bracteoles linear–lanceolate, several. Fruit oblong–ovoid, flattened, with winged ridges. Jul–Sep. Damp grassland, open woods. B, GB, DK, SF, F, D, NL, N, S.

913

914 Scots Lovage *Ligusticum scoticum*
Branched leafy hairless hollow-stemmed perennial to 90cm. Leaves fleshy, twice 3-lobed, the lobes ovate to wedge-shaped, toothed or shallowly lobed, glossy, and with inflated leaf-stalks sheathing stem. Flowers white, in umbels with 5–20 primary rays, with linear bracts and bracteoles. Fruit oblong–ovoid with very prominent ridges, to 8mm. Jun–Jul. Coastal rocks, cliffs, and shingle. GB, DK, IRL, IS, N, S. **175**

915 Conioselinum tataricum
Hairless perennial up to 1·5m, with lower leaves long-stalked, 2–3-pinnate with lobes oblong to linear, often pinnately lobed; upper leaves with much-inflated leaf-stalk and small blade. Flowers white; petals broadly ovate, notched with incurved apex; sepals absent. Fruit elliptic, flattened, with winged ridges. Jul. Stony places. SF, N.

916

916 Wild Angelica *Angelica sylvestris*
Robust erect perennial up to 2m, with stems usually tinged purple. Leaves 2–3-pinnate, up to 60cm long, with oblong–ovate acutely toothed lobes, and leaf-stalks strongly sheathing at the base; upper leaves reduced to inflated sheaths more or less encircling young umbels. Flowers white or pinkish, in umbels with numerous primary rays; bracts few or absent; bracteoles bristle-like. Petals lanceolate; sepals minute. Fruit ovate, flattened, with wings wider than fruit. Jul–Sep. Damp grassy places, woods, cliffs. Throughout area covered.

917 Garden Angelica *Angelica archangelica*
Differs from **916** in its fruit which has thick corky wings (wings thin in **916**). Stems often tinged pink. Leaf-blades

more deeply lobed and the terminal lobe 3-lobed. Flowers greenish-white to cream. Jun–Jul. Damp places, by the sea. DK, SF, D, NL, IS, N, S; int B, GB, F. **191**

918 Marsh Angelica *Angelica palustris*
Distinguished by its broadly ovate whitish sepals (sepals minute in **916**, **917**). Biennial or perennial up to 120cm, with sharply angled stems. Petals white; bracteoles numerous, linear–lanceolate with whitish margin. Fruit with prominent dorsal ridges. Jul–Aug. Wet places. D.

919 Lovage *Levisticum officinale*
Stout strong-smelling perennial up to 2·5m, with upper branches opposite or whorled. Lower leaves up to 65cm long, 2–3-pinnate, glossy, with long wedge-shaped toothed or lobed lobes. Flowers greenish-yellow, in umbels with 12–20 primary stout furrowed rays; bracts numerous, lanceolate-pointed, down-curved; bracteoles several fused at base. Fruit yellow or brown, ovoid–oblong with thick winged marginal ridges and low narrow-winged dorsal ridges. Jun–Aug. Grassy places, in mountains. Native of Iran. Int B, DK, SF, F, D, NL, N, S.

919

PEUCEDANUM
LOBES OF LOWER LEAVES LINEAR OR NARROWLY LANCEOLATE, NEVER FINELY TOOTHED

920 Hog's Fennel *Peucedanum officinale*
Much branched hairless dark green perennial with smooth stems up to 2m. Lower leaves up to 60cm long, 2–6 times 3-lobed, the lobes narrowly linear and narrowed at both ends, with prominent mid-rib. Flowers yellow, in umbels nodding in bud, later erect; primary rays 10–40, bracts 0–3; bracteoles bristle-like several. Fruit narrow elliptic to narrowly ovate, with wing c. 1–3 times as wide as fruit. Jul–Sep. Grassy places, especially by the sea. GB, F, D.

921 *Peucedanum lancifolium*
Distinguished by the lobes of the lower leaves linear entire, and upper stem leaves pinnate or entire. Perennial up to 120cm. Flowers white or pale yellowish-white. Bracts and bracteoles 4–7, linear, down-curved, persistent. Fruit elliptic, with rather thick wing to 1mm and thick prominent dorsal ridges. Aug–Oct. Wet meadows, marshes. F.

920

PEUCEDANUM
LOBES OF LOWER LEAVES OVATE OR OBLONG, TOOTHED OR LOBED; OR LEAVES PINNATE

922 *Peucedanum carvifolia*
Nearly hairless perennial up to 1m, branched with

313

grooved stems above. Basal leaves oblong in outline, shining, 1-pinnate with lobes usually 2–3 times further divided into linear segments; upper leaves pinnate with linear–lanceolate lobes. Flowers yellowish to greenish-white, in umbels with 6–18 very unequal primary rays; bracts absent; bracteoles one or few. Fruit broadly elliptic with slender dorsal ridges. Jun–Sep. Meadows, open woods, damp bushy places. B, F, D, NL.

923 *Peucedanum oreoselinum*
Perennial with solid-ribbed, often reddish stems up to 1m. Lower leaves 2- to 3-pinnate, triangular in outline; lobes ovate and pinnately lobed and with narrowly winged stalks, terminal lobe rhombic toothed; upper stem-leaves less divided, with inflated leaf-stalks. Flowers white or pinkish; petals covered with small swellings. Bracts and bracteoles linear–lanceolate, down-curved. Fruit obovate. Jul–Sep. Dry meadows, open woods. F, D, S.

924 Milk Parsley *Peucedanum palustre*
Hairless perennial to 160cm, with angled and furrowed hollow stem, often purplish. Lower leaves 2- to 6-pinnate, triangular in outline, with ultimate lobes linear–oblong entire to 2- to 3-lobed with white leathery apex. Flowers white, in umbels with 20–40 primary rays; bracts and bracteoles 4 or more, lanceolate with white margins, unequal, down-curved. Sepals ovate blunt; petals with small swellings above. Fruit elliptic, with thick wings and prominent dorsal ridges. Jun–Jul. Marshes, fens, damp meadows. B, GB, DK, SF, F, D, NL, N, S. **175**

925 Masterwort *Peucedanum ostruthium*
Hairless perennial with rounded hollow stems with fine longitudinal ridges. Lower leaves 2- to 3-lobed, triangular in outline; lobes ovate to lanceolate, irregularly toothed, up to 10cm; leaf-stalks of stem-leaves much inflated. Flowers white or pinkish; in umbels with 30–60 primary rays; bracts absent; bracteoles few, bristle-like. Fruit rounded flattened, with broad wings nearly as wide as the fruit. Jun–Jul. Grassy places in hills and mountains, woods, rocky places. F, D; int B, GB, DK, N, S.

925

926 Wild Parsnip *Pastinaca sativa*
Rough-hairy strong smelling biennial up to 1m; basal leaves pinnate with 5–11 broad toothed leaflets. Flowers yellow in umbels with 9–20 angled and unequal primary rays; bracts and bracteoles 0–2, soon falling. Fruit elliptic, winged. Jun–Sep. Grassy and waste places. B, GB, F, D, NL; int DK, SF, IRL, N, S. **217**

927 Hogweed *Heracleum sphondylium*
Variable stout biennial or perennial with stems 1–3m. Leaves variable, 1- to 3-pinnate with very broad toothed

leaflets; larger stem leaves usually with 5 leaflets often pinnately lobed, densely hairy. Flowers white, rarely pink, in umbels up to 20cm across, with petals of outer flowers larger than petals of inner flowers. Primary rays 12–25; bracts few or absent; bracteoles usually present. Fruit elliptic to rounded, flattened, hairless, broadly winged. Jun–Oct. Grassy places, roadsides, hedges, woods. Throughout area covered, except IS. **175**

928 Giant Hogweed *Heracleum mantegazzianum*
Massive biennial or perennial 2–5m, with stout hollow stem up to 10cm across, usually with conspicuous purple blotches. Leaves up to 3m, variously divided with pinnately lobed lobes up to 130cm. Flowers white, rarely pinkish, in umbels up to 50cm across; primary rays 50–150; petals to 12mm. A very variable species. A poisonous plant that can burn the skin. Jun–Jul. Damp ground, waste places. Native of Caucasus. Int GB, DK, SF, F, D, IRL, NL, N, S. **175**

929 Hartwort *Tordylium maximum*

929

Stout bristly hairy annual or biennial up to 130cm, with hollow stem, usually much branched and with deflexed bristles. Leaves pinnate, the lower with ovate or rounded toothed lobes with heart-shaped base; upper leaves with narrow lanceolate lobes. Flowers white or purple, the 2–3 outer petals larger. Primary rays 5–15; bracts and bracteoles numerous awl-shaped. Fruit rounded flattened, with thickened lobed margin, bristly hairy. Jun–Aug. Grassy and waste places. GB, F; int B, D.

930 Sermountain *Laserpitium latifolium*
Nearly hairless greyish perennial up to 1·5m, with ribbed solid stem, branched above. Leaves very large 2-pinnate, with ovate, toothed and stalked lobes, with prominent mid-rib; leaf-stalks of lower leaves laterally compressed, upper strongly inflated. Flowers white, in umbels with 25–40 primary rays, with numerous deflexed narrow bracts with membranous margins; bracteoles few, awl-shaped. Fruit ovoid, with wide undulate wings. Jun–Aug. Mountain woods, rocks, scrub. DK, SF, F, D, N, S; int B.

931 *Laserpitium prutenicum*
Differs from **930** in primary umbels having numerous bracts with hairy margins (bracts not hairy-margined in **930**). Hairy biennial up to 1m, with slender angled stem, branched above. Lower leaves 2–3-pinnate, with lanceolate to elliptic toothed, stalkless or short-stalked lobes, bristly hairy beneath. Flowers white or yellowish-tinged, with usually 12–20 primary rays in umbel; bracts and bracteoles numerous, linear-lanceolate, membranous, deflexed. Fruit broadly ellipsoid with bristly-hairy ridges. Jun–Aug. Grassy places, woods. F, D.

932

933

936

932 Knotted Hedge-parsley *Torilis nodosa*
Usually procumbent annual, 10–50cm. Leaves 1–2-pinnate, with deeply pinnately lobed segments. Flowers pinkish-white, in leaf-opposed umbels; primary rays very short with umbels densely clustered; bracts absent; bracteoles longer than the almost stalkless flowers. Fruit linear to ovoid, with straight spreading spines. May–Aug. Waste places, dry grasslands, arable fields. B, GB, F, IRL, NL; int D.

933 Spreading Hedge-parsley *Torilis arvensis*
Usually an erect annual up to 1m, with variable 2-pinnate to 3-lobed leaves, with lobes coarsely toothed or nearly entire. Flowers white, in umbels with 4–12 primary rays; bracts 0–1; bracteoles numerous. Fruit ovoid, with long curved bristles. Very variable species. Jun–Aug. Arable fields. B, GB, F, D, NL.

934 Upright Hedge-parsley *Torilis japonica*
Erect annual up to 125cm, with leaves 1- to 3-pinnate. Flowers pink or white, in umbels with 5–12 primary rays; bracts 4–6; bracteoles about equalling flower stalks. Outer petals only slightly larger than inner. Fruit with recurved spines. Jun–Sep. Waste places, roadsides. Throughout area covered, except IS.

935 Small Bur-parsley *Caucalis platycarpos*
Annual with branched stems up to 40cm, with leaves 2- to 3-pinnate, the leaflets pinnately divided into oblong or lanceolate lobes. Flowers white or pink, in umbels with 2–5 primary rays; bracts usually absent; bracteoles linear–lanceolate. Sepals small; petals with incurved apex. Fruit ovoid flattened, the 3 primary ridges with line of hairs, secondary ridges with spines. May–Jul. Fields, hedges, waysides. F, D.

936 Greater Bur-parsley *Turgenia latifolia*
Annual up to 60cm with pinnate leaves, with lanceolate to oblong toothed or pinnately lobed leaflets, hairy, with often hairy margins. Flowers white, pink or purplish, in long-stalked umbels with 2–5 primary rays with 3–5 bracts; bracteoles 5–7 broadly lanceolate to oblong with papery margins. Fruit with 2–3 rows of spines on most ridges. May–Aug. Cultivated and disturbed ground, waysides. B, F, D; int GB.

937 *Orlaya grandiflora*
Annual with simple or branched stem up to 40cm. Leaves 2–3-pinnate with ultimate lobes oblong; upper stem-leaves entire or pinnately lobed. Its white flowers have the outer petals up to 8 times as long as the other petals. Umbels with 5–12 primary rays with 5–8 lanceolate bracts; bracteoles with membranous margins. Fruit ovoid–lanceolate with spines on dorsal ridges in 2–3 rows. Jun–Sep. Calcareous fields. B, F, D. **175**

938 Wild Carrot *Daucus carota*

Biennial with stems 25–100cm. Leaves 2–3-pinnate with ultimate leaflets linear to lanceolate, the upper stem leaves bract-like. Flowers white or purplish, in umbels to 15cm across; primary rays variable in number; bracts 1–2-pinnately lobed; bracteoles of outer umbels 3-lobed, or inner entire. Fruit with slender primary ridges and a single row of spines on secondary ridges. A very variable species. Jun–Sep. Fields, waysides, meadows. Throughout area covered, except IS.

Ssp. *gummifer* has fleshy shiny leaves, stems less than 40cm, and spines on fruit upcurved. Sea cliffs and sand-dunes.

Ssp. *sativa*, with a large orange edible taproot, is the cultivated carrot. **176**

Fruits of Carrot Family

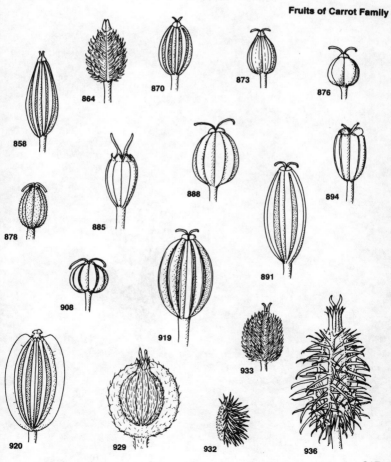

DIAPENSIA FAMILY

Diapensiaceae

Dwarf shrubs. Flowers 5-merous. Fruit a capsule; seeds small. Arctic and alpine plants.

939 Diapensia *Diapensia lapponica*
Small evergreen cushion-forming shrublet 2–6cm, with leathery spoon-shaped leaves in dense rosettes. Flowers white, solitary on short stalks, with bracts and bracteoles. Calyx deeply 5-lobed, leathery; petals 5, ovate, spreading; stamens with wide flattened filaments. Capsule ovoid. May–Jun. Rock-crevices, stony mountain pastures. GB, SF, IS, N, S. **176**

939

WINTERGREEN FAMILY

Pyrolaceae

Rhizomatous perennial herbs. Leaves simple, uppermost scale-like. Flowers 5-merous. Fruit a capsule; seeds small. Plants of woods, acid heaths and mountains.

PYROLA
STYLE NOT EXPANDED INTO A DISK BELOW STIGMA

940 Common Wintergreen *Pyrola minor*
Hairless perennial up to 20cm or more, with broadly elliptic usually blunt-toothed leaves with leaf-stalks shorter than blade, in a rosette. Flowers white or lilac-pink, globular, 5–7mm, in a terminal spike-like cluster. Style short, straight, included in the petals. Jun–Aug. Woods, moors, humus-rich soils. Throughout area covered.

941 *Pyrola norvegica*
Differs from **940** in having curved exserted style much longer than the petals, and bracts lanceolate, equalling or shorter than flower-stalks. Stem up to 20cm; leaves rounded to elliptic. Flowers white or lilac, broadly bell-shaped, 1–2·5cm across. Calyx-lobes ovate-lanceolate pointed. Jul. Bare places in mountains. SF, N, S.

940

PYROLA
STYLE EXPANDED INTO A DISK BELOW STIGMA

942 Intermediate Wintergreen *Pyrola media*
Stem up to 30cm, with leaves ovate to rounded, with rounded teeth; leaf-stalk shorter or equalling blade. Distinguished by its style which is straight and longer than petals and with a disk below stigma. Flowers white or pink, globular, 7–10mm across; calyx triangular-ovate, spreading. Jun–Aug. Woods, moors, heaths. GB, DK, SF, F, D, IRL, N, S.

943 Yellow Wintergreen *Pyrola chlorantha*
Stem up to 30cm, with oblong–ovate, rounded–toothed leaves, pale green above darker beneath; leaf-stalk longer than blade. Flowers yellowish-green, broadly bell-shaped, 8–12mm across, in a terminal spike-like cluster. Style longer the petals, curved. Jun–Jul. Coniferous woods, rocks. B, DK, SF, F, D, N, S.

944 Round-leaved Wintergreen *Pyrola rotundifolia*
Differs from **943** in having lanceolate pointed calyx-lobes up to 4·5mm (calyx-lobes triangular to 2mm in **943**).

Flowers white or bell-shaped, 8–12mm across; style up to 1cm, much longer than the petals. Perennial up to 30cm, with rounded to ovate, toothed leaves; stem-leaves oblong–lanceolate. Jun–Jul. Woods, wet places. Throughout area covered, except IS.

945 Serrated Wintergreen *Orthilia secunda*
Distinguished by its one-sided spike-like cluster of greenish-white flowers each 5–6mm across, with much longer protruding straight style. Perennial with stem up to 25cm, with ovate to broadly elliptic pointed, pale green leaves, in a basal rosette from a short creeping stock; stem leaves lanceolate, numerous. Jun–Aug. Woods, rock ledges, in hills and mountains. GB, DK, SF, F, D, IRL, IS, N, S; int B. **199**

946

946 One-flowered Wintergreen *Moneses uniflora*
Distinguished by its solitary drooping white flower 1·3–2cm across, with long protruding style, borne on erect leafless stem up to 15cm. Leaves rounded to ovate–elliptic, toothed, with a short leaf-stalk. May–Jun. Coniferous woods, moors. GB, DK, SF, F, D, NL, N, S; int B.

947 Umbellate Wintergreen *Chimaphila umbellata*
Dwarf shrub with rhizomes and flowering stems up to 30cm. Leaves oblanceolate, toothed, leathery, mostly whorled or alternate, short-stalked. Flowers pinkish 3–7, nodding, in a terminal umbel. Petals rounded, 5–6mm; style very short, thick. Jun–Jul. Coniferous woods, rocks. DK, SF, F, D, N, S.

948 Yellow Bird's-nest *Monotropa hypopitys*
Yellowish-white saprophytic perennial, without green chlorophyll, with stout erect stem up to 25cm, covered with many ovate whitish-brown scales, each up to 13mm long, overlapping below. Flowers yellowish, in terminal elongated cluster, at first down-curved, later erect. Sepals oblong/spoon-shaped; petals swollen at base up to 13mm, erect with recurved apices; stamens shorter. Fruit globular. Jun–Aug. Damp coniferous and oak woods, sand-dunes. Throughout area covered, except IS.

HEATH FAMILY

Ericaceae

Small shrubs. Leaves simple, small, evergreen. Petals fused into inflated bell- or urn-shaped tube. Fruit a capsule, berry or drupe. Major component of the vegetation of heaths, moors, bogs, tundra and acid soils on mountains. They have fungi in intimate association with their roots (mycorrhiza).

ERICA
STAMENS INCLUDED IN COROLLA

949 Cross-leaved Heath *Erica tetralix*
Dwarf greyish undershrub with weak ascending stems up to 70cm. Leaves linear, in whorls of 4, with long bristly glandular hairs on margin. Flowers pale pink, in a terminal umbel. Sepals bristly hairy; corolla urn-shaped with spreading or recurved lobes; anthers included in corolla. Ovary hairy. Jun–Oct. Bogs, wet heaths, pinewoods. Throughout area covered, except IS. **261**

950 Dorset Heath *Erica ciliaris*
Differs from **949**: has broader ovate to lanceolate leaves in whorls of 3, and larger bright reddish-pink flowers 8–12mm (flowers 5–9mm in **949**). Flowering spikes elongated; ovary hairless. Dwarf shrub up to 80cm. Apr–Oct. Bogs, heaths, open woods. GB, F, IRL. **262**

951 Mackay's Heath *Erica mackaiana*
Densely branched bushy dwarf shrub 5–60cm, with oblong leaves 4–5mm, in whorls of 4, ciliate and spreading throughout. Flowers pinkish-purple, in terminal umbels. Corolla urn-shaped with spreading or recurved lobes, 5–7mm. Ovary hairless. Jul–Sep. Moors. IRL.

952 Bell Heather *Erica cinerea*
Dwarf shrub up to 75cm, with ascending branches. Leaves linear, in whorls of 3, hairless, with inrolled margins. Flowers reddish-purple in a terminal elongated cluster or an umbel. Sepals lanceolate, hairless, with papery margins; corolla urn-shaped, 4–7mm, with spreading or erect lobes; stamens included. Ovary hairless. Jul–Sep. Heaths, rocky ground, woods, moorlands. B, GB, F, D, IRL, NL, N. **262**

951

ERICA
STAMENS LONGER THAN COROLLA, WITH ANTHERS PROTRUDING

953 Irish Heath *Erica erigena*
Erect shrub up to 120cm, with linear leaves in whorls of 4,

hairless and with a white line beneath. Flowers pink, in elongated clusters, often branched. Corolla tubular with erect lobes, with anthers slightly longer. Mar–May. Heaths, bogs, wet moors. F, IRL.

954 Cornish Heath *Erica vagans*
Dwarf spreading or ascending shrub with flexuous stems up to 60cm. Leaves in whorls of 4–5, linear to oblong, mostly hairless, spreading or down-turned. Flowers lilac-pink or white, in a dense leafy inflorescence to 10cm long. Corolla bell-shaped with erect lobes; anthers dark, longer. Jul–Sep. Heaths, woods. GB, F, IRL. **245**

955 Heather *Calluna vulgaris*
Dwarf shrub up to 80cm, freely branched. Leaves oblong–lanceolate, in opposite rows, clasping stem with basal lobes. Flowers pale purple, in leafy stalked spike-like clusters; 6–8 bracteoles crowded beneath flowers. Sepals oblong, petal-like and longer than the deeply lobed corolla; stamens 8. Jul–Sep. Heaths, moors, bogs, woods, sand-dunes. Throughout area covered. **261**

953

956 *Cassiope tetragona*
Spreading or ascending shrublet up to 30cm, with oblong–lanceolate blunt overlapping leaves in 4 rows closely adpressed to stem. Flowers creamy-white, solitary, bell-shaped 6–8mm, axillary, stalked in short lax cluster. Sepals yellowish, thin papery stiff, shorter than corolla. Jul. Heaths, tundra. SF, N, S.

957 Cassiope *Cassiope hypnoides*
Differs from **956** in having alternate acute, not grooved leaves (deeply grooved in **956**), not closely adpressed to stem. Mat-forming dwarf shrublet with spreading branched stems up to 15cm. Flowers terminal, stalked, with sepals crimson with papery margin; corolla white, broadly bell-shaped. Jun–Aug. Streams, damp heaths, tundra, by late snow patches. SF, IS, N, S. **176**

958 Arctic Rhododendron
Rhododendron lapponicum
Spreading evergreen dwarf shrub, with branched stems up to 50cm. Leaves ovate, leathery dark green, densely brownish scaly beneath, with inturned margin. Flowers purple, broadly bell-shaped, 8–15mm, in stalked clusters of 3–6. Calyx-lobes triangular, with hairy margin. Stamens 6–8. Jun. Dry heaths, stony places, in mountains. SF, N, S.

959 Labrador Tea *Ledum palustre*
Evergreen dwarf shrub up to 120cm, either spreading or erect, with young stems brown-hairy. Leaves linear to broadly oblong, leathery, brown-hairy beneath, with incurved margin. Flowers white, numerous in dense

958

terminal umbels. Petals 5, free, obovate, spreading, 4–8mm. Stamens 8–10. May–Jul. Bogs, heaths, coniferous woods. SF, D, N, S; int GB. **176**

960 Trailing Azalea *Loiseleuria procumbens*
Mat-forming hairless shrublet, rooting freely. Leaves oblong, opposite, with incurved margin, and mid-rib prominent beneath. Flowers pink, c. 6mm, solitary or in small terminal umbels. Corolla broadly bell-shaped, 5-lobed; sepals lanceolate, red; stamens 5. May–Jul. Dry stony and peaty places on arctic heaths and in mountains. GB, SF, F, D, IS, N, S.

961 Blue Heath *Phyllodoce caerulea*
Dwarf evergreen shrublet with erect or ascending freely branched stems up to 35cm. Leaves alternate, crowded linear to linear–oblong blunt, leathery, with margin strongly incurved. Flowers lilac to pinkish-purple, pendulous, urn-shaped with short lobes, up to 12mm, borne on long glandular-hairy stalks several in a terminal cluster. Stamens 10, included in corolla. Jun–Jul. Heaths on mountains, moors. GB, SF, F, IS, N, S. **245**

962 St Dabeoc's Heath *Daboecia cantabrica*
Evergreen dwarf shrub with spreading or ascending weak stems usually up to 35cm, or longer if supported by other shrubs. Leaves variable, narrowly lanceolate to narrowly ovate, with white-woolly undersides. Flowers reddish-purple, pendulous, in lax terminal cluster of 3–9. Corolla urn-shaped with 4 short spreading lobes, 9–14mm; stamens 8. May–Oct. Heaths, open woods, rocky ground. F, IRL. **262**

963 Bearberry *Arctostaphylos uva-ursi*
Prostrate mat-forming evergreen much-branched undershrub up to 1·5m. Leaves obovate to oblanceolate entire, rather leathery dark shining green above. Flowers greenish-white to pink, nearly globular with short recurved lobes, 5–6mm. Calyx-lobes rounded. Fruit berry-like, bright red when ripe. Apr–Jul. Moors, rocky ground, open woods. Throughout area covered, except B. **245**

964

964 Alpine Bearberry *Arctostaphylos alpinus*
Differs from **963** in having leaves saw-toothed and not evergreen. Fruit black with ripe, succulent. Prostrate under-shrub up to 60cm. Flowers white. May–Jul. Heaths, dry stony places, mainly in mountains. GB, SF, F, D, N, S.

965 Shallon *Gaultheria shallon*
Erect evergreen shrub up to 1·7m, forming dense thickets. Leaves broadly ovate pointed with rounded or heart-shaped base, finely toothed. Flowers pinkish-white, in spike-like clusters on previous year's shoots.

Corolla urn-shaped with recurved lobes. Fruit a capsule surrounded by fleshy calyx, berry-like, dark purple. May–Jun. Sandy and peaty soils. Native of N. America. Int GB, F.

966 *Pernettya mucronata*
Small evergreen erect or spreading shrub up to 1m. Leaves elliptic–lanceolate, spine-tipped, leathery. Flowers white, drooping on short stalk shorter than the subtending leaf. Corolla urn-shaped, with recurved acute lobes, 5–6mm. Berry globular, purple, pink or white. May–Jun. Native of Chile. Naturalized locally in GB, IRL.

967 Bog Rosemary *Andromeda polifolia*
Erect or ascending evergreen dwarf shrub up to 35cm. Leaves linear to oblong, dark green above, silvery-hairy beneath, margin usually incurved. Flowers bright pink fading to white, drooping, in short spike-like clusters. Corolla urn-shaped, with recurved lobes, 5–8mm; calyx-lobes triangular, reddish. Fruit a dry capsule. May–Jun. Bogs, wet heaths. Throughout area covered, except IS.

968 Leatherleaf *Chamaedaphne calyculata*
Small evergreen shrublet up to 50cm, with elliptic-oblong leaves covered with brownish scales beneath. Flowers white, drooping, in axils of leaf-like bracts, in a drooping or horizontal one-sided spike-like cluster. Corolla cylindrical 5–6mm, lobed to $\frac{1}{3}$ its length; calyx-lobes rounded, hairy-margined. Fruit a capsule, drooping. Jun. Bogs, meadows, wet woods. SF, S.

968

VACCINIUM
COROLLA DIVIDED ALMOST TO BASE

969 Cranberry *Vaccinium oxycoccos*
Slender spreading evergreen undershrub up to 80cm. Leaves ovate to oblong, shining green above, whitish beneath. Flowers pinkish-red, in terminal spike-like clusters of 2–5, with softly hairy flower-stalk. Corolla with 4 ovate, spreading or down-curved petals; stamens and style prominent. Fruit a red berry. Jun–Aug. Peat-bogs. Throughout area covered, except IS. **234**

970 Small Cranberry *Vaccinium microcarpum*
Differs from **969** in having flower-stalks hairless and leaves triangular–ovate, not more than 2·5mm wide. Flowers smaller. Berry 5–8mm wide, pear-shaped to ellipsoid. Jun. Peat-bogs. GB, SF, D, IS, N, S.

971 American Cranberry *Vaccinium macrocarpon*
Like **969** but flowers not borne terminally; corolla-lobes 6–10mm (5–6 in **969**) and bracteoles ovate–elliptic, 1mm or more wide (bracteoles linear–oblong not more than

971

0·5mm wide in **969**). Berry larger, 1–2cm wide, edible. Jun–Aug. Native of N. America. Nat GB, D, NL.

VACCINIUM
COROLLA DIVIDED TO NOT MORE THAN HALF-WAY TO BASE

972 Cowberry *Vaccinium vitis-idaea*
Small evergreen undershrub up to 30cm, often much less, with spreading arching stems. Leaves elliptic to oblong or obovate, blunt, leathery, dark-green above, paler gland-dotted beneath. Flowers white or pink, 4–5-lobed, in short crowded clusters. Corolla 5–8mm, bell-shaped with lobe half as long as tube. Filaments of stamens hairy. Fruit a red globular berry. May–Jun. Moors, heaths, coniferous woods, tundra. Throughout area covered. **176**

973 Bog Bilberry *Vaccinium uliginosum*
Branched undershrub up to 75cm or more, with deciduous obovate, blunt, hairless, blue-green leaves. Flowers white, usually tinged pink, 1–3 on short scaly branches. Corolla urn-shaped with 4–5 short recurved lobes; calyx-lobes rounded, reddish. Berry globular to elliptic, bluish black. May–Jun. Moors, heaths, coniferous woods, tundra. Throughout area covered, except IRL.

974 Bilberry *Vaccinium myrtillus*
Deciduous undershrub up to 35cm or more, freely branched, with twigs acutely 3-angled. Leaves ovate pointed, finely toothed, bright green. Flowers pale green, tinged pink, solitary or paired. Corolla globular 4–6mm with short recurved lobes; calyx scarcely lobed with wavy or entire margin. Berry globular, bluish-black, sweet-tasting. Apr–Jul. Heaths, moors, open woods on acid soils. Throughout area covered. **234**

CROWBERRY FAMILY

Empetraceae

Small shrubs. Leaves alternate or whorled, 'heath'-like. Flowers small, 3-merous, in short, axillary racemes. Fruit a drupe.

975 Crowberry *Empetrum nigrum*

Spreading mat-forming or ascending undershrub up to 25cm, with linear–oblong dark green shiny leaves, with incurved whitish glandular margin. Flowers either male or female on each plant, in short lateral clusters. Sepals and petals greenish-pink to reddish-purple, with stamens much longer. Fruit a black berry-like drupe with purplish bloom. Apr–Jun. Moors, bogs. Throughout area covered. Ssp. *hermaphroditum*, with usually bisexual flowers and stamens usually persistent in fruit, occurs in N. Europe to c. 60°N. **268**

975

PRIMROSE FAMILY

Primulaceae

Annual, biennial or perennial herbs. Leaves alternate, simple. Flowers showy, regular, 5- to 7-merous. Fruit a capsule, with many seeds.

PRIMULA
FLOWERS YELLOW

976 Primrose *Primula vulgaris*
Perennial with a lax rosette of oblanceolate to obovate, irregularly toothed wrinkled leaves. Flowers scented, pale yellow with darker centre, borne individually on leafless long-haired stalks, arising from the leaf rosette. Corolla 2–4cm across, with spreading notched lobes; calyx tubular, angled, with lanceolate pointed lobes. Feb–May. Woods, scrub, grassy banks, sea-cliffs, mountains. Throughout area covered, except IS, S. **218**

977 Cowslip *Primula veris*
Long flower stalks bear a one-sided umbel of many bright yellow flowers with orange spots at base of petal lobes. Leaves in a lax rosette, more or less ovate, toothed, white-woolly beneath, abruptly contracted into a leaf-stalk. Flowers 8–28mm across; calyx bell-shaped, with triangular lobes. Apr–May. Meadows, pastures. Throughout area covered, except IS. **218**

978 Oxlip *Primula elatior*
Differs from **977** in having calyx-lobes long-pointed, and mature capsule as long or longer than calyx (calyx-lobes acute, capsule shorter than calyx in **977**). Flowers pale yellow, 1·5–2·5cm across, in a terminal umbel, on stems 10–30cm. Apr–May. Meadows, woods. B, GB, DK, F, D, NL, S; int SF, N. **218**

PRIMULA
FLOWERS LILAC, PINK, PURPLE OR VIOLET

979 Birdseye Primrose *Primula farinosa*
Flowers usually lilac-pink with yellow throat, rarely purple or white, with up to 20 flowers in a terminal umbel, on stems up to 20cm. Leaves oblanceolate to elliptic, blunt-toothed, green above and usually white-mealy beneath, in a basal rosette. Corolla 8–16mm across; sepal-teeth pointed or blunt. May–Jul. Damp, grassy places in hills and mountains. GB, DK, SF, F, D, S. **262**

980

980 Scottish Primrose *Primula scotica*
Like **979**, but flowers dark purple with yellow throat,

5–8mm across, usually 1–6 on stem 5–6cm. Sepal-teeth blunt; stigma 5-lobed. Leaves mealy beneath. May–Jun, Jul–Aug. Sand-dunes, coastal cliffs. Endemic to GB (N. Scotland).

981 *Primula scandinavica*
Differs from **980** in having larger flowers 9–12mm across, with stigma globular, not lobed, on stems 4–10cm in a cluster of 2–8 flowers. Jun. Meadows, by streams. N, S.

982 *Primula stricta*
Distinguished by the absence of white mealy hairs on stems and leaves. Flowers violet or lilac, 4–9mm across, with oblong notched lobes, borne in a terminal cluster of 1–15, on a stem 2–30cm. Calyx-teeth glandular, with marginal hairs. Leaves narrowly obovate to oblanceolate, entire or toothed, sometimes mealy beneath. Jun. Damp. Mountain meadows, cliffs. SF, IS, N, S.

983 *Primula nutans*
Distinguished by the absence of white meal on leaves, and with styles of different length. Flowers lilac or pink with yellow centre, in umbels of 1–10, on stem 1–30cm. Corolla 1–2cm across; calyx with 5 distinct ribs. Bracts usually eared at base. Leaves ovate to nearly rounded, somewhat fleshy, with leaf-stalk twice as long as blade. Jun. Damp meadows, usually near the sea. SF, N, S.

ANDROSACE
SLENDER ANNUALS OR BIENNIALS

984 Northern Androsace *Androsace septentrionalis*
Annual with rosette of basal leaves, and erect stems bearing an umbel of 5–30 long-stalked white or pink flowers. Flowering stem leafless, 8–30cm; corolla 4–6mm across; calyx lobed to the middle. Leaves oblong to elliptic, toothed. May–Jul. Grassy places, in mountains. DK, SF, F, D, N, S.

985 *Androsace maxima*
Differs from **984** in having bracts below umbels leaf-like and equalling or longer than the flower-stalks at flowering. (Bracts shorter than leaf-stalks in **984**). Flowers white or pink, 6mm across, in many-flowered umbel, on stem 3–15cm. Bracts fused at base. Calyx enlarging in fruit, densely hairy. Apr–May. Dry open places, grasslands. F, D.

984

986 *Androsace elongata*
Distinguished by its tiny white flowers c. 3mm across, with petals shorter than the calyx-lobes. Annual with a rosette of lanceolate to oblanceolate leaves with fine marginal hairs. Flower stems 4–10cm, usually many,

densely hairy, with many flowers in a lax umbel and with flower stalks much longer than the bracts. Calyx glandular-hairy. Apr–May. Dry open places, fields, vineyards. F, D.

ANDROSACE
LAX MAT-FORMING PERENNIAL

987

987 *Androsace lactea*
Almost hairless loosely tufted perennial, with linear stalkless leaves in rosettes. Flowers white, up to 12mm across, borne in umbel of 1–4, on stems 3–15cm; flower stalks much longer than linear–lanceolate bracts. Calyx hairless. Jun–Aug. Dry open places, rocks, screes. F, D.

988 Alpine Snowbell *Soldanella alpina*
Hairless mat-forming perennial with rounded to kidney-shaped leaves, long-stalked, all basal. Flowers violet or blue-violet, nodding, 2–4 borne on stems up to 15cm, which elongate in fruit. Corolla 8–13mm long, divided to half-way or more into 4–5 linear lobes. Apr–Aug. Pastures, stony places in mountains. F, D. **276**

989 Water Violet *Hottonia palustris*
Submerged aquatic perennial; flowering stems borne above water with whorls of violet flowers. Leaves all submerged, pinnate with linear lobes, alternate or in whorls. Flowers 3–2·5cm across, with yellow throat, in whorls of 3–9, in a long erect cluster up to 40cm. Calyx equalling corolla-tube, lobed nearly to base. May–Jul. Shallow, still water. B, GB, DK, F, D, NL, S; int IRL. **246**

990 Sowbread *Cyclamen hederifolium*
Perennial with a globular flattened tuber 3–15cm across, rooting mainly from the upper surface. Leaves appearing after flowering, heart-shaped, toothed, angled or lobed. Flowers pale pink or white with darker blotches, solitary, nodding. Petals up to c. 2cm, with eared bases. Flower-stalks coiling in fruit. Aug–Nov. Woods. F; int GB. **246**

991 Cyclamen *Cyclamen purpurascens*
Differs from **990** in having petals not eared at base, and flowers appearing when leaves are fully developed. Tuber 2–3cm, globular, rooting all over. Leaves broadly heart-shaped or kidney-shaped, not angled. Flowers reddish-pink, very fragrant, with dark blotch at throat; style slightly longer. Jun–Oct. Woods. F, D. **262**

992 Yellow Pimpernel *Lysimachia nemorum*
Evergreen creeping perennial with stems up to 45cm. Leaves opposite, ovate–lanceolate acute, short-stalked.

Flowers yellow, in axils of middle leaves, on slender stalks. Calyx with linear–lanceolate lobes; petals spreading, 6–8·5mm. May–Sep. Woods, damp shady places. B, GB, DK, F, D, IRL, NL, N, S.

993 Creeping Jenny *Lysimachia nummularia*
Differing from **992** in having broadly ovate to rounded gland-dotted leaves, and larger ovate overlapping calyx-lobes. Flowers yellow, solitary on short stalks. Petals 8–18mm, with ovate lobes, dotted with black glands. Jun–Aug. Lake shores, ditches, wet grasslands. B, GB, DK, F, D, IRL, NL, N, S; int SF. 218

994 Yellow Loosestrife *Lysimachia vulgaris*
Hairy perennial with erect stems up to 160cm. Leaves opposite or in whorls of 3–4, ovate to lanceolate, dotted with black or orange glands, short-stalked. Flowers yellow, in a terminal branched cluster which is leafy below and with linear bracts above. Corolla 1·5–2cm across; calyx with lobes with red margin. Jul–Aug. Fens, wet woods, river-banks, lake shores. Throughout area covered, except IS. 218

994

995 Dotted Loosestrife *Lysimachia punctata*
Differs from **994** in having flowers in axillary clusters of 2 or more (not in terminal clusters as in **994**). Stems up to 90cm or more, with opposite leaves or leaves in whorls of 3–4, lanceolate to elliptic acute, dotted with glands beneath. Flowers yellow, 3·5cm across, with ovate to lanceolate glandular-hairy lobes; calyx glandular-hairy. Jul–Oct. Marshy fields and riversides. Native of S Europe. Int B, GB, DK, SF, F, D, NL, N, S. 218

996 Tufted Loosestrife *Lysimachia thyrsiflora*
Distinguished by its dense axillary ovoid clusters of yellow flowers, from axils of middle stem-leaves. Usually hairless erect perennial up to 70cm, with opposite lanceolate stalkless leaves, with numerous black glands. Flowers with 7 sepals and petals; corolla 4–6mm long with linear–lanceolate lobes, stamens longer. Calyx-lobes linear. Jun–Jul. Fens, marshes, bogs. B, GB, DK, SF, F, D, NL, N, S. 218

997 Fringed Loosestrife *Lysimachia ciliata*
Flowers yellow, solitary or rarely 2, axillary; corolla with red basal blotches. Perennial up to 130cm; leaves opposite or in whorls of 4, ovate to lanceolate, hairy only on margin, stalked. May–Jun. Waste places, lake shores. Native of N. America. Locally naturalized in B, GB.

998 Lake Loosestrife *Lysimachia terrestris*
Flowers yellow in spike-like cluster; corolla streaked and dotted with red and black; bulbils usually present in axils of leaves. Perennial with stems up to 80cm, with lanceolate stalkless leaves. Corolla 5·5–7mm, lobes

lanceolate. Damp places, lake margins. Native of N. America. Naturalized locally in GB.

999 Chickweed Wintergreen *Trientalis europaea*
Hairless perennial with usually unbranched stem 5–30cm, with leaves in a whorl at apex of stem. Leaves obovate to lanceolate, stalkless. Flowers white tinged pink, 11–19mm across, usually solitary, stalked. Petals 5–8, spreading, ovate pointed; calyx-teeth linear. May–Aug. Coniferous woods, moors, heaths. Throughout area covered, except IRL. **176**

1000 Sea Milkwort *Glaux maritima*
Fleshy perennial with erect or spreading stems, rooting at the nodes, 5–30cm. Leaves on rhizomes broadly triangular, papery; stem-leaves elliptic to obovate entire, in 4 ranks, stalkless. Flowers white to purple or pink, 3–6mm across, stalkless, axillary. Petals absent; calyx lobes petal-like, blunt with broad translucent margin. June–Aug. Salt-marshes, salt-meadows, coastal rocks. Throughout area covered. **246**

1001 Scarlet Pimpernel *Anagallis arvensis*
Annual or biennial with erect or ascending 4-angled stems, 5–50cm. Leaves ovate to lanceolate, usually opposite, upper leaves narrower. Flowers red, blue or flesh-coloured, in axils of upper leaves, with spreading petals 4–7mm across. Calyx-lobes narrow lanceolate, fine-pointed; lobes of corolla usually with marginal hairs. Variable species. Apr–Sep. Cultivated ground, waste places, sand-dunes. Throughout area covered, except IS. **229**

1002 Blue Pimpernel *Anagallis foemina*
Like **1001** but lobes of corolla without marginal hairs, or few hairs. Flowers blue with wedge-shaped toothed lobes; calyx concealing corolla in bud (not concealing corolla in bud in **1001**). Leaves lanceolate. May–Jul. Cultivated ground, waste places, coastal sands. Throughout area covered, but mostly as a casual, except IRL, IS. **276**

1003 Bog Pimpernel *Anagallis tenella*
Slender spreading perennial rooting at the nodes, with stems up to 15cm. Leaves rounded to broadly elliptic, opposite, short-stalked. Flowers pink, rarely white, 6–10mm, born in axils of middle leaves. Petal-lobes lanceolate long-stalked. May–Sep. Damp turf, bogs, marshes, ditches, lake shores. B, GB, F, D, IRL, NL.

1004 Chaffweed *Anagallis minima*
Erect annual with stems usually 1–4cm. Leaves ovate entire, alternate. Flowers white or pink, 2mm across, almost stalkless in axils of leaves. Calyx-lobes much longer than corolla. Jun–Aug. Bare ground, damp sandy places. Throughout area covered, except IS.

331

1005 Brookweed *Samolus valerandi*
Hairless perennial with a basal rosette of leaves and erect leafy stems 5–60cm. Leaves obovate to spoon-shaped, entire, stalkless. Flowers white or pink, in a terminal spike or branched spike-like cluster. Flowers 2–3mm across. Calyx bell-shaped with blunt teeth, half as long as the bell-shaped 5-lobed corolla. Capsule globular. Jun–Aug. Marshes, ditches, wet sands. Throughout area covered, except IS, N. **177**

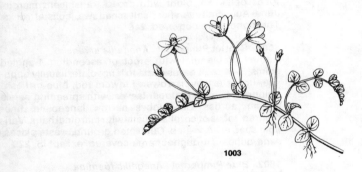

1003

SEA-LAVENDER FAMILY

Plumbaginaceae

Perennial or rarely annual herbs. Leaves all basal, simple, often fleshy. Flowers small, aggregated into lax or dense long-stalked inflorescences; bracts papery. Calyx persistent. Fruit 1-seeded, dry, papery. Plants of coastal habitats, especially salt-marshes and cliffs.

1006 Thrift *Armeria maritima*
Low mat-forming perennial, with tufts of linear leaves, and erect leafless stems 3–30cm, bearing a terminal dense rounded head of pink flowers. Flower-heads 1–3cm across, with a sheath below. Outer involucral-bracts finely pointed, usually with papery margins, inner bracts papery. Calyx funnel-shaped, with a ribbed tube and papery limb; corolla funnel-shaped with 5 petals, 8–10mm across. A very variable species. Apr–Aug. Salt-marshes, sand-dunes, cliffs, heaths, mine spoil heaps, mountain grasslands. Throughout area covered, except NL. **246**

1007 Common Sea-lavender *Limonium vulgare*
Low mat-forming perennial, with elliptic to broadly lanceolate stalked leaves, and flowering stems branched above, up to 70cm. Leaves in a basal rosette with leaf-stalks half as long as oblanceolate spoon-shaped blade. Flowers lilac to reddish, 5–6mm across, in dense or lax one-sided flat-topped branched inflorescence, with papery bracts. Calyx funnel-shaped, 5-lobed; corolla with short tube with broad rounded petals. Jul–Sep. Salt-marshes. B, GB, DK, F, D, NL, S. **276**

1008 Lax-flowered Sea-lavender *Limonium humile*
Like **1007** but a smaller plant up to 40cm, with flowering stems branched in upper half and somewhat angled. Flowers in longer spikes 3–5cm, erect, with 2–3 spikelets per centimetre (spikes 1–2cm, spreading, with 6–8 spikelets per centimetre in **1007**). Aug–Sep. Salt-marshes. GB, DK, F, D, IRL, N, S.

1009 Matted Sea-lavender *Limonium bellidifolium*
Distinguished from **1007** by its spoon-shaped acute leaves, with usually 3 parallel veins (leaves with branched veins in **1007**). Stems branched almost from the base with zig-zag branches, many non-flowering, spreading or ascending to 30cm. Leaves often absent at flowering. Flowers pale pink, in dense spreading spikes, each spikelet 1–3-flowered; bracts with papery margins. Jun–Aug. Dry salt-marshes. GB, F.

1010 Rock Sea-lavender *Limonium binervosum*
Hairless perennial up to 30cm, with oblanceolate leaves

1008

333

in a basal rosette. Flowers blue-violet, with wide overlapping petals, in dense erect spikes, with spikelets 6–8 per centimetre on major terminal branches; inflorescence without non-flowering branches. A variable species that has been split into a number of microspecies. Jun–Sep. Coastal cliffs, rocks and shingle. GB, F, IRL.

1011 *Limonium paradoxum*
Like **1010** but leaves very small, 1-veined, c. 1·5×0·5cm (leaves 4–5·5cm in **1010**). Inflorescence 5–15cm; spikes reduced to clusters of 2–3 spikelets. Jun–Sep. Coastal cliffs. GB.

1012 *Limonium recurvum*
Differs from **1010** in having 8–10 spikelets per centimetre, closely set so that the outer bracts overlap those of the adjacent spikelets in the same row. Leaves 4–8mm wide, blunt, 3-veined at base. Flowering spikes up to 3cm, spreading, often recurved. Jun–Sep. Coastal cliffs. GB, IRL.

1013 *Limonium transwallianum*
Differs from **1012** in having narrower leaves 3–6mm wide, 1-veined, apex blunt with a fine tip. Spikes spreading; petals narrow, not overlapping in bud. Jul–Sep. Coastal rocks. GB.

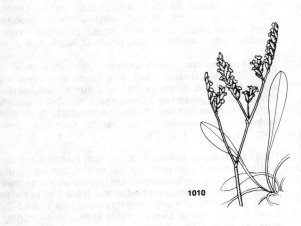

1010

GENTIAN FAMILY

Gentianaceae

Annual or perennial herbs. Leaves opposite, usually sessile. Simple. Flowers 4- to 5-merous, regular. Corolla tubular; corolla-lobes contorted in bud. Stamens 4–5, inserted on corolla tube. Fruit a capsule, with many small seeds. Plants mostly of grassland, and in the mountains.

1014

1014 Yellow Centaury *Cicendia filiformis*
Small slender erect annual 2–14cm, with simple or little-branched stem. Leaves linear, few, soon withering. Flowers yellow, 3–6mm across. Calyx bell-shaped with short triangular lobes; corolla with ovoid tube and 4 short lobes. Capsule egg-shaped. May–Oct. Damp bare places, often by sea. B, GB, F, D, IRL, NL.

1015 Yellow-wort *Blackstonia perfoliata*
Erect hairless blue-green annual, 10–60cm, with distinctive upper leaves which are opposite and fused round stem. Leaves triangular–ovate, basal leaves in a rosette, not fused. Flowers yellow, 8–15mm, with a very short tube and 6–8 spreading lobes. Calyx with short tube and 6–12 linear lobes shorter than the petals. Jul–Oct. Grassy places, sand-dunes. B, GB, F, D, IRL, NL. **219**

CENTAURIUM
ANNUALS OR BIENNIALS WITHOUT NON-FLOWERING SHOOTS

1016 Common Centaury *Centaurium erythraea*
Very variable biennial 10–50cm, with usually one stem, branched above. Rosette-leaves obovate to elliptic, 3–7-veined, stem leaves much smaller and narrower, often acute, 3-veined. Flowers pink, in dense clusters in a rather flat-topped inflorescence. Corolla tubular with 5 spreading lobes half as long as tube; calyx with linear lobes. Jun–Sep. Grasslands, sand-dunes. Throughout area covered, except SF, IS, N. **246**

1017 Seaside Centaury *Centaurium littorale*
Distinguished from **1016**, by its narrow 1-veined blunt stem leaves, and rosette leaves 3-veined, not more than 5mm wide. Biennial up to 25cm, with several stems, branched above; rosette-leaves 1–2cm. Flowers pink, stalkless, in a dense flat-topped cluster. Jul–Aug. Sand-dunes, sandy ground. Throughout area covered, except IS.

1018 Lesser Centaury *Centaurium pulchellum*
Annual up to 20cm, without basal rosette of leaves. Leaves ovate–lanceolate acute, increasing in length up

stem. Flowers pinkish-purple, rarely white, in lax branched flat-topped cluster, or solitary. Calyx nearly equalling corolla-tube; corolla lobes 2–4mm. Jun–Sep. Open places, grassy places near sea. Throughout area covered, except IS.

1019 Slender Centaury *Centaurium tenuiflorum*
Annual up to 25cm, with stem with 5–9 internodes, branched above; stem leaves ovate to elliptic, increasing in length up stem. Flowers reddish-pink, 12–14mm across, in dense erect flat-topped cluster. Calyx nearly equalling corolla-tube; corolla-lobes 3–4mm. Jul–Sep. Damp grassy places by sea. GB, F.

CENTAURIUM
PERENNIALS WITH SPREADING NON-FLOWERING SHOOTS

1020 Perennial Centaury *Centaurium scilloides*
Many spreading non-flowering stems, and ascending flowering stems to 30cm. Lower leaves rounded to rhombic, short-stalked, upper leaves lanceolate, stalkless. Flowers pink, 1·5–2cm, solitary or few in a cluster. Calyx ¾ as long as corolla-tube; corolla-lobes 5, 8–9mm. Jul–Aug. Coastal grassland. GB, F.

GENTIANA
FLOWERS YELLOW

1021 Great Yellow Gentian *Gentiana lutea*
Robust perennial with stout erect unbranched stem 0·5–2m. Leaves elliptic to broadly ovate, blue-green, conspicuously 5–7-veined. Flowers yellow, densely crowded in axillary and terminal clusters, partially surrounded by large leafy bracts. Flowers c. 2·5cm long with 5–9 spreading lobes much longer than corolla-tube. Jun–Aug. Grassy places in mountains. F, D. **219**

1022 Spotted Gentian *Gentiana punctata*
Like **1021** but lobes of corolla not more than ½ as long as corolla-tube. Flowers greenish-yellow, with dark purple spots; corolla-lobes erect. Jul–Sep. Grassland, open woods, rocks in mountains. F, D. **229**

GENTIANA
FLOWERS BLUE OR PURPLE, CROWDED INTO A TERMINAL HEAD

1023 Purple Gentian *Gentiana purpurea*
Distinguished by its cluster of reddish-purple flowers with dark purple spots, and papery calyx which is split down one side. Corolla 1·5–2·5cm long. Stems erect up to 60cm, with ovate–acute, stalked, strongly 5–7-veined leaves. Flowers usually in small terminal clusters,

sometimes with few axillary clusters below. Jun–Sep. Grassy and rocky places. F, D, N. **268**

1024 Cross Gentian *Gentiana cruciata*
Stems usually several, up to 40cm, from a basal rosette of leaves and with numerous stem leaves. Leaves oblong–ovate, 3-veined, sheathing at base. Flowers blue, 2–2·5cm long, with long tube and 4 short lobes, densely clustered up stem. Calyx with broad triangular teeth, ⅓ as long as corolla-tube. Jun–Sep. Dry grassy places, open woods. B, F, D, NL.

GENTIANA
FLOWERS BLUE OR PURPLE; SOLITARY OR FEW, NOT IN A TERMINAL HEAD; LOWER LEAVES NOT FORMING A ROSETTE

1025 Willow Gentian *Gentiana asclepiadea*
Perennial with simple erect stem up to 60cm. Leaves lanceolate to ovate pointed, stalked, with 3–5 conspicuous veins. Flowers blue, usually with reddish-purple spots within, 1–3 in leaf-axils. Corolla 3·5–5cm long, with small blunt lobes between petal lobes; calyx-teeth shorter than calyx-tube. Aug–Sep. Woods, damp fields, marshes, damp rocks. F, D. **276**

1026 Marsh Gentian *Gentiana pneumonanthe*
Perennial with slender erect stems up to 40cm. Leaves linear to ovate–lanceolate, 1-veined, stalkless. Flowers blue with greenish lines, 2·5–5cm long, with small acute lobes between petal lobes, usually in a terminal cluster of 1–6. Calyx with linear–lanceolate lobes about as long as calyx-tube. Aug–Sep. Wet places, heaths, bogs. B, GB, DK, F, D, NL, N, S. **283**

GENTIANA
FLOWERS BLUE; LOWER LEAVES FORMING A ROSETTE

1027 *Gentiana clusii*
Perennial with mature rosette leaves elliptic to oblong–lanceolate. Flowers dark blue, solitary, terminal, on stem up to 8cm. Corolla 4–7cm, obconical with 5 blunt lobes with small lobes between. Calyx green, leafy, with 5 triangular lobes usually more than ½ as long as calyx-tube. May–Aug. Calcareous grassland, mountain pastures. F, D. **276**

1028 Spring Gentian *Gentiana verna*
Low tufted perennial with flowering stems arising from rosettes of lanceolate to elliptic–acute leaves with margin with small projections; stem leaves 1–3 pairs. Flowers deep blue, 1·5–2·5cm long, with corolla-tube greenish-blue with white lines, and lobes spreading with small bifid lobes between. Calyx-tube 5-angled, with

much shorter lobes. Apr–Jun. Grassy places on limestone hills and mountains. GB, F, D, IRL. **283**

GENTIANA
ANNUALS

1029 Alpine Gentian *Gentiana nivalis*
Annual 1–15cm, with simple or branched stem. Leaves ovate to elliptic, margins with small weak projections. Flowers intense blue, solitary, terminal, to c. 1·5cm long. Calyx with angled but not winged tube, and narrow triangular acute lobes $\frac{1}{2}$–$\frac{2}{3}$ length of tube. Jun–Sep. Grasslands, heaths, woods, in mountains. GB, SF, F, D, IS, N, S.

1030 Bladder Gentian *Gentiana utriculosa*
Like **1029** but calyx-tube angled with wings 2–3mm wide; calyx-lobes lanceolate, $\frac{1}{3}$ to $\frac{1}{2}$ as long as calyx-tube. Flowers intense blue, 1·5–2cm long. Annual up to 25cm. May–Aug. Damp fields, marshes, heaths. F, D. **284**

1029

GENTIANELLA
COROLLA NOT FRINGED WITH HAIRS IN THROAT

1031 Fringed Gentian *Gentianella ciliata*
Biennial up to 30cm, with lower leaves spoon-shaped and stem leaves narrowly lanceolate pointed. Flowers blue, 2·5–5cm long, with 4 spreading ovate lobes with long marginal hairs. Calyx-lobes equal, $\frac{1}{2}$ as long as corolla. Aug–Oct. Grassland, wood margins. B, GB, F, D, NL.

1032 *Gentianella detonsa*
Differs from **1031** in having hairs on lobes of corolla much shorter than width of lobes, and corolla-lobes with toothed apex. Annual or biennial with stem leaves linear-lanceolate. Flowers dark blue, 2·5–4cm long. Jul. Damp places, mainly by the sea. IS, N.

1033 Northern Gentian *Gentianella aurea*
Annual or biennial with erect branches arising from the base, up to 15cm. Stem leaves 2–3 times as long as wide. Flowers pale yellow, rarely blue, 4–5-lobed, small and crowded at ends of branches, closely subtended by the broad uppermost leaves. Corolla 7–10mm; calyx-teeth equal. Jul. Lake margins and seashores. IS, N, S.

1031

GENTIANELLA
COROLLA FRINGED WITH HAIRS IN THROAT

1034 Field Gentian *Gentianella campestris*
Annual or biennial 2–35cm, with simple or branched stem bearing a spike-like or branched inflorescence.

Leaves strap-shaped to broadly lanceolate. Flowers bluish-lilac to white, 8–10cm across, with 4 triangular lobes with hairs at the base, and corolla-tube twice as long as calyx. Calyx-lobes broadest below middle, margins with small projections, or with hairs. Jul–Sep. Grasslands, heaths. Throughout area covered. **246**

1035 Autumn Gentian *Gentianella amarella*
Annual or biennial with erect simple or branched stem 5–30cm, or more, with lower branches not reaching the upper branches. Stem leaves ovate to narrowly lanceolate. Flowers dull purple, blue, pink or whitish, with 4–5 lobes. Corolla usually 12–18mm long, and corolla-tube fringed with hairs in throat, less than twice as long as calyx; calyx-lobes erect. Jul–Sep. Grassy places, sand-dunes. Throughout area covered, except NL. **262**

1036 Dune Gentian *Gentianella uliginosa*
Like **1035** but upper internode and terminal flower stalk forming at least half the height of the plant (less than half the height in **1035**). Upper leaves ovate to ovate–lanceolate. Calyx-lobes unequal, spreading. Annual or biennial branched from the base, 1–15 cm. Flowers blue, with corolla-tube about as long as the longest calyx-lobe. Aug–Sep. Damp meadows, sand-dunes. GB, DK, SF, D, NL, N, S.

1037 Early Gentian *Gentianella anglica*
Differs from **1036** in having upper leaves lanceolate and calyx-lobes nearly equal and adpressed to corolla-tube. Flowers dull purple, with corolla c. $1\frac{1}{2}$ times as long as calyx. May–Jun. Grasslands, damp places in sand-dunes. Endemic to GB.

1038 German Gentian *Gentianella germanica*
Biennial up to 40cm, usually branched from the base. Stem leaves ovate to ovate–triangular, hairless. Flowers violet, pink or whitish, 1–4cm, with corolla-tube longer than calyx and with 5 spreading lobes. Calyx-lobes equal in length, hairless. Aug–Sep. Grasslands, marshes. B, GB, F, D, NL.

1039 Slender Gentian *Gentianella tenella*
Annual or biennial, usually 2–10cm, with basal leaves spoon-shaped and stem leaves elliptic, 1–4 pairs. Flowers blue or dull violet, rarely white or yellowish, with 4 spreading lobes, 6–12mm with long fringe of scales in throat of corolla. Calyx divided nearly to base into 4 lobes. Jul–Aug. Pastures, screes, river-gravels, in mountains. SF, F, D, IS, N, S.

1040 Marsh Felwort *Swertia perennis*
Hairless perennial up to 60cm, with 4-angled brownish, red or purplish stems. Lower leaves crowded, ovate to

elliptic, narrowed to a winged leaf-stalk; upper leaves usually opposite, stalkless and clasping stem. Flowers blue, violet, greenish-yellow or white, with darker dots or lines. Corolla with 4–5 lobes 6–16mm, each lobed with fringed nectaries. Calyx-lobes narrow pointed. Variable species. Jul–Sep. Wet places in mountains. F, D. **247**

1041 *Lomatogonium rotatum*
Annual with 4-angled stem up to 25cm. Lower leaves spoon-shaped, upper linear–lanceolate. Flowers solitary, on long leafless branches, pale blue or white, with usually 5 lobes. Corolla 12–16mm long; calyx-lobes longer than corolla, linear–lanceolate. Wet places. Native of N. & C. Asia and N. America. Int IS.

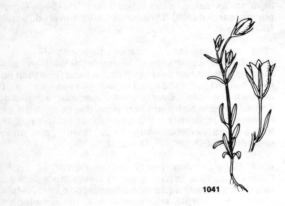

1041

BOGBEAN FAMILY

Menyanthaceae

Similar to Gentianaceae, but aquatic perennials. Leaves mostly alternate.

1042 Bogbean *Menyanthes trifoliata*
Aquatic perennial with a stout creeping underwater rhizome, and leaves borne above water, with 3 leaflets; flowering stems up to 35cm. Leaves with obovate to rhombic, short-stalked leaflets; leaf-stalks sheathing below. Flowers pink or white, stalked, with shorter ovate bracts, in a long cluster. Corolla c. 1·5cm across, with 5 spreading lobes fringed with white hairs; calyx-lobes ovate. Apr–Jun. Shallow pools and lakes, wet places in bogs, fens. Throughout area covered. **247**

1043 Fringed Water-lily *Nymphoides peltata*
Aquatic perennial with floating rounded leaves, and yellow flowers 3–4cm across, borne above water. Stems creeping and floating, to 1·6m; leaf-stalks sheathing at base. Flowers in axillary clusters of 2–5, long-stalked, with lobes of corolla 5, fringed with conspicuous hairs; calyx-lobes oblong–lanceolate. Jun–Sep. Still waters, slow-flowing rivers. B, GB, F, D, NL; int DK, S. **219**

DOGBANE FAMILY

Apocynaceae

Poisonous perennial herbs (or shrubs). Leaves opposite, simple. Flowers solitary, regular, 5-merous. Fruit of 2 follicles.

1044 Lesser Periwinkle *Vinca minor*
Creeping or ascending evergreen, with lanceolate to elliptic hairless leaves with rounded or wedge-shaped base. Flowers blue-violet, long-stalked from leaf axils. Corolla 2·5–3cm across, with 5 spreading lobes and corolla-tube 1·2–1·5cm long. Calyx-lobes narrow ovate to triangular, hairless. Fruit ovoid. Feb–May. Woods, hedges, rocks. B, F, D, NL; int GB, DK, IRL, N, S. **277**

1045 Greater Periwinkle *Vinca major*
Distinguished from **1044** by larger blue-purple flowers 3–5cm, narrow calyx-lobes; margin fringed with conspicuous hairs. Leaves ovate with margin fringed with hairs, long-stalked. Flowering stems to 30cm. Fruit cylindrical. Apr–Jun. Woods, hedges, shady rocks. F; int GB, IRL. **277**

MILKWEED FAMILY

Asclepiadaceae

Perennial herbs, sometimes climbing. Leaves opposite. Flowers regular, in axillary or terminal clusters. Corolla 5-lobed. Stamens united in a ring. Fruit of 2 follicles.

1046 Vincetoxicum *Vincetoxicum hirundinaria*
Erect, nearly hairless, often twining perennial up to 120cm. Leaves broadly ovate to broadly lanceolate acute, hairy on veins and margin beneath. Flowers white or yellow, 3–10mm across, in a rather flat-topped lax cluster. Corolla-lobes 5, ovate, fleshy, with membraneous scales ⅔ as long as lobes. Fruit a pair of spindle-shaped follicles. Very variable species. May–Aug. Woods, scrub, dry banks, screes. B, DK, SF, F, D, NL, N, S. **200**

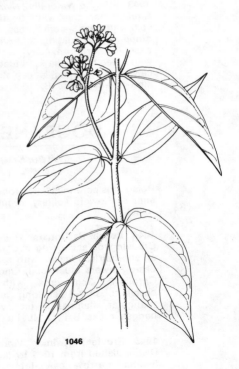

1046

MADDER FAMILY

Rubiaceae

Annual or perennial herbs. Leaves simple, in whorls. Flowers small, in terminal and axillary clusters, regular 4- to 5-merous. Sepals minute. Fruit dry, indehiscent, divided into two 1-seeded units, or fleshy and 1-seeded.

1047 Field Madder *Sherardia arvensis*
Small tufted annual up to 40cm; 4-angled stems with down-curved prickles, and 4–6 lanceolate leaves in each whorl. Flowers lilac, 2–3m across, in a dense terminal cluster surrounded by 8–10 leaf-like bracts fused together at their bases. Corolla funnel-shaped, 4–6mm long, with 4 spreading lobes. Fruit with two rough bristly lobes crowned with calyx-teeth. May–Sep. Cultivated ground, dry grasslands, lawns. Throughout area covered, except IS. **277**

1048 Squinancywort *Asperula cynanchica*
Tufted perennial with numerous nearly hairless stems 10–35cm, arising from a woody rootstock. Leaves in whorls of 4, linear fine-pointed. Flowers pale purplish to whitish, c. 5mm across, in a much branched inflorescence. Corolla broadly funnel-shaped, with corolla-tube to 1½ times as long as the 4 spreading lobes. Fruit rough, with swellings. A very variable species. Jun–Sep. Calcareous grasslands, open woods, sand-dunes. B, GB, F, D, IRL, NL. **177**

1049 Dyer's Woodruff *Asperula tinctoria*
Distinguished by its leaves in whorls of 4–6, and its white flowers, pink outside, with 3 lobes. Perennial, with orange stolons, and erect robust 4-angled stems 25–80cm. Leaves lanceolate to linear, 3-veined. Flowers narrowly funnel-shaped, 3–4mm long, in a broadly ovoid inflorescence; bracts oval. Jun–Jul. Rocky slopes, grassy and bushy places. DK, SF, F, D, N, S. **177**

1050 Blue Woodruff *Asperula arvensis*
Annual with stems 10–55cm, and leaves mostly in whorls of 6–8. Lower leaves broadly lanceolate, upper narrower. Flowers bluish-violet, with 4-lobed salver-shaped corolla 4–6mm across, in dense heads surrounded often by large bristly-hairy bracts. May–Jun. Fields, waste places. F, D, NL; int DK, N, S. **277**

GALIUM
ANNUALS

1051 Cleavers *Galium aparine*
Relatively robust scrambling annual, with often stout

4-angled stems 80–180cm. Leaves oblanceolate, in whorls of 6–9, covered in hooked bristles. Flowers whitish, 1·5–1·7mm across, in few-flowered axillary clusters. Fruit covered with dense hooked bristles. Very variable species. Jun–Aug. Woods, scrub, hedges, cultivated ground, seashores. Throughout area covered, except IS. **177**

1052 False Cleavers *Galium spurium*
Differs from **1051** in its smaller greenish-yellow flowers 0·8–1·3mm across, and its smaller fruit 2–3mm (fruit 3–5mm in **1051**), either smooth, or with hooked bristles. Weak or stout scrambling annual to 1m or more, with leaves in whorls of 6–10, oblanceolate and with a long awned apex. Jun–Aug. Hedges, scrub, sand-dunes, cultivated fields. B, DK, SF, F, D, NL, N, S; int GB.

1053 Corn Cleavers *Galium tricornutum*
Differs from **1052** and **1053**, in having inflorescence and flower-stalks curved inwards after flowering. Fruit warty. Leaves hairless above. Jun–Sep. Cultivated fields, waste ground. B, F, D, NL, N, S; int GB.

1054 Wall Bedstraw *Galium parisiense*
Annual with spreading or ascending much-branched weak stems up to 30cm, angled and with downwardly directed prickles. Leaves 5–7 in a whorl, at first spreading then down-curved, margin with forward-directed prickles. Flowers greenish within and reddish outside, 0·5–1mm across, in a long pyramidal or ovoid inflorescence. Very variable species. Jun–Jul. Walls, sandy places. B, GB, F, D.

GALIUM
PERENNIALS. LEAVES NEVER IN WHORLS OF MORE THAN 4

1055 *Galium rotundifolium*
Perennial with slender creeping rooting stolons, and slender mostly hairless stems up to 20cm. Leaves ovate to nearly rounded, shortly stalked, nearly hairless. Flowers white sometimes greenish, 3–3·5mm, with spreading petals, in rather few-flowered flat-topped lax inflorescence with few bracts. Fruit with spreading hooked hairs. May–Jul. Woods. F, D, S; int DK, NL, N.

1056 Northern Bedstraw *Galium boreale*
Perennial with rooting stolons and erect stout 4-angled stems 30–65cm. Leaves long lanceolate, widest below middle, blunt, usually hairless. Flowers white, 3–4mm across, with spreading lobes, in dense terminal clusters. Fruit hairless or with adpressed hairs. Jul–Aug. Grassy places, open woods, bushy places. Throughout area covered. **177**

GALIUM
PERENNIALS; AT LEAST SOME LEAVES IN WHORLS OF MORE THAN 4.

1057 Woodruff *Galium odoratum*
Perennial with creeping underground stems and erect 4-angled stems up to 25cm, stems hairless except at nodes. Leaves in whorls of 6–9, lanceolate, to 5cm, widest in the middle or above middle. Flowers white, funnel-shaped, with 4 spreading lobes 4–7mm across, in a terminal long-stalked cluster. Fruit covered with hooked hairs. May–Jun. Woods on calcareous soils. Throughout area covered, except IS. **177**

1058 *Galium triflorum*
Differs from **1057** in having smaller greenish-white flowers 1·5–3·5mm across, with spreading pointed lobes, in a narrow pyramidal inflorescence. Jul–Aug. Coniferous woods. SF, N, S.

GALIUM
PERENNIALS; OVARY AND FRUIT HAIRLESS

1059 *Galium trifidum*
Distinguished by its tiny 3-lobed white flowers which are 1·5mm across. Middle stem-leaves linear to narrowly lanceolate. Inflorescence few-flowered; flower-stalks reflexed after flowering. Fruit smooth. Jun–Jul. Bogs, wet places. SF, F, N, S.

1060 Common Marsh Bedstraw *Galium palustre*
Perennial with slender spreading or erect stems 15–70cm. Leaves in whorls of 4–6, middle stem-leaves narrowly to broadly oblanceolate, blunt. Flowers with 4 acute lobes, 3–4·5mm, white, in spreading axillary clusters in a lax pyramidal inflorescence. Fruit hairless. Jun–Jul. Marshes, fens, ditches. Throughout area covered. **178**

1059

1061 Slender Marsh Bedstraw *Galium debile*
Differs from **1060** in having narrowly linear leaves, and submerged autumn leaves very narrow, flaccid (submerged leaves similar to stem-leaves in **1060**). Flowers white, in obconical inflorescence with ascending branches. May–Jul. Pond margins. GB, F.

1062 Fen Bedstraw *Galium uliginosum*
Like **1060** but distinguished by its 6–8 finely pointed leaves in each whorl, and fruit remaining green when dry. Perennial with weak spreading or ascending rough stems, with recurved prickles on the angles, 10–100cm. Leaves narrowly lanceolate, narrowed to an awned apex. Flowers white, 2·5–3mm across, with 4 acute lobes, in a narrow branched cluster. Fruit hairless. Jul–Aug. Marshes, fens, wet places. Throughout area covered.

1062

345

1063 Lady's Bedstraw *Galium verum*
Distinguished by its golden-yellow fragrant flowers, with spreading ovate lobes. Stems 10–120cm, with 4 raised lines, usually finely hairy. Leaves in whorls of 8–12, shining and usually hairy above, densely finely hairy beneath, margin usually incurved. Inflorescence usually branched, dense ovoid. Corolla 2–3·5mm across, with spreading lobes. Fruit usually hairless. Jun–Aug. Meadows, hedge banks, sand-dunes. Throughout area covered. **219**

1064 *Galium sylvaticum*
Stems stout, bushy, rounded, hairless, up to 1m. Leaves in whorls of 6–8, broadly oblanceolate to elliptic, widest above the middle, blue-green, margins toothed, rough. Flowers white, 2–3mm across, cup-shaped with acute lobes, in a lax broadly ovoid inflorescence. Fruit bloomed. Jun–Jul. Woodlands, scrub. B, F, D, NL.

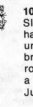

1065 Hedge Bedstraw *Galium mollugo*
Slender erect or spreading perennial 30–150cm, with hairless stems arising from a reddish rootstock with long underground stolons. Leaves in whorls of 6–8, oblong to broadly oblanceolate, abruptly narrowed above, with rough prickled margins. Flowers white, 2–3mm across, in a lax broadly ovoid, much-branched inflorescence. Jun–Sep. Grassy places, hedgerows. B, GB, F, D, NL. **178**

1066 Upright Hedge Bedstraw *Galium album*
Like **1065** but with whitish flowers 3–5mm across, and flower stalks usually shorter than the diameter of the flowers. Inflorescence rather dense, and branches less spreading after flowering. May–Jun. Open habitats. B, GB, DK, F, D, NL; int SF, IRL, IS, N, S.

1066

1067 Heath Bedstraw *Galium saxatile*
Slender straggling perennial with sparsely branched hairless stems, 5–35cm. Leaves mostly in whorls of 6–7, the lower obovate, the upper oblanceolate, with short apical awn, and margin with forwardly directed bristles. Flowers white, 2·5–4mm across, funnel-shaped at base and with spreading lobes. Fruit with acute swellings. Jun–Aug. Heaths, pastures and scrub on acid soils. B, GB, DK, F, D, IRL, NL, N, S; int SF.

1068 Slender Bedstraw *Galium pumilum*
Lax tufted perennial with slender stems up to 30cm. Leaves in whorls of usually 8–9, narrowly oblanceolate, somewhat sickle-shaped, pointed, with few backwardly-directed prickles. Flowers creamy-white, 2–3mm across, in a lax open inflorescence. Fruit with blunt swellings. Jun–Aug. Open woods, calcareous grasslands. B, GB, DK, F, D, NL; int SF, S.

1069 Limestone Bedstraw *Galium sterneri*
Like **1068** but fruit covered with acute swellings. Tufted
perennial with many non-flowering stems, and flowering
stems up to 15cm or more, usually hairless, often red at
base. Leaves mostly in whorls of 7–8, narrowly
oblanceolate, margin with many curved
backwardly-directed prickles. Inflorescence compact,
pyramidal; flowers creamy-white. Jun–Jul. Dry
grassland, rocky ground. GB, DK, D, IRL, N.

1070 *Galium glaucum*
Perennial with stout rounded 4-ridged stems up to 80cm.
Leaves linear to needle-shaped, in whorls of 8–10, with
incurved margins with 1–2 rows of teeth. Flowers white,
4–6mm across, broadly cup-shaped with tube shorter
than lobes. May–Jul. Forest margins, dry grassland,
stony places. B, F, D.

1071 Crosswort *Cruciata laevipes*
Perennial with slender stems 20–60cm, with spreading
hairs, and slender creeping rootstock. Leaves in whorls
of 4, broadly lanceolate to ovate, 3-veined, hairy,
yellowish in flowering region. Flowers yellow, c. 2–3mm
across, in dense axillary clusters of 5–9. Fruit smooth,
becoming wrinkled when dry. May–Jul. Grassland, open
woods, hedgerows. B, GB, F, D, NL; int IRL. **219**

1072 Wild Madder *Rubia peregrina*
Stout scrambling perennial 50–120cm, woody at base;
stem 4-angled, with hooked bristles. Leaves in whorls of
4–8, linear to broadly ovate–elliptic, dark green, leathery.
Flowers yellowish-green, 4–6mm across, with 5
spreading lobes, in stalked clusters longer than the
subtending leaves. Fruit fleshy, usually only 1-seeded.
Jun–Aug. Hedges, thickets, scrub, usually near sea. GB,
F, IRL. **200**

1070

PHLOX FAMILY

Polemoniaceae

Annual or perennial herbs. Flowers regular 5-merous; petals forming tube. Fruit a capsule. Mainly North American family.

1073 Jacob's Ladder *Polemonium caeruleum*
Leafy perennial up to 90cm, with pinnate leaves with usually 10–12 pairs of ovate–lanceolate leaflets and a terminal leaflet, lower leaflets stalked. Flowers blue, 8–15mm across, in a terminal branched inflorescence. Corolla with 5 spreading ovate lobes and a short tube; calyx-lobes lanceolate. Fruit a globular capsule. Jun–Jul. Grassy places, open woods in hills and mountains. GB, SF, F, D, IS, N, S; int B, DK, NL. **277**

1073

CONVOLVULUS FAMILY

Convolvulaceae

Annual or perennial herbs, usually climbing. The Dodders *Cuscuta* are all parasitic. Leaves alternate. Flowers regular, 5-merous; bell-, urn- or funnel-shaped. Fruit a capsule.

1074

1074 Greater Dodder *Cuscuta europaea*
Reddish parasite with twining stems up to 1m, with colourless scale-like leaves. Flowers pinkish-white, 3–4mm, in numerous clusters 1–5cm across. Corolla bell-shaped, with triangular to ovate blunt lobes; calyx obconical, shorter or about as long as corolla-tube, lobes ovate. Commonly parasitic on nettles, hops, hedge bindweed and other plants. Jun–Aug. Throughout area covered, except IRL, IS.

1075 Dodder *Cuscuta epithymum*
Stem much-branched, often reddish or purplish, with scale-like leaves. Flowers white or pink, 3–4mm, in dense globular clusters up to 1cm across. Corolla 5-lobed, lobes triangular acute spreading; stamens longer, anthers often purple-tinged. Calyx usually shorter than corolla-tube with lobes triangular acute. Parasitic on shrubs and herbs, commonly on heather, gorse, and clover species. Jul–Aug. Throughout area covered, except IS. **235**

1076 Flax Dodder *Cuscuta epilinum*
Distinguished by its yellowish flowers 3mm across, in rounded stalkless clusters c. 1cm across. Corolla urn-shaped, lobes 5, ovate–triangular, shorter than corolla-tube; calyx-lobes acute. Stems nearly simple or sparingly branched. Commonly parasitic on flax and other *Linum* species. Jul–Aug. Native of S-W. Asia. Int SF, F, D, NL, N, S.

1077 Sea Bindweed *Calystegia soldanella*
Hairless perennial, with creeping rather than twining stems, up to 50cm or more, and with kidney-shaped, somewhat fleshy leaves. Flowers pink, 3–5cm across, funnel-shaped; calyx longer than ovate bracts. Jun–Sep. Coastal sands, shingle. B, GB, DK, F, D, IRL, NL. **247**

1078 Hedge Bindweed *Calystegia sepium*
Hairless or hairy, strongly twining climbing perennial 1–3mm, with heart-shaped to arrow-shaped leaves. Flowers white or pink, 3–6cm across, funnel-shaped; bracteoles longer than calyx, either flat or strongly inflated. Jun–Sep. Hedges, bushy places, fens, wood verges. Throughout area covered, except IS.

1079 Great Bindweed *Calystegia silvatica*
Flowers usually white, 5–9cm across, with bracteoles
1·5–4cm wide when flattened, sac-like at base and
longer, concealing calyx. Straggling climbing perennial,
with arrow-shaped leaves with rounded angle between
lobes. Jul–Sep. Hedges, open ground. F; int GB, IRL. **247**

1080 Hairy Bindweed *Calystegia pulchra*
Differs from **1078** in having pink flowers 5–7·5cm across,
and leaves arrow-shaped with an oblong or more or less
parallel angle. Stems, leaves and flower-stalks hairy.
Jul–Sep. Naturalized from gardens; int B, GB, DK, F, D,
IRL, NL, S.

1081 Field Bindweed *Convolvulus arvensis*
Perennial with slender climbing or trailing stems up to
2m. Leaves triangular to linear, spear- or arrow-shaped.
Flowers white or pink, broadly funnel-shaped, 1–1·5cm
across, borne 1–3 on axillary stalks about as long as the
subtending leaves. Sepals blunt or with notched apex.
Variable in leaf shape and hairyness. Jun–Sep. Cultivated
and waste ground. Throughout area covered, except IS.
247

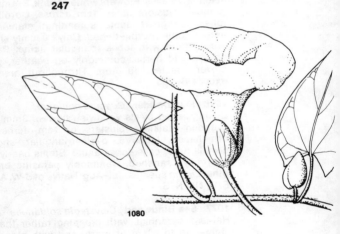

1080

BORAGE FAMILY

Boraginaceae

Annual or perennial herbs, frequently bristly. Flowers usually regular, in 2-ranked, coiled clusters. Calyx 5-toothed; corolla 5-lobed, tubular or bell-shaped, often blue. Stamens 5. Fruit of 4 nutlets.

1082 Heliotrope *Heliotropium europaeum*
Erect, widely branched, greyish-hairy foetid annual 10–40cm. Leaves ovate to ovate, with wedge-shaped or rounded base, stalked. Flowers white or lilac, 2–4mm across, sepals linear–oblong to narrowly triangular, spreading after flowering; bracts absent. Jun–Oct. Cultivated ground, roadsides, rocks. F, D. **178**

1083 Common Gromwell *Lithospermum officinale*
Perennial with one or several stems up to 1m, much branched above, from a stout rhizome. Leaves lanceolate, rough-hairy, the middle and upper stalkless. Flowers white or yellowish, 6–8mm across, in leafy terminal and axillary clusters. Corolla with cylindrical tube about as long as the oblong blunt calyx-lobes, and corolla with 5 blunt lobes. Nutlets 4, ovoid, smooth, white. Jun–Jul. Hedges, thickets, wood margins. Throughout area covered, except IS. **200**

1084 Field Gromwell *Buglossoides arvensis*
Annual with usually one erect bristly-hairy stem 10–50cm, or more. Stem leaves oblong to linear. Flowers white, or with a blue zone about the middle of the corolla-tube, rarely purplish, funnel-shaped, 6–9mm. Calyx-lobes linear, unequal, same length or longer than corolla-tube. Nutlets 4, with numerous swellings, brownish. May–Jun. Cultivated fields, dry open places. Throughout area covered, except IS.

1085 Purple Gromwell *Buglossoides purpurocaerulea*
Densely hairy perennial with erect unbranched flowering stems 15–60cm, arising from a creeping rhizome. Leaves lanceolate to narrowly elliptic, very acute, hairy. Flowers 5-lobed, at first reddish-purple, then bright blue. Corolla-tube 14–19mm long, in 2–3 short leafy clusters; calyx with linear acute, bristly hairy lobes. Nutlets nearly globular, smooth shining, white. May–Jun. Scrub, wood margins. B, GB, F, D. **277**

1086 Viper's Bugloss *Echium vulgare*
Bristly hairy biennial with one or several flowering stems 20–90cm. Leaves elliptic to lanceolate, the lower narrowed to a short stalk, the upper narrower, stalkless. Flowers blue to blue-violet, in numerous lateral clusters, in a long terminal spike. Corolla tubular 2-lipped

1–1·9cm, with 4–5 much longer stamens; flower-buds red. Jun–Sep. Fields, dry grassland, sand and shingle beaches. Throughout area covered, except IS. **277**

1087 Purple Viper's Bugloss *Echium plantagineum*
Differs from **1086** in having larger blue flowers becoming pink, 1·8–3cm, and usually only 2 stamens protruding from the corolla. Softly hairy annual or biennial up to 60cm. Basal leaves ovate with prominent veins, upper oblong to lanceolate with heart-shaped base. May–Sep. Sandy places, cliffs. GB, F. **263**

1088 Lungwort *Pulmonaria obscura*
Low downy perennial up to 30cm, with a thin creeping rhizome. Summer-leaves heart-shaped, the lower long-stalked, the upper clasping stem; lower leaves enlarging after flowering, leaves unspotted or with faint green spots. Flowers reddish to bluish-violet, 10–12mm across. Corolla bell-shaped, with 5 blunt lobes; calyx with short broad lobes. Nutlets smooth, shining. Mar–May. Woods, copses. B, DK, SF, F, D, S; int GB.

1089 *Pulmonaria officinalis*
Very similar to **1088** and often included with it. Differs in having leaf-blades of summer leaves with distinct white spots, and uniform bristly hairs (hairs unequal in **1088**). Leaf-stalks of summer-leaves shorter than blade. Mar–Jun. Open woods. B, DK, F, D, NL, S; int GB. **263**

1090 Narrow-leaved Lungwort *Pulmonaria longifolia*
Distinguished by its summer-leaves which are 6–9 times as long as wide, usually spotted, inflorescence remaining dense. Flowers violet to blue-violet, up to 6mm across, in a dense cluster which does not elongate after flowering; calyx-teeth half as long as calyx-tube. Apr–May. Woods. GB, F.

1091 *Pulmonaria angustifolia*
Like **1090** but summer-leaves with stiff uniform bristles, and without long glandular hairs (summer-leaves with long and short bristles, and with scattered glandular hairs in **1090**). Flowers bright blue. Summer-leaves unspotted, 6–9 times as long as wide. Apr–Jun. Woods, meadows. DK, F, D, S.

1092 Common Comfrey *Symphytum officinale*
Stout erect perennial with winged stem 50–120cm, often branched. Leaves ovate–lanceolate pointed, the middle and upper stalkless, continuing as a wing down stem. Flowers violet-purple, pinkish or whitish, many in a flat-topped cluster; corolla cylindrical 12–18mm long, with recurved lobes, and triangular scales in throat; calyx with lanceolate lobes. Nutlets black, smooth shining. May–Jun. Damp grassland, river banks. B, GB, F, D, NL; int DK, SF, IRL, N, S. **277**

1091

1093

1093 Rough Comfrey *Symphytum asperum*
Like **1092** but leaves all stalked, or upper leaves nearly stalkless but not continuing as a wing down stem. Flowers pink, turning blue; corolla tubular 11–17mm and with scales tongue-shaped; calyx with rounded lobes. Nutlets net-veined, rough. Jun–Jul. Waste places. Native of S-W. Africa. Int B, GB, DK, SF, F, IRL, NL, S.

1094 Russian Comfrey *Symphytum ×uplandicum*
Like **1092** but upper leaves stalkless and shortly winged down stem. Flowers pink at first, turning blue, or persistently violet, 12–18mm; corolla scales triangular. Calyx-lobes pointed. Jun–Aug. Roadsides, hedgebanks, woods. Int B, GB, DK, SF, F, IRL, NL, N, S. **278**

1095 Tuberous Comfrey *Symphytum tuberosum*
Perennial, having a stout rhizome with alternate thick and thin sections, and simple or little-branched rough-hairy stem up to 40cm, or more. Basal leaves long-stalked, absent at flowering; lower stem-leaves elliptic to lanceolate, the upper stalkless, shortly and narrowly continuing down stem. Flowers pale yellow, 13–19mm, lobes with down-curved tips; calyx-lobes narrowly lanceolate. Jun–Jul. Woods. GB, F, D; int IRL. **200**

1096 White Comfrey *Symphytum orientale*
Distinguished by its white flowers 14–18mm long, with lobes not recurved, scales in corolla tongue-shaped, and calyx lobed to $\frac{1}{3}$–$\frac{2}{3}$. Flowering stem up to 70cm or more, much branched; rhizome spindle-shaped. Leaves ovate to rounded, densely and softly hairy, the upper stalkless, not running down stem. Apr–May. Damp shady places. Native of Turkey. Int GB, F. **247**

1097 Creeping Comfrey *Symphytum ibiricum*
Distinguished by its pale yellow flowers, on ascending or spreading flowering stems up to 40cm, from a slender creeping rhizome. Leaves ovate–elliptic, all stalked. Calyx lobed nearly to base. Apr–May. Hedges, grassland. Native of the Caucasus. Int GB. **200**

1098 Alkanet *Anchusa officinalis*
Bristly-hairy perennial, with erect stems to 80cm. Leaves lanceolate, the lower stalked. Flowers violet-reddish, rarely white or yellow, in several dense flat-topped clusters. Corolla 7–15mm across, corolla-tube equalling or longer than calyx; calyx divided half-way or almost to base into lanceolate lobes. Nutlets ovoid. Jun–Aug. Dry grassy places. DK, F, D, NL, N, S; int B, SF. **284**

1099 Large Blue Alkanet *Anchusa azurea*
Like **1098** but with violet or deep blue flowers 1–1·5cm across, and calyx divided almost to base into linear lobes. Rough hairy perennial, up to 1·5m. Apr–Jun. Woods, meadows, waste places. F; int D. **278**

1100 Yellow Alkanet *Anchusa ochroleuca*
Distinguished by its pale yellow flowers 7–10mm or more across, with corolla-tube $1\frac{1}{2}$ times as long as calyx-lobes. Usually a soft hairy perennial up to 80cm. Jul–Aug. Waste places. Native of S-E. & E-C. Europe. Int NL.

1101 Bugloss *Anchusa arvensis*
Rough hairy annual with ascending stems up to 60cm. Leaves linear to broadly lanceolate, with undulate margin, toothed; upper leaves clasping stem. Flowers blue, rarely white, 4–6mm across, with broad unequal blunt lobes, in a forked cluster. Corolla-tube curved; calyx with linear-lanceolate lobes. Nutlets with sparse swellings. Apr–Sep. Arable fields, sandy places. Throughout area covered, except IS.

1102 Borage *Borago officinalis*
Rough-hairy annual with robust often branched stems up to 70cm. Basal leaves ovate to lanceolate, stalked, upper leaves clasping stem. Flowers bright blue, rarely white, 2–3cm across, in lax branched leafy cluster. Corolla with spreading lanceolate lobes and white scales at base and with very short or almost absent tube; anthers conspicuous, dark purple. Calyx with linear-lanceolate lobes, enlarging in fruit and pressed together. May–Sep. Waste places, vineyards; also widely cultivated as a herb. F; int GB, D, NL. **278**

1103 Oysterplant *Mertensia maritima*
Spreading mat-forming greyish-hairy perennial up to 60cm; leaves fleshy, spoon-shaped to lanceolate, the lower long-stalked, the upper stalkless. Flowers pink, becoming blue and pink, in branched clusters with leaf-like bracts. Corolla 6mm across; bell-shaped with 5 ovate–triangular lobes; calyx-lobes ovate. Nutlets fleshy. Jun–Aug. Coastal sands and shingle in the northern part of area covered. GB, DK, IRL, IS, N, S. **284**

1104 Madwort *Asperugo procumbens*
Rough hairy annual with spreading or climbing stems up to 70cm. Leaves lanceolate, the lower opposite or in a whorl, stalked, the upper stalkless. Flowers purplish, becoming dark violet, funnel-shaped, 2–3mm across, solitary or paired in leaf axils. Nutlets with dense fine swellings and surrounded by enlarged toothed sepals. May–Nov. Cultivated fields, waste ground. DK, SF, D, N, S; int F, NL, GB.

1104

MYOSOTIS
CALYX WITH STRAIGHT ADPRESSED HAIRS POINTING TOWARDS APEX

1105 Tufted Forget-me-not *Myosotis laxa*
Annual or biennial to 50cm, branched from base, with adpressed hairs on stem. Flowers bright blue, up to 5mm

across, in long clusters; lower flower-stalks down-curved in fruit. Nutlets ovoid–blunt, dark brown. Jun–Aug. Wet places. Throughout area covered, except IS.

1106 Water Forget-me-not *Myosotis scorpioides*
Biennial or perennial with creeping rhizomes and runners; stem up to 1m. Leaves oblong to oblong-lanceolate, usually with adpressed forward-pointing hairs. Flowers pale blue, 4–8mm across; style often protruding. Calyx-teeth broadly triangular, with short straight adpressed hairs. Nutlets ovoid, narrowly bordered. May–Sep. Wet places, stream margins, ditches. Throughout area covered. **284**

1107 Creeping Forget-me-not *Myosotis secunda*
Differs from **1106** in its calyx which is divided at flowering at least half-way into narrow triangular lobes, open saucer-shaped, to 5mm across, spreading and falling at maturity. Annual or biennial up to 40cm, with rooting stolons. Flowers bright blue, to 8mm across. Nutlets black. May–Aug. Wet places. GB, F, IRL.

1107

1108 Pale Forget-me-not *Myosotis stolonifera*
Like **1107** but smaller with hairs of base of stem adpressed (with spreading hairs in **1107**). Stolons numerous, much branched. Flowers 4–5mm across; calyx 3mm in fruit (calyx 5mm in fruit in **1107**). Jun–Aug. Wet places. GB.

1109 Jersey Forget-me-not *Myosotis sicula*
Differs from **1108** in having no stolons. Annual or biennial with stems either short and little branched, or up to 50cm and much branched, with hairs on stems and leaves adpressed and forward pointing. Flowers bright blue, to 3mm across, saucer-shaped, in 2 distinct rows on stems. Calyx up to 6mm in fruit; calyx-tube twice as long as lobes. Nutlets brown. May. Wet places. F.

MYOSOTIS
CALYX WITH HOOKED HAIRS, OR HAIRS OF 2 KINDS, EITHER BRISTLE-LIKE, HOOKED, OR SPREADING, OR SOME SHORTER.

1110 Field Forget-me-not *Myosotis arvensis*
Grey-haired variable perennial with robust stems, branched from the base, up to 60cm. Lower oblanceolate narrowed below, upper stalkless. Flowers bright blue, 3–5mm across, more or less saucer-shaped, not flat. Calyx up to 7mm, in fruit, closed, with many spreading hooked hairs. Nutlets dark brown to black, pointed, shining. Apr–Oct. Disturbed ground, sand-dunes. Throughout area covered.

1111 Wood Forget-me-not *Myosotis sylvatica*
Stems much-branched, very leafy, up to 50cm. Leaves

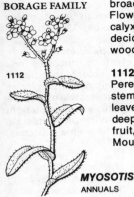

1112

MYOSOTIS
ANNUALS

1116

broadly to narrowly ovate or elliptic, usually not stalked. Flowers bright blue, 8mm across, but often smaller; calyx-lobes narrow–triangular, open, with hooked hairs, deciduous. Nutlets ovoid, with rim. May–Jun. Damp woods. B, GB, DK, F, D, NL, N, S; int SF. **284**

1112 Alpine Forget-me-not *Myosotis alpestris*
Perennial with short rhizome and long fleshy roots; stems 5–35cm. Basal leaves stalked or stalkless, stem leaves very variable, ovate to linear. Flowers bright or deep blue, up to 9mm across. Calyx much enlarged in fruit, densely hairy. Nutlets black, shining. Jul–Sep. Mountain rocks and meadows. GB, F, D.

1113 Early Forget-me-not *Myosotis ramosissima*
Small branched annual often only 2–3cm, but sometimes up to 40cm. Basal leaves in a rosette, lanceolate, with soft spreading hairs; stem with spreading hairs below and appressed hairs above. Flowers bright blue, saucer-shaped, up to 3mm across, in lax inflorescence. Calyx lobed to half-way and with down-curved hooked hairs at base, falling in fruit. Nutlets brown, without rim. Apr–Jun. Dry, sandy places, often by sea. Throughout area covered, except IS.

1114 Changing Forget-me-not *Myosotis discolor*
Distinguished by its flowers which are at first yellow or cream, changing to pink, violet or blue. Annual with slender stems often branched from the base, up to 30cm. Leaves lanceolate to narrow–obovate, the lower blunt, the upper acute. Flowers c. 2mm across, saucer-shaped; corolla-tube blue to violet. Nutlets dark brown, with wide rim. May–Jun. Heaths, sandy fields, dry banks. Throughout area covered, except SF.

1115 *Myosotis stricta*
Distinguished from **1114** by its smaller blue flowers c. 1mm across, and lower surface of leaves and base of stem with hooked hairs (without hooked hairs in **1114**). Annual, much branched from the base, up to 30cm, with hairs on stem pointing upwards. Calyx with dense hooked and appressed hairs, calyx-lobes closed, not falling. Nutlets brown, with rim keeled at apex. May–Jun. Dry sandy places. Throughout area covered, except GB, IRL.

1116 Bur Forget-me-not *Lappula squarrosa*
Annual or biennial with erect often branched stems up to 70cm, with dense or sparse, spreading and appressed hairs. Leaves oblong to narrowly lanceolate, the lower

short-stalked the upper stalkless. Flowers pale blue, 2–4mm across, in a branched cluster. Calyx lobed almost to base, enlarging in fruit. Nutlets with 2–3 rows of hooked spines, and surrounded by spreading calyx. Jun–Jul. Waste places, dry grasslands, fallow fields. F, S; int DK, SF, D, NL, N.

1117 Blue-eyed Mary *Omphalodes verna*

Low creeping perennial with stolons, and stem 5–20cm. Basal leaves ovate to heart-shaped, acute, long-stalked, sparsely hairy, stem leaves smaller stalkless or short-stalked. Flowers blue with yellow folds, bell-shaped, 8–10mm across, with elliptic lobes and with swellings in throat, in lax terminal cluster. Nutlets hairy, winged. Mar–May. Damp woods, hedges. Native of S-C. Europe. Int B, GB, F, D, NL. **285**

1118 *Omphalodes scorpioides*

Biennial with solitary axillary blue flowers with yellow centre, 3–4mm. Stems up to 40cm, spreading or ascending, leaves lanceolate to spoon-shaped, bristly-hairy, lower leaves opposite, stalked, upper stalkless. Calyx enlarging to 5mm in fruit. Nutlets winged, hairy. Apr–Jun. Damp shady places. D.

1119 Houndstongue *Cynoglossum officinale*

Biennial with hairy winged stems up to 60cm, smelling of mice when bruised. Stem-leaves oblong to lanceolate with greyish-silky adpressed hairs, the lower stalked, the middle leaves stalkless or clasping stem. Flowers dull purple, 5–6mm, with a short cylindrical tube, with spreading lobes, and 5 scales closing the throat. Nutlets flattened-ovoid, with thick border, and short barbed spines. May–Aug. Dry stony and grassy places, sand-dunes. Throughout area covered, except IS. **268**

1120 Green Houndstongue
Cynoglossum germanicum

Differs from **1119** in having green leaves with sparse bristly hairs, nearly hairless above, and nutlets without a thick border. Flowers dull red-purple, c. 5mm across. May–Jul. Woods, hedges, banks. B, GB, F, D.

1120

VERBENA FAMILY

Verbenaceae

Perennial herbs. Leaves opposite or whorled. Flowers tubular, 4- to 5-merous, somewhat bilaterally symmetrical. Fruit of 4 nutlets.

1121 Vervain *Verbena officinalis*
Perennial with erect 4-angled stems 30–60cm. Leaves rhombic in outline, opposite, the lower deeply 1–2 times lobed with larger terminal lobe, the upper leaves nearly entire, smaller, stalkless. Flowers pale pink, 2–5mm, many in a dense slender branched cluster without bracts. Corolla with tube twice as long as calyx and with 5 unequal blunt lobes; calyx tubular with 5 unequal teeth. Fruiting spikes 10–25cm; nutlets reddish-brown, ribbed. Jul–Sep. Roadsides, waste ground. Throughout area covered, except SF, IS, N, S. **278**

STARWORT FAMILY

Callitrichaceae

Annual or perennial, aquatic herbs. Leaves opposite. Flowers axillary. Sepals and petals absent; stamen 1 only. Fruit of 4 drupelets.

CALLITRICHE
ALL LEAVES SUBMERGED

1122 Autumnal Water-starwort
Callitriche hermaphroditica
Submerged yellowish aquatic plant up to 50cm, with all leaves submerged, linear widest at base and tapering towards notched apex. Flowers solitary, one-sexed, without petals, in leaf-axils; bractoles absent; styles spreading, downcurved, soon falling. Fruit with 4 lobes, usually broadly winged towards apex. May–Sep. Lakes, rivers, canals. GB, DK, SF, D, IRL, NL, IS, N, S.

1123 Short-leaved Water-starwort   *Callitriche truncata*
Differs from **1122** in having fruit wider than long, and wings of lobes narrow or absent (fruit longer than wide in **1122**). Very slender and entirely submerged, often reddish plant; leaves linear with almost parallel sides. Jun–Sep. Pools, ditches. B, GB, F, †IRL.

1123

1124 Common Water-starwort *Callitriche stagnalis*
Annual or perennial with narrow elliptic submerged
leaves, and rosettes of broadly elliptic to nearly rounded
short-stalked floating leaves; or in terrestrial plants
growing on damp mud, all leaves broadly elliptic to
nearly rounded. Flowers solitary, or both male and
female in same leaf-axil. Fruit rounded, pale brown, with
4 broadly winged lobes; style down-curved, persistent in
fruit. May–Sep. Springs, slow-flowing waters, wet mud.
Throughout area covered, except SF. **191**

1124

1125 Blunt-fruited Water-starwort
Callitriche obtusangula
Distinguished by its floating rosettes of 12–20 often
fleshy rhombic leaves; in terrestrial plants, leaves
narrowly rhombic or elliptic, fleshy, often
yellowish-green. Fruit elliptic, brown, with rounded, not
winged lobes. May–Sep. Fresh and brackish waters. B,
GB, F, D, IRL, NL.

1126 *Calitriche cophocarpa*
Differs from **1125** in its smaller rounded fruit 0·8–1·2mm,
and lobes with distinct but blunt margins (fruit 1·5mm,
with rounded, scarcely distinct margin in **1125**). Apr–Oct.
Slow-moving waters. Throughout area covered, except
IRL, IS.

1127 Various-leaved Water-starwort
Callitriche platycarpa
Submerged leaves linear; floating leaves elliptic, in
rosettes, often dark green. Fruit rounded, 1·5mm, brown,
with lobes narrowly winged, and styles erect or
spreading in fruit. May–Sep. Still or flowing waters. B,
GB, DK, F, D, IRL, NL, N, S.

1127

1128 *Callitriche palustris*
Distinguished by its obovate fruits with the lobes winged
only at the apex. Submerged leaves, narrowly linear,
floating rosettes with elliptic to nearly rounded leaves;
leaves elliptic in terrestrial forms. Fruit obovate, blackish,
with erect style which soon falls. May–Oct. Shallow still
waters. GB, DK, SF, F, D, NL, IS, N, S.

1129 Intermediate Water-starwort
Callitriche hamulata
Usually robust; submerged linear leaves with broad,
deeply notched apex, floating rosettes with elliptic to
obovate leaves; terrestrial plants with elliptic, dark green
leaves. Fruit rounded, 1·2–1·5mm, with lobes narrowly
winged, styles pressed to sides of fruit. Apr–Sep. Neutral
or acid slow-flowing waters, lakes. Throughout area
covered.

1130 Pedunculate Water-starwort
Callitriche brutia
Like **1129** but a slender plant with fruit usually longer than wide and lobes broadly winged. Submerged leaves linear, not widened at apex; floating rosettes with elliptic to obovate leaves; terrestrial growth forms with elliptic, dark green leaves. Apr–Sep. Still, often shallow waters. B, GB, DK, F, IRL, IS, N, S.

MINT FAMILY

Labiatae

Annual or perennial herbs, and small shrubs. Leaves opposite, usually simple. Flowers bilaterally symmetrical, in whorl-like clusters. Petals 5-lobed, forming hooded tube, with a prominent lip (or all lobes forming lip). Stamens usually 4. Fruit of 4 1-seeded nutlets. Many species are aromatic when bruised, and have been cultivated for scent or flavouring.

1131 Bugle *Ajuga reptans*
Perennial with long stolons, and erect stems 10–40cm; stems hairy on opposite sides at each node. Lower leaves ovate, entire or toothed, stalked, the upper leaves smaller. Flowers blue, rarely pink or white, in clusters in axils of leafy bracts, in a spike-like inflorescence. Corolla 14–17mm long, with upper lip entire and lower 3-lobed, corolla-tube longer than calyx and stamens longer than corolla-tube. Apr–Aug. Meadows, waysides, woods. B, GB, DK, F, D, IRL, NL, N, S; int SF. **285**

1132 Blue Bugle *Ajuga genevensis*
Differs from **1131** in having upper part of stem hairy on all sides. Stamens conspicuous, longer than corolla-tube, and filaments hairy; upper bracts often bluish, shorter than flowers. Perennial with erect stems up to 40cm, without stolons. Flowers bright blue, rarely white or pink, upper lip with 2 teeth. Apr–Jun. Calcareous grasslands, sunny slopes. B, F, D, NL; int SF. **285**

1133

1133 Pyramidal Bugle *Ajuga pyramidalis*
Differs from **1132** in having stamens only slightly longer than corolla-tube, and filaments hairless; upper bracts bluish, longer than flowers. Perennial up to 30cm, without stolons. Leaves obovate, entire or rounded–toothed. Flowers pale blue-violet, rarely pink or white, 1–1·8cm; corolla-tube longer than calyx and upper lip entire. May–Aug. Mountain meadows, rocky places. Throughout area covered, except NL.

1134 Ground Pine *Ajuga chamaepitys*
Readily distinguished by its deeply 3-lobed leaves with linear segments, and similar bracts subtending flowers. Usually annual, with branched stem up to 30cm. Flowers yellow with red or purple markings, rarely entirely purple, 7–15mm; corolla-tube about equalling calyx and upper lip of corolla entire; stamens longer than corolla-tube, filaments hairy. Apr–Oct. Chalk grassland, arable fields. B, GB, F, D, NL. **220**

1135 Cut-leaved Germander *Teucrium botrys*
Distinguished by its leaves which are divided into narrow

361

lobes. Hairy annual up to 30cm, with stalked leaves, once or twice divided. Flowers pinkish-purple, shaggy-haired, with corolla-tube shorter than calyx, in a lax inflorescence. Calyx shaggy-haired, glandular, conspicuously enlarged at base, net-veined, with triangular nearly equal teeth shorter than calyx-tube. Jun–Oct. Dry stony places. B, GB, F, D, NL. **247**

1136 Wood Sage *Teucrium scorodonia*
Dwarf hairy shrub, with erect branched stems up to 50cm or more. Leaves triangular–ovate with heart-shaped base, with rounded teeth, wrinkled, stalked. Flowers greenish-yellow, rarely white or red, in long, simple or branched, lax spike-like cluster. Corolla 9mm, shaggy-haired, stamens much longer. Calyx bell-shaped, 2-lipped with lips shaggy-haired and half length of calyx-tube, which is curved and swollen at base. Jun–Sep. Heaths, scrub. B, GB, F, D, IRL, NL, N; int DK, S. **200**

1137 Water Germander *Teucrium scordium*
Softly hairy perennial, smelling of garlic when crushed, with spreading stolons, and erect branched stems up to 60cm. Leaves ovate to oblong, coarsely toothed, stalkless or nearly so. Flowers pinkish, in axils of leafy bracts. Corolla 7–10mm, corolla-tube slightly longer than calyx which is shaggy-haired with teeth c. $\frac{1}{3}$ as long as enlarged calyx-tube. Jun–Aug. Wet places, marshes, ditches. Throughout area covered, except SF, IS, N.

1137

1138 Wall Germander *Teucrium chamaedrys*
Dwarf undershrub with hairy annual stems up to 50cm. Leaves all similar, up to 2cm, oblong to narrowly obovate, entire or toothed. Flowers pale to deep purple, rarely white, in lax or dense inflorescence longer than wide. Corolla 9–10mm, hairy; calyx bell-shaped, curved, with triangular nearly equal lobes $\frac{2}{3}$ as long as tube. Very variable species. May–Sep. Dry ground, banks, woods. B, F, D, NL; int GB. **263**

1139 Mountain Germander *Teucrium montanum*
Low spreading undershrub with yellowish-white flowers in a terminal rounded cluster. Leaves narrowly elliptic, entire, stalkless, white-hairy beneath, margin inrolled. Flowers 5-lobed, with spoon-shaped lateral lobes; calyx 7–10mm. May–Aug. Dry rocky and stony ground. B, F, D, NL.

1140 Skullcap *Scutellaria galericulata*
Low creeping perennial with rooting stolons, and erect simple or branched stems up to 50cm or more. Leaves ovate–lanceolate with heart-shaped base, remotely and shallowly rounded toothed. Flowers blue-violet, 1–1·8cm, in remote axillary pairs in axils of leafy bracts, in a spike-like cluster. Corolla 2-lipped, with curved tube much longer than the 2-lipped calyx. Jun–Sep. Fens,

damp meadows, streamsides. Throughout area covered, except IS. **278**

1141 Spear-leaved Skullcap *Scutellaria hastifolia*
Distinguished from **1140** by its arrow-shaped entire leaves, and its glandular-hairy calyx. Flowers blue-violet, 1·5–2cm, with corolla-tube conspicuously curved. Bracts similar to leaves but shorter than flowers (usually longer towards base of inflorescence in **1140**). Jul–Aug. Damp grassland, muddy places. DK, SF, F, D, S; int B, GB. **278**

1142 Lesser Skullcap *Scutellaria minor*
Distinguished from **1141** by its smaller pink flowers with an almost straight corolla-tube. Smaller perennial with stems usually 10–20cm, and leaves ovate–lanceolate, almost entire; bracts entire. Jun–Oct. Wet heaths. B, GB, F, D, IRL, NL, S.

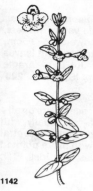

1142

1143 *Scutellaria columnae*
Flowers in a one-sided spike-like cluster, purplish with whitish lower lip, 1–2·2cm; corolla-tube very long, strongly curved, hairy. Perennial up to 1m. Bracts shorter than flowers. Leaves ovate with heart-shaped base, rounded-toothed. Jun–Jul. Woods. Native of Balkan peninsula. Int F, NL.

1144 White Horehound *Marrubium vulgare*
Perennial with white-woolly stems up to 45cm. Leaves rounded to broadly ovate, deeply and irregularly rounded-toothed, wrinkled above and densely white-woolly beneath. Flowers white, c. 1·5cm, in globular clusters in axils of much longer leaves. Calyx with 10 spreading hooked teeth; corolla little longer than calyx, 2-lipped, the upper 2-lobed, the lower 3-lobed. Jun–Nov. Waste places, roadsides, downs. Throughout area covered, except SF, IS, N; int IRL. **178**

1145 Bastard Balm *Melittis melissophyllum*
Strong smelling perennial with erect hairy stems 30–70cm. Leaves oblong to ovate, toothed, stalked. Flowers purple, white, pink, or sometimes variegated, 2·5–4cm. Corolla 2-lipped, upper lip weakly hooded, lower 3-lobed, tube much longer than calyx. Calyx 2-lipped. A variable species. May–Jun. Woods, hedge banks, sandy places. B, GB, F, D. **248**

GALEOPSIS
PLANTS WITH RIGID OFTEN YELLOWISH HAIRS; STEMS SWOLLEN AT NODES

1146 Common Hemp-nettle *Galeopsis tetrahit*
Coarsely hairy annual with angled stems with adpressed hairs on opposite sides of stems, up to 50cm. Leaves lanceolate to broadly ovate, pointed, toothed. Flowers pink with darker markings, rarely white or pale yellow,

1147

1·5–2cm or more. Corolla 2-lobed, middle lobe of lower
lip broad and flat; calyx tubular, 5-toothed, with bristly
hairs. Jul–Sep. Arable fields, open woods, fens, heaths.
Throughout area covered. **249**

1147 *Galeopsis bifida*
Like **1146** but flowers smaller, rarely more than 1·5cm,
and mid-lobe of lower lip narrower, distinctly notched,
with margin down-curved. A shorter, more slender, more
bristly annual. Jul–Sep. Arable fields, woods, fens,
heaths. Throughout area covered, except IS.

1148 Large-flowered Hemp-nettle *Galeopsis speciosa*
Differs from **1146** in having larger pale yellow flowers,
with large purple blotch on lower lip; flowers 2·5–3·5cm;
calyx-teeth with bristly ribs. Stem up to 1m, with leaves
ovate to ovate–lanceolate, toothed. Jul–Sep. Arable
fields. Throughout area covered, except IS; int IRL. **220**

1149 *Galeopsis pubescens*
Differs from **1146** in having dense adpressed hairs on all 4
sides of stem. Flowers bright pinkish-red usually with
yellow blotches, 2–2·5cm, with broad rounded central
lobe of lower lip. Annual up to 50cm, with ovate pointed
toothed leaves. Jul–Aug. Woods, hedges, waysides. F, D;
int B, NL.

GALEOPSIS
PLANTS LACKING RIGID HAIRS; STEMS NOT SWOLLEN AT NODES

1150 Red Hemp-nettle *Galeopsis angustifolia*
Annual with erect stems up to 40cm, with soft curved
hairs, with or without glandular hairs. Leaves narrow
linear to lanceolate, rarely ovate, with wedge-shaped
base, entire or toothed. Flowers deep reddish-pink with
yellow blotches, 14–24mm, in small dense whorls; calyx
whitish, with closely adpressed hairs. Jul–Sep.
Cultivated ground, bare stony places. B, GB, DK, F, D, NL;
int IRL, S. **263**

1151 Downy Hemp-nettle *Galeopsis segetum*
Differs from **1150** in having pale yellow flowers, and
leaves and calyx covered with dense soft-silky hairs, and
bracteoles of lower whorls shorter than calyx-tube.
Annual up to 50cm, with stem 4-angled and with curved
and glandular hairs. Leaves lanceolate to ovate,
wedge-shaped at base, toothed. Calyx softly hairy,
glandular, $\frac{1}{4}$–$\frac{1}{3}$ as long as corolla. Jul–Oct. Arable fields,
waysides. B, GB, DK, F, D, NL. **179**

1152 Broad-leaved Hemp-nettle
Galeopsis ladanum
Differs from **1150** in having green calyx, with spreading
hairs, and leaves broadly ovate to ovate–lanceolate.

Flowers deep pink with yellow blotches, 15–28mm.
Annual with stem up to 40cm, with curved spreading
glandular hairs. Jul–Oct. Waste places, cultivated
ground. B, DK, SF, F, D, NL, N, S.

LAMIUM
ANNUALS WITH FLOWERS USUALLY LESS THAN 2CM LONG

1154

1153 Red Dead-nettle *Lamium purpureum*
Hairy spreading or ascending annual 10–40cm, with
ovate to rounded, toothed leaves. Flowers
pinkish-purple, 1–1·8cm, lower lip heart-shaped with
mid-lobe 2-lobed, and lateral lobes tiny acute, upper lip
entire; corolla-tube straight, longer than calyx. Feb–Dec.
Cultivated ground, waste places. Throughout area
covered; int IS. **249**

1154 Cut-leaved Dead-nettle *Lamium hybridum*
Like **1153**, but leaves and bracts deeply and irregularly
toothed, and upper leaves with blade running down
leaf-stalk. Flowers pink with darker spots, 1–1·5cm.
Mar–Nov. Arable fields, waste ground. Throughout area
covered, except IS.

1155 Northern Dead-nettle *Lamium moluccellifolium*
Like **1153** but calyx-teeth longer, 8–12mm, and longer
than calyx-tube (calyx 5–7mm, teeth not longer than tube
in **1153**). Flowers pinkish-purple, 1·4–2cm, with straight
corolla-tube longer than calyx; upper-lip entire, lower-lip
heart-shaped. Hairy annual, up to 40cm. May–Sep.
Cultivated ground. GB, DK, SF, D, IRL, N, S; int IS.

1156 Henbit Dead-nettle *Lamium amplexicaule*
Readily distinguished by its heart-shaped shallowly
lobed stalkless bracts surrounding the whorls of
pinkish-purple flowers. Hairy annual up to 30cm, with
rounded, toothed or lobed leaves. Corolla 1·4–2cm, with
straight corolla-tube much longer than calyx; upper lip
entire, lower lip 2-lobed. Mar–Oct. Weed of cultivation.
Throughout area covered; int IS. **249**

LAMIUM
PERENNIALS WITH FLOWERS MORE THAN 2CM LONG

1157 White Dead-nettle *Lamium album*
Readily distinguished by its whorls of white flowers in the
axils of the upper leaf-like bracts. Hairy perennial up to
80cm, with triangular–ovate, coarsely toothed, stalked
leaves. Flowers 2–2·5cm, with curved corolla-tube about
as long as calyx; upper-lip hairy, entire or toothed, the
lateral lobes with 2–3 small teeth, lower-lip heart-shaped.
Mar–Nov. Roadsides, waste places. Throughout area
covered; int IRL, IS. **178**

1158 Spotted Dead-nettle *Lamium maculatum*
Differs from **1157** in having pink, purple or brownish-purple, rarely white flowers, and lateral lobes of corolla 1-toothed. Hairy perennial up to 80cm, with triangular–ovate coarsely toothed, often white-spotted leaves. Flowers 2–3·5cm, corolla-tube curved upwards, upper-lip entire, lower-lip heart-shaped. A very variable species. Apr–Sep. Fields, hedges, wood verges, fen carr; widely cultivated. B, F, D, NL; int GB, S. **249**

1159 Yellow Archangel *Lamiastrum galeobdolon*
Readily distinguished by its bright yellow flowers with brownish markings, in whorls in the axils of upper leafy bracts. Erect perennial with stems up to 60cm, with lanceolate to ovate coarsely toothed leaves, with cut-off or slightly heart-shaped base. Flowers 1·5–2·5cm, with straight corolla-tube with a ring of hairs within, lower-lip with 3 more or less equal lobes. Calyx-teeth $\frac{1}{4}$ as long as calyx-tube. May–Jun. Woods. Throughout area covered, except IS; int SF, N. **220**

1160 Motherwort *Leonurus cardiaca*
Erect perennial 30–200cm, with lower leaves 5–7-lobed, the lobes toothed or shallowly lobed; upper leaves 3-lobed. Flowers white or pink, 8–12mm, upper-lip hooded, densely hairy on back, lower-lip 3-lobed; corolla-tube shorter than calyx. Calyx bell-shaped, prominently 5-veined, with 5 spine-tipped teeth. Jul–Sep. Waysides, waste places. B, DK, SF, F, D, NL, N, S; int GB. **249**

1161 False Motherwort *Leonurus marrubiastrum*
Differs from **1160** in having entire coarsely toothed leaves, and flowers pale pink 5–7mm, scarcely exceeding calyx. Grey-hairy perennial up to 125cm. Jul–Sep. Watersides, meadows, hedges, waste places. D; int F.

1162 Black Horehound *Ballota nigra*
Branched, foetid-smelling hairy perennial up to 130cm. Leaves ovate to rounded, softly hairy, usually short-stalked. Flowers lilac, 12–15mm, many in dense clusters subtended by leaf-like bracts, in a terminal spike. Corolla with lower lip 3-lobed; calyx with erect triangular awned lobes, 10-veined. Jun–Oct. Hedgerows, waste places. Throughout area covered, except SF, IS, N. **263**

STACHYS
BRACTEOLES AS LONG OR LONGER THAN CALYX-TUBE; PERENNIALS

1163 Betony *Stachys officinalis*
Erect nearly hairless to densely hairy perennial 10–100cm. Leaves oblong to oblong–ovate with heart-shaped base, coarsely toothed. Flowers bright

1163

reddish-purple, rarely pink or white, many in a dense cylindrical spike. Corolla 12–18mm, with corolla-tube longer than calyx, upper-lip entire, lower-lip 3-lobed. Calyx with 5 bristly, awned teeth. Jul–Sep. Woods, heaths, grassland. Throughout area covered, except IS; int SF, N.

1164 Downy Woundwort *Stachys germanica*
Perennial with woolly, not glandular hairs, 30–100cm, with oblong to oblong–ovate leaves with heart-shaped base, green above, grey-woolly beneath. Flowers pink or purple, 1·5–2cm. Calyx with unequal teeth. Jun–Sep. Hedgerows, wood verges, rocky places. B, GB, F, D.

1165 Limestone Woundwort *Stachys alpina*
Differs from **1164** in having stems with glandular hairs, at least above. Flowers dull purple, rarely tinged with yellow, 1·5–2·2cm. Perennial 30–100cm, with leaves oblong or ovate, with heart-shaped base, toothed, grey or grey-green. Calyx teeth unequal. Jun–Oct. Open woods, ravines, damp rocks. B, GB, F, D. **249**

STACHYS
BRACTEOLES ABSENT OR NOT MORE THAN HALF AS LONG AS CALYX-TUBE; PERENNIALS

1166 Hedge Woundwort *Stachys sylvatica*
Erect glandular-hairy perennial up to 120cm. Leaves ovate pointed, coarsely toothed, all stalked. Flowers dull reddish-purple with white markings, rarely white or pink, finely hairy, in crowded terminal interrupted spike. Corolla 1·3–1·8cm; calyx half as long as corolla, with triangular teeth as long as or slightly shorter than calyx-tube. Jul–Aug. Woods, hedgerows, shady waste places. Throughout area covered, except IS. **268**

1167 Marsh Woundwort *Stachys palustris*
Differs from **1166** in having lanceolate, short-stalked or stalkless leaves, and dull purple flowers. Hairy perennial up to 120cm, usually not glandular. Flowers 1·2–1·5cm, in whorls forming a long terminal interrupted spike. Calyx usually not glandular. Jul–Sep. Damp places, cultivated land. Throughout area covered, except IS. **250**

1168 Yellow Woundwort *Stachys recta*
Erect or ascending perennial up to 1m, nearly hairless and not glandular. Leaves oblong to ovate, with rounded or wedge-shaped base, the upper leaves narrower, stalkless, all toothed. Flowers pale yellow, hairy, 1·5–2cm, in many whorls in a crowded spike. Calyx-teeth shorter than calyx-tube, with triangular spine-tipped teeth. Very variable species. Jun–Oct. Calcareous grasslands, open woods. B, F, D. **229**

1169 Annual Woundwort *Stachys annua*
Like **1168** with pale yellow or white flowers, sometimes
with red spots, in whorls, the upper crowded. Flowers in
clusters of 2–6 (6–16 in **1168**). Corolla 1–1·6cm, with tube
longer than calyx; calyx glandular-hairy, teeth half as
long as calyx-tube. Usually an annual to 40cm. Leaves
lanceolate pointed with rounded or wedge-shaped base,
toothed, nearly hairless. Jun–Oct. Arable fields,
vineyards. B, F, D, NL; int DK, N, S. **201**

1170 Field Woundwort *Stachys arvensis*
Erect or spreading-hairy annual up to 40cm, with ovate
leaves, blunt-toothed, the upper stalkless. Flowers white,
pale pink or purple, scarcely longer than calyx, in whorls
of 4–6, in a short spike-like cluster. Corolla 6–8mm; calyx
hairy, with teeth as long as calyx-tube. Apr–Oct. Arable
fields, damp soils. B, GB, DK, F, D, IRL, NL, S.

1171 Catmint *Nepeta cataria*
Erect grey-hairy aromatic perennial up to 1m. Leaves
ovate, pointed with heart-shaped base, toothed, grey
woolly-haired beneath, stalked. Flowers white with small
purple spots, in a spike-like cluster with lower whorls
distant. Corolla 7–10mm, slightly longer than calyx,
upper-lip erect entire, lower-lip 3-lobed. Calyx ovoid,
teeth spreading. Jun–Sep. Hedgerows, wood verges,
clearings. B, GB, F, NL; int DK, SF, D, IRL, N, S. **250**

1172 Ground Ivy *Glechoma hederacea*
Softly hairy to nearly hairless perennial, with creeping
rooting stems, and ascending flowering stems 10–50cm.
Leaves kidney-shaped to rounded/heart-shaped, with
blunt teeth, all stalked. Flowers pale violet with purple
spots on lower lip, 2–3 in leaf axils. Corolla 1·5–2·2cm,
upper-lip flat, lower 3-lobed; calyx 2-lipped, hairy.
Mar–May. Woods, grasslands, hedge banks. Throughout
area covered, except IS. **278**

1173 *Dracocephalum thymiflorum*
Erect sparsely hairy annual up to 60cm. Lower leaves
ovate–lanceolate with heart-shaped base, saw-toothed,
hairless, with leaf-stalk longer than blade; upper leaves
ovate with wedge-shaped base and shorter leaf-stalks.
Flowers blue-lilac, in whorls, in an interrupted spike.
Corolla 7–9mm, only slightly longer than calyx-tube.
May–Jun. Native of USSR. Int DK, SF, S.

1174 *Dracocephalum ruyschiana*
Perennial with erect or ascending stems up to 60cm.
Leaves linear-lanceolate blunt, with incurved margin,
hairless, upper stalkless. Flowers blue to violet, rarely

pink or white, in whorls forming a dense terminal spike.
Corolla 2–2·8cm, 2-lipped, upper lip 2-lobed, lower lip
3-lobed, corolla-tube widening above. Jul–Sep. Dry
grasslands, open woods. F, D, N, S.

1175 Selfheal *Prunella vulgaris*
Hairy perennial with spreading or erect flowering stems
up to 50cm. Leaves ovate, entire or shallowly toothed,
stalked. Flowers deep blue-violet, rarely pink or white, in
dense terminal cylindrical spike, usually with leaves
directly below and bracts purplish, hairy. Corolla
1·3–1·5cm, 2-lipped, upper-lip hooded, the lower
toothed. Calyx 2-lipped, teeth unequal. Jul–Aug. Waste
places, woodlands, grasslands. Throughout area
covered. **278**

1176 Cut-leaved Selfheal *Prunella laciniata*
Like **1175** but flowers yellowish-white, and at least the
upper leaves pinnately lobed. Densely hairy perennial
with stems up to 30cm. Inflorescence dense and
subtended by leaves; corolla 1·5–1·7cm. Calyx with teeth
of lower lip linear–lanceolate with marginal hairs.
Jul–Oct. Dry grassy places. B, F, D; int GB. **200**

1177 Large Selfheal *Prunella grandiflora*
Distinguished from **1175** by its larger deep violet flowers
with whitish tube 2·5–3cm, in a terminal cluster and
without leaves directly below flower cluster. Perennial up
to 60cm; leaves ovate to ovate–lanceolate, entire or
toothed. Calyx-teeth awned. Jun–Aug. Calcareous
grassland, open woods. B, DK, F, D, S. **279**

1178 Balm *Melissa officinalis*
Erect branched glandular-hairy aromatic perennial up to
1·5m. Leaves broadly ovate to oblong, deeply toothed,
stalked. Flowers pale yellow, becoming whitish or pink,
in axillary whorls, in a long leafy spike. Corolla 8–15mm,
2-lipped, with curved tube enlarged above, upper-lip
notched, lower-lip 3-lobed. Calyx 2-lipped, upper-lip
3-toothed, lower 2-toothed, all awl-shaped,
glandular-hairy. Jul–Sep. Scrub, shady places. F; int B,
GB, DK, D, IRL, S.

1178

1179 Basil Thyme *Acinos arvensis*
Hairy annual with many stems, to 40cm. Leaves small,
lanceolate to ovate, to 1·5cm, entire or toothed,
conspicuously veined beneath. Flowers violet with white
marks on lower-lip, in whorls of 3–8, not longer than leafy
bracts, and in lax terminal spike. Corolla 7–10mm,
2-lipped with tube twice as long as calyx. Calyx
conspicuously ribbed, inflated at base. May–Sep. Scrub,
dry pastures, arable fields. Throughout area covered,
except IS.

1180 Wood Calamint *Calamintha sylvatica*
Hairy, strongly aromatic perennial up to 80cm, with

stolons. Leaves ovate to nearly rounded, almost entire to coarsely toothed. Flowers pink or lilac, with white spots on lower-lip, in opposite axillary stalked clusters. Corolla 1–2·2cm, 2-lipped, upper-lip entire or notched, lower 3-lobed. Calyx 2-lipped, upper-lip 3-toothed, lower 2-toothed, longer. Jul–Sep. Shady grassy places. B, GB, F, D, IRL, NL.

1181 Lesser Calamint *Calamintha nepeta*
Differs from **1180**: smaller white flowers 1–1·5cm, and hairs in throat of calyx protruding after flowering (not protruding in **1180**), and lower teeth of calyx without or with few long hairs (lower teeth with dense long hairs in **1180**). Flowers white or lilac, in a many-flowered cluster. Plant greener than **1180**. Jul–Sep. Calcareous grassland, dry banks. GB, F; int D. **250**

1182 Wild Basil *Clinopodium vulgare*
Hairy branched perennial 30–80cm, with ovate, shallowly toothed leaves with rounded or wedge-shaped base, stalked. Flowers pinkish-purple, in dense whorls in axils of upper leaves; bracts linear with feathery hairs. Corolla 2-lipped, 1·2–2·2cm; calyx 2-lipped, calyx-tube curved, teeth awl-shaped. Jun–Oct. Scrub, hedges, open woods, calcareous grassland. Throughout area covered, except IS. **264**

1183 Hyssop *Hyssopus officinalis*
Erect or spreading aromatic perennial up to 60cm. Leaves linear to oblong blunt, entire, hairless to shaggy-haired, stalkless or almost so. Flowers blue-violet, rarely white, in whorls in a long spike. Corolla 2-lipped, upper lip notched, the lower spreading 3-lobed and with mid-lobe notched; stamens longer. Calyx tubular with 5 equal teeth. Jul–Sep. Dry banks, hills, old walls. F; int B, D, NL. **279**

1184 Marjoram *Origanum vulgare*
Aromatic downy perennial with stems up to 90cm, branched above. Leaves ovate, entire or shallowly toothed, usually glandular-hairy, stalked. Flowers purple-violet or greenish, in lax ovoid or oblong clusters in a more or less flat-topped inflorescence. Corolla 4–7mm, 2-lipped; calyx bell-shaped with 5 equal teeth. Bracts ovate, leafy, usually purplish. A very variable species. Jul–Sep. Grasslands, woods, hedges on calcareous soils. Throughout area covered, except IS. **250**

1185 Breckland Thyme *Thymus serpyllum*
Aromatic perennial with long creeping branches, rooting at the nodes and with flowering stems up to 10cm, hairy all round. Leaves linear to elliptic, nearly stalkless, with marginal hairs at base. Flowers purple, 6–8mm, usually in dense rounded clusters; corolla 2-lipped, with straight

tube and stamens longer. Calyx 2-lipped. A very variable
species. Jun–Sep. Sandy grasslands, heaths, pinewoods, sand-dunes. B, GB, DK, SF, F, D, NL, N, S. **264**

1186 Large Thyme *Thymus pulegioides*
Like **1185**, but flowering stem 4-angled, hairy on angles
only, and runners absent, stems to 25cm or more,
sometimes branched. Leaves ovate, blunt, usually hairy
at base. Flowers pink-purple, up to c. 6mm, usually in
elongated cluster, interrupted below. Calyx-teeth hairy
on margin. A very variable species. Jun–Oct. Dry
grassland, waysides. B, GB, DK, F, D, NL, N, S; int SF.

1187 Wild Thyme *Thymus praecox*
Small much-branched tufted perennial with numerous
creeping stems, and flowering stems borne in rows, up to
10cm, each with a basal cluster of small leaves. Leaves
mostly obovate to rounded, with bristly-hairy margin at
base. Flowers purple, in dense globular heads; calyx
bell-shaped. A very variable species. May–Aug.
Calcareous grassland and rocks. B, GB, F, D, IRL, NL, IS,
and N.

1188 Gipsywort *Lycopus europaeus*
Hairy odourless perennial up to 120cm, with creeping
rhizomes. Leaves broadly lanceolate to elliptic,
pinnately-lobed at base, and coarsely toothed at apex,
upper leaves and bracts often undivided, but coarsely
toothed. Flowers white with few purple spots, up to c.
4mm, in dense many-flowered clusters in axils of bracts.
Corolla-tube shorter than calyx and with 4 nearly equal
lobes; stamens 2, longer than corolla. Calyx bell-shaped
with 5 equal spiny teeth. A very variable species.
Jun–Sep. Watersides, marshes. Throughout area
covered, except IS. **179**

MENTHA
BRACTS LIKE LEAVES. INFLORESCENCE TERMINATED BY LEAVES OR VERY
SMALL FLOWER CLUSTER

1189 Pennyroyal *Mentha pulegium*
Slender, spreading or ascending, nearly hairless or hairy
strong-smelling perennial up to 40cm. Leaves narrowly
elliptic, entire or with 6 teeth on each margin, hairy
beneath. Flowers lilac, 4·5–6mm, in many-flowered
clusters with leaf-like bracts, in a long interrupted spike.
Calyx with 5 unequal teeth, hairy in throat. A very variable
species. Aug–Sep. Wet places, sandy soils. B, GB, F, D,
IRL, NL. **279**

1190 Corn Mint *Mentha arvensis*
Hairy green perennial up to 60cm, with a sickly scent.
Leaves broadly lanceolate to ovate, shallowly toothed.
Flowers lilac, rarely pink or white, in dense clusters in

1189

371

axils of leafy bracts, and with apex of inflorescence leafy.
Calyx with 5 more or less equal broadly triangular teeth,
without hairs in throat. Jul–Aug. Damp arable fields, wet
meadows. Throughout area covered, except IS.

1191 Whorled Mint *Mentha ×verticillata*
Like **1190** but more robust and more hairy; calyx
2·5–3·5mm, with hairy tube and teeth more or less
triangular pointed. Upper bracts ovate to
ovate-lanceolate, not fine-pointed. Usually a sterile
hybrid. May–Oct. B, GB, DK, SF, F, D, IRL, NL, N, S.

1192 Bushy Mint *Mentha ×gentilis*
Perennial, up to 90cm, often red-tinged, with pungent
smell, hairless or hairy. Leaves ovate–lanceolate, densely
hairy. Flowers in remote whorls, with leafy bracts
decreasing in size of inflorescence. Calyx bell-shaped,
hairless below, teeth usually awl-shaped with marginal
hairs. Ditches, waste ground. Frequently cultivated and
escaping. Throughout area covered, except IS.

1193 *Mentha ×smithiana*
Differs from **1191** in having calyx-tube hairless; plant with
a pungent scent, and stamens usually longer than
corolla. Robust perennial up to 1·5m. Ditches, hedge
banks, waste ground. B, GB, F, D, IRL, NL.

MENTHA
BRACTS SMALL, INCONSPICUOUS; FLOWERS IN TERMINAL SPIKES OR HEADS

1194 Water Mint *Mentha aquatica*
Pleasantly aromatic, often purplish, hairy perennial up to
90cm. Leaves ovate, toothed, stalked. Flowers lilac, in
terminal rounded or cylindrical heads of 1–3 whorls, and
usually with axillary whorls below and with
inconspicuous narrow bracts hidden by flowers. Corolla
with 4 nearly equal lobes, stamens usually longer; calyx
with equal teeth, hairy. Jul–Oct. Swamps, marshes, fens,
by rivers and ponds. Throughout area; int IS. **250**

1195 Peppermint *Mentha ×piperita*
Differs from **1194** in having leaves and calyx hairless or
nearly so, and plant sterile. Perennial up to 90cm with
lilac-pink flowers in many whorls in an oblong or
rounded spike. Stamens not protruding. Aug–Sep. Waste
places. Hybrid garden escape. B, GB, DK, F, D, IRL, NL.

1196

1196 Spearmint *Mentha spicata*
Strongly sweet-scented perennial with erect stem up to
1m. Leaves lanceolate, toothed, smooth or rough,
hairless or densely hairy, almost stalkless. Flowers lilac,
pink or white, 3mm across, usually in spike-like
inflorescence, but variable. Calyx bell-shaped, hairless. A
very variable species. Jun–Oct. Damp and waste places.

Widely cultivated; int throughout area covered, except SF, IS.

1197 Round-leaved Mint *Mentha suaveolens*
Like **1196** but stem and leaves hairy, and leaves not more than 4·5cm, with numerous branched hairs beneath (leaves 5–9cm, without branched hairs beneath in **1196**). Perennial up to 1m, with sickly sweet scent. Leaves ovate–oblong to nearly rounded, toothed, usually grey- or white-woolly beneath. Flowers whitish or pinkish, in many whorls forming a dense terminal spike, interrupted and branched below. B, GB, F, D, NL; int DK, IRL, S.

1198 Horse Mint *Mentha longifolia*
Like **1196** but leaves oblong–elliptic, green- to grey-woolly above, grey- or white-woolly beneath. Flowers lilac or white, in many whorls forming a terminal usually branched spike up to 10cm long. Very variable perennial up to 1·2m, with a musty scent. Jul–Sep. Damp roadsides, waste places, ditches. B, F, D, S.

1198

1199 Meadow Clary *Salvia pratensis*
Erect glandular-hairy perennial, branched above, up to 1m. Basal leaves ovate with heart-shaped base, toothed, long-stalked, stem leaves smaller, few, stalkless. Flowers blue-violet, rarely white or pink, in a branched lax inflorescence. Corolla 2–3cm, 2-lipped, lower lip 3-lobed; calyx 2-lipped, upper lip curved, teeth unequal, glandular hairy; bracts less than half as long as calyx. Variable in flower size and shape. Apr–Aug. Calcareous grassland, roadsides. B, GB, F, D, NL; int S. **279**

1200 Wild Clary *Salvia verbenaca*
Distinguished from **1199** by its pinnately lobed leaves, and much smaller blue, lilac or white flowers, 6–10mm. Erect perennial 20–80cm. A variable species. Jun–Aug. Dry pastures, rocky banks, sand-dunes. GB, F, IRL. **279**

1201 Whorled Clary *Salvia verticillata*
Perennial with erect often unbranched stem 30–80cm. Leaves ovate–triangular, simple or with 1–2 pairs of small lobes. Flowers blue-lilac, 8–15mm; corolla-tube slightly longer than calyx, and upper-lip narrowed at base; 15–30 in each cluster. May–Aug. Roadsides, grasslands, margins of fields. F; int B, GB, DK, D, NL, N, S. **268**

1202 Wild Sage *Salvia nemorosa*
Hairy perennial with densely adpressed hairs, up to 60cm. Basal leaves oblong with heart-shaped or rounded base, toothed, grey-felted beneath, stalked; stem leaves more or less stalkless. Flowers blue-violet, rarely pink or white, 8–12mm, in dense inflorescence with whorls of 2–6 flowers; bracts ovate, violet, overlapping in bud. Jun–Jul. Grassland, waste places. D; int GB, F, N, S.

1202

NIGHTSHADE FAMILY

Solanaceae

Annual or perennial herbs, or shrubs. Flowers regular, tubular or bell-shaped, usually 5-merous. Stamens 5, joined to corolla-tube. Fruit a capsule or a berry. Several members of this family are extremely poisonous.

1203 Deadly Nightshade *Atropa bella-donna*
Stout, leafy, very poisonous perennial, branched above 50–150cm. Leaves large, ovate pointed, unequal in size, opposite above. Flowers bell-shaped, 2·5–3cm, 5-lobed, brownish-purple outside, greenish-yellow and violet-veined within. Fruit a large shining black berry to 2cm. Jun–Sep. Wood margins, clearings, hedges. B, GB, IRL, F, D, NL; int DK, S. **269**

1204 Henbane *Hyoscyamus niger*
Sticky-hairy poisonous, strong-smelling perennial 30–80cm, with oblong toothed or lobed leaves, the upper clasping stem. Flowers funnel-shaped 2–3cm across, yellowish with conspicuous network of violet veins, clustered at apex of stem. Fruit a globular capsule, encircled by papery calyx. Jun–Oct. Sandy places, waysides, often near the sea. Throughout area covered, except IS. **201**

1205 Bittersweet *Solanum dulcamara*
Climbing shrub-like perennial, 0·5–2m. Leaves broadly lanceolate, the lower deeply lobed, the upper entire. Flowers violet-purple, 1–1·5cm across, with 5 spreading pointed lobes, which later curve downwards, and with conspicuous yellow anthers in a cone; flowers in lax branched stalked clusters, arising opposite the leaves. Fruit a globular red berry, 1–1·5cm. May–Sep. Damp woods and scrub, waste ground, river-banks, coastal shingle. Throughout area covered, except IS. **279**

1207

1206 Black Nightshade *Solanum nigrum*
Hairless or hairy branched annual 10–60cm, distinguished by its white flowers and black berries. Leaves ovate to rhomboid, entire or toothed. Flowers in a lax cluster, with spreading petals, c. 5mm across, petals later down-curved; anthers in conspicuous yellow column. Fruit a black poisonous berry. Jun–Oct. Waste places, cultivated ground. Throughout area covered, except IS. **179**

1207 Hairy Nightshade *Solanum luteum*
Differs from **1206** in having usually greyish, softly hairy more deeply lobed leaves. Flowers white. Fruit red, orange or yellowish-brown. Jun–Sep. Waste places, arable land. F, D; int B, DK, NL, S.

1208

1208 Green Nightshade *Solanum sarrachoides*
Like **1206** with white flowers, but berries green when ripe,
with calyx conspicuously enlarged in fruit, and enclosing
at least its lower half. Jul–Oct. Waste places, cultivated
fields. Native of Brazil. Int GB, F, D.

1209 Thorn-apple *Datura stramonium*
Hairless strong-smelling annual 20–200cm. Leaves ovate
pointed, deeply toothed or lobed, up to 20cm long.
Flowers large, trumpet-shaped, up to 10cm, white, rarely
violet, with 5 acute lobes. Fruit egg-shaped, 3·5–7cm
long, green, covered with spines. Jul–Oct. Waste ground,
cultivated fields, roadsides; sporadic in occurrence.
Native of America. Int throughout area covered, except
SF, IS.

1210 Small Tobacco Plant *Nicotiana rustica*
Sticky-hairy, strong-smelling leafy annual up to 1·5m.
Leaves ovate to elliptic, leaf-stalk not winged. Flowers
tubular/bell-shaped, usually 3–4cm, greenish-yellow, in
clusters. Fruit an ovoid capsule. Jun–Aug. Native of N.
America. Int B, DK, F, D, NL. **201**

1211 Tobacco Plant *Nicotiana tabacum*
Differs from **1210** in having winged leaf-stalk, or leaf-stalk
absent. Perennial 1–3m, leaves elliptic to lanceolate, to
50cm. Flowers greenish-cream with pinkish margin
3·5–5·5cm, numerous in a branched cluster. Jul–Sep.
Naturalized from cultivation. Native of S. America. Int B,
DK, F, D, NL.

FIGWORT FAMILY

Scrophulariaceae

Annual or perennial herbs, or small shrubs. Leaves usually opposite. Flowers more or less 5-merous; petals fused, but variable in structure. Stamens 2 or 5. Fruit a capsule, with many seeds. A number of species are semi-parasitic or parasitic.

1213

1212 Gratiola *Gratiola officinalis*
Hairless perennial up to 50cm, with 4-angled stem above. Leaves linear to lanceolate, toothed, stalkless. Flowers white, usually veined and tinged purplish-red, tubular, weakly 2-lipped, 1–1·2cm, solitary, long-stalked from the axils of upper leaves. Fruit a capsule. May–Oct. Ditches, river-banks, wet meadows. B, F, D, NL. **179**

1213 Mudwort *Limosella aquatica*
Spreading hairless annual with creeping runners. Leaves mostly narrowly elliptic, long-stalked, in basal rosette. Flowers pinkish or whitish, 3mm, solitary, stalked, from lower leaves. Fruit ovoid, down-curved. Jun–Sep. Ditches, lake-shores, mud. Throughout area covered.

1214 Monkey Flower *Mimulus guttatus*
Hairless perennial, except for glandular-hairy inflorescence, with stout hollow stems, up to 50cm. Leaves broadly ovate and irregularly toothed, the upper stalkless. Flowers c. 4cm, bright yellow and usually red-spotted in throat, with 2-lipped cylindrical tube; calyx-teeth unequal. Jul–Sep. By streams. Native of west N. America. Int throughout area covered, except IS. **229**

1215 Musk *Mimulus moschatus*
Glandular-sticky perennial with spreading or ascending stems up to 35cm. Leaves ovate, finely toothed or entire. Flowers pale yellow, sometimes red-striped in throat, c. 2cm, mostly from axils of leaves; calyx with nearly equal teeth. Jul–Aug. Damp shady places. Native of West N. America. Int B, GB, F, D, NL. **220**

1216

1216 Blood-drop Emlets *Mimulus luteus*
Like **1214** but inflorescence hairless. Flowers yellow with red patches on throat, long-stalked. Stems spreading; leaves narrower, pointed, more regularly toothed. Jun–Sep. By streams. Native of Chile. Int GB (north).

VERBASCUM
FLOWERS SOLITARY IN AXILS OF BRACTS

1217 Moth Mullein *Verbascum blattaria*
Erect biennial up to 120cm, with stem 4-angled, usually

unbranched and hairless below, with sticky hairs above. Basal leaves oblong to lanceolate, toothed or lobed. Flowers yellow, rarely white, long-stalked, 2–3cm across. Stamens 5, the lower 2 with purple hairs on filaments. Jun–Aug. Waste places, bare ground. B, F, D, NL; int GB.

1218 Twiggy Mullein *Verbascum virgatum*
Differs from **1217**, in having 2–5 flowers often in the axils of lower bracts, and flower-stalks much shorter than calyx (flowers 1 to each bract; flower-stalks much longer than calyx in **1217**). Usually glandular-hairy throughout. Bracts toothed, bracteoles usually present. Jun–Sep. Waste places, fallow fields. GB, F.

1219 Purple Mullein *Verbascum phoeniceum*
Erect perennial 30–100cm, distinguished by its violet flowers (flowers rarely yellow). Basal leaves ovate, entire or shallowly toothed, stem leaves few, small. Flowers up to 3·5cm across, in a lax unbranched spike, with lanceolate bracts usually shorter than flower-stalks. Stamens 4–5 with violet hairs on filaments. May–Jul. Dry grasslands, scrub. D; int NL.

VERBASCUM
AT LEAST LOWER BRACTS WITH CLUSTERS OF FLOWERS. ANTHERS OF LOWER STAMENS EXTENDING DOWN FILAMENT

1220 Great Mullein *Verbascum thapsus*
Erect greyish felty-hairy perennial up to 2m, with elliptic to oblong pointed leaves with blades running down stem. Flowers pale yellow, up to 3·5cm across, in a long dense unbranched terminal spike; flowers several in axils of each bract. Stamens with white hairs on filaments. Jul–Sep. Waste places, wood verges, dry banks. Throughout area covered, except IS. **220**

1221 Orange Mullein *Verbascum phlomoides*
Greyish, white or yellowish woolly biennial up to 120cm, with stem-leaves ovate to lanceolate pointed, not or very shortly running down stem. Flowers yellow, sometimes orange-yellow, 2–5·5cm across, with petals woolly-haired on outside, usually in an unbranched spike. Stamens with filaments with white or yellow hairs. Jun–Sep. Waste ground, sandy and stony places. F, D; int B, GB, NL.

1222 *Verbascum densiflorum*
Differs from **1221** in having stem-leaves and bracts with blades running down stem; bracts long-pointed, to 4cm. Flowers pale yellow, to 3·5cm across. Jul–Aug. Waste ground, dry fields, wood clearings. B, DK, F, D, NL, S.

1223 Hoary Mullein *Verbascum pulverulentum*
Densely white-woolly biennial up to 120cm, with basal
leaves obovate, oblong to oblanceolate, stalkless or
short-stalked, upper leaves usually without blade
running down stem. Flowers yellow, up to 2·5cm across,
in branched inflorescence; bracts linear. Stamens 5,
anthers kidney-shaped, filaments with white hairs.
Jul–Aug. Roadsides. B, GB, F, D. **264**

1224 White Mullein *Verbascum lychnitis*
Sparsely grey-hairy biennial up to 1·5m, with basal leaves
ovate to oblanceolate, green above, white-woolly
beneath, stalked. Flowers white or pale yellow, c. 2cm
across, in freely branched inflorescence. Stamens 5, with
kidney-shaped anthers and with white or yellowish hairs
on filaments. Jun–Sep. Dry sparsely grassy places, waste
places. B, GB, DK, F, D, NL; int F, S. **201**

1225 Dark Mullein *Verbascum nigrum*
Erect biennial; purplish ridged stem with star-shaped
hairs, up to 120cm. Basal leaves heart-shaped, toothed,
dark green above, paler and more hairy beneath with
star-shaped hairs. Flowers in a long spike-like
inflorescence, yellow, rarely white, up to 2·5cm across,
with conspicuous purple hairs on stamen filaments.
Jun–Sep. Dry grassy places. B, GB, DK, SF, F, D, NL, N, S.
201

1226 French Figwort *Scrophularia canina*
Distinguished by its lower leaves which are pinnately
divided into linear to oblong toothed lobes. Flowers dark
purplish-red, usually 4–5mm, 2-lipped, usually 5–11 in
each cluster, forming a cylindrical inflorescence.
Jun–Aug. Waste places, bare ground. F, D. **269**

1228

1227 Yellow Figwort *Scrophularia vernalis*
Distinguished by its pale greenish-yellow flowers,
6–8mm, which are not 2-lipped; staminode absent.
Glandular-hairy biennial or perennial up to 1m, with
broadly ovate deeply double-toothed leaves. Apr–Jun.
Woods, scrub, old walls, bare ground. F, D; int B, GB, DK,
NL, S.

1228 Balm-leaved Figwort *Scrophularia scorodonia*
Downy perennial up to 1m or more, with ovate to
lanceolate double-toothed leaves, with heart-shaped
base. Bracts mostly leaf-like. Flowers dull purple, to
12mm, with a rounded staminode. Calyx-lobes with
broad papery margin. Jun–Sep. Hedges, riversides,
meadows, sand-dunes. GB, F.

1229 Common Figwort *Scrophularia nodosa*
Hairless perennial with sharply 4-angled stem,
40–100cm. Leaves ovate to narrowly ovate, double-
toothed, with heart-shaped or cut-off base. Flowers
green with purplish-brown upper lip, up to 1cm;
staminode oval. Jun–Sep. Damp shady places.
Throughout area covered, except IS.

1230 Water Figwort *Scrophularia auriculata*
Differs from **1229**; has a broadly winged 4-angled stem,
and calyx-lobes with papery margin more than 0·5mm
wide (papery margin less than 0·5mm wide in **1229**).
Leaves ovate to elliptic, simple or with one pair of lobes at
base, toothed. Bracts linear. Flowers greenish with purple
upper lip, up to 9mm; staminode rounded. Jun–Sep.
Damp places, watersides. B, GB, F, D, IRL, NL. **269**

1231 Green Figwort *Scrophularia umbrosa*
Differs from **1230** in having stems broadly winged, and
leaves without basal lobes. Flowers olive-brown; calyx
margin more or less toothed; staminode wider than long,
2-lobed. Jun–Aug. Damp shady places. B, GB, DK, F, D,
IRL, NL.

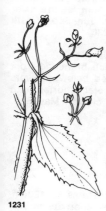

1232 Daisy-leaved Toadflax *Anarrhinum bellidifolium*
Hairless biennial or perennial, to 80cm, with basal leaves
narrowly elliptic, irregularly toothed, tapering to
leaf-stalk; stem-leaves divided into 3–5 narrow acute
lobes. Flowers pale lilac to blue, 4–5mm, with a short
curved spur, upper-lip 2-lobed, lower-lip 3-lobed;
stamens 4. Flowers in a slender leafless spike. Mar–Aug.
Dry ground, rocks, walls, coniferous woods. F, D.

1231

1233 Snapdragon *Antirrhinum majus*
Downy branched perennial 30–100cm. Leaves linear to
ovate with wedge-shaped base. Flowers pink or purple,
rarely yellow, 3–4·5cm, in a terminal spike. Corolla with
wide cylindrical tube, 2-lipped, the upper-lip 2-lobed, the
lower-lip 3-lobed and with rounded projections closing
the mouth of the tube. May–Oct. Rocks, walls, dry places.
F; int B, GB, D, IRL, NL.

1234 Lesser Snapdragon *Misopates orontium*
Erect sparsely branched annual 10–50cm. Leaves linear
to narrowly elliptic, opposite below, alternate above.
Flowers pink, 1–1·7cm, pouched at base, equalling or
shorter than the unequal linear calyx-lobes. Flowers
stalked, in a lax terminal spike-like cluster. Jul–Oct.
Cultivated ground. B, GB, F, IRL, NL; int DK, D, S.

1235 Small Toadflax *Chaenorhinum minus*
Glandular-hairy annual 5–40cm, with linear to oblong,
entire greyish leaves. Flowers pale purple, 5–9mm, with a
short blunt spur, stalked, in a lax cluster. Jun–Oct. Arable
1234 land, dry banks. Throughout area covered, except IS.

LINARIA
FLOWERS PREDOMINANTLY YELLOW

1236 Common Toadflax *Linaria vulgaris*
Erect greyish-hairy perennial 30–90cm, with linear to narrowly elliptic crowded leaves. Flowers yellow with orange spot on lower lip, 2·5–3·3cm, with a short straight spur shorter than lower lip; flowers in a dense spike-like cluster. Calyx-lobes ovate to oblanceolate, more or less equal. Jul–Oct. Waste places, hedgebanks, fields. Throughout area covered, except IS. **220**

1237 Prostrate Toadflax *Linaria supina*
Annual to perennial, spreading or ascending, 5–30cm, with linear to oblanceolate leaves in whorls below and alternate on upper part of stem. Flowers pale yellow 1·3–2cm, with nearly straight spur 1–1·5cm, few in a lax or dense cluster. Sepals linear, blunt. Jun–Sep. Waste places, sandy ground. F; int GB, S. **230**

1238 Sand Toadflax *Linaria arenaria*
Glandular-hairy annual 5–15cm, much branched from the base. Leaves lanceolate, whorled below. Flowers yellow, tiny, 4–7mm; spur often violet, shorter than corolla. Flowers few, in a short lax cluster. May–Sep. Sand-dunes. F; int GB (N. Devon).

1238

LINARIA
FLOWERS PREDOMINANTLY PURPLE, LILAC OR WHITE

1239 Pale Toadflax *Linaria repens*
Greyish hairless perennial with erect stems 30–120cm. Leaves linear, in whorls, sometimes alternate above. Flowers white to pale lilac with violet veins, in a long dense spike-like cluster. Corolla 8–15mm, with a straight conical spur, half as long as corolla; calyx-lobes narrowly lanceolate. Jun–Sep. Dry grassy places, bare ground. B, F, D; int GB, DK, SF, IRL, NL, N, S.

1240 Purple Toadflax *Linaria purpurea*
Greyish hairless perennial up to 60cm or more, with numerous linear leaves. Flowers bright violet, occasionally pink, 9–12mm, with a long curved spur as long as the corolla. Flowers in a long slender rather dense cluster. Jun–Aug. Bare ground, walls. Native of Italy. Int GB, IRL. **264**

1241 Jersey Toadflax *Linaria pelisseriana*
Hairless blue-green annual up to 50cm, with linear leaves. Flowers bluish-violet with white centre, 1·5–2cm, with upper lip very long with parallel lobes; spur 7–9mm, straight. Flowers in dense cluster. Seeds disk-like with marginal wing. May–Jul. Bare disturbed ground, sandy places. F.

1242 *Linaria arvensis*
Blue-green annual with erect stem up to 50cm, with
linear leaves. Flowers pale blue-lilac, tiny, 4–7mm, with
short strongly curved spur, in a dense spike-like cluster.
Apr–Sep. Cultivated ground, sandy places, rocks, open
ground. F, D.

1243 Ivy-leaved Toadflax *Cymbalaria muralis*
Trailing usually hairless, often pinkish perennial up to
60cm. Leaves rounded or kidney-shaped, with 5–9
shallow lobes, long-stalked. Flowers solitary, long-
stalked in axils of leaves, lilac with yellow centre,
9–15mm, spur curved a third as long as corolla. Apr–Nov.
Rocks, stony ground, walls. Native of S. Europe. Int B,
GB, DK, F, D, IRL, NL, N, S. **251**

1244 Sharp-leaved Fluellen *Kickxia elatine*
Glandular-hairy mostly prostrate annual, branched from
the base, up to c. 50cm. Leaves triangular with pointed
basal lobes, stalked. Flowers yellowish or bluish with
violet upper-lip, 7–9mm, spur straight: flowers solitary,
stalked, from axils of leaves. Jul–Oct. Bare ground,
cultivated fields. Throughout area covered, except SF,
IS, N; int DK, IRL, S.

1244

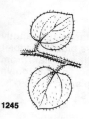

1245 Round-leaved Fluellen *Kickxia spuria*
Differs from **1244** in having ovate leaves with rounded or
heart-shaped base, and flower-stalks woolly-haired
(hairless in **1244**). Flowers yellow, 1–1·5cm, with deep
purple upper lip; spur curved. Jul–Oct. Arable fields. B,
GB, F, D, NL; int DK.

1245

1246 Foxglove *Digitalis purpurea*
Erect downy biennial or perennial 50–180cm. Basal
leaves ovate to lanceolate, lower long-stalked, upper
leaves stalkless usually densely glandular, hairy. Flowers
large, purple or pale pink, spotted within, numerous in a
long spike-like cluster. Corolla broadly tubular with
shallow lobes, 4–5·5cm; calyx-lobes ovate, lanceolate to
elliptic. Jun–Aug. Wood margins, heaths and scrub on
acid soil. B, GB, F, D, IRL, N, S; int DK, NL. **264**

1247 Large Yellow Foxglove *Digitalis grandiflora*
Distinguished by its inflated bell-shaped pale yellow
flowers, with brown spots within, in a long slender spike.
Perennial up to 1m, with ovate–lanceolate finely toothed,
hairless, shining leaves. Corolla 4–5cm, 2-lipped.
Jun–Aug. Woods, rocks in mountains. B, F, D. **202**

1248 Small Yellow Foxglove *Digitalis lutea*
Distinguished from **1247** by its smaller pale yellow
flowers 1·5–2·2cm, with slender cylindrical corolla-tube,
with recurved lateral lobes, and without spots within.
Perennial up to 1m, with oblong–oblanceolate toothed or

381

nearly entire leaves. Flowers many, in a dense spike-like cluster. Jun–Aug. Woods, stony hillsides. B, F, D. **202**

1249

1249 Fairy Foxglove *Erinus alpinus*
Low tufted sticky-hairy perennial 5–20cm. Leaves oblanceolate, toothed at least towards apex, lower leaves stalked. Flowers bright purple, 6–9mm across, with cut-off or notched lobes, the upper 2 narrower than the lower 3, in a somewhat flat-topped cluster. May–Oct. Rocks, screes, stony grasslands; also naturalized on walls. F; int GB, IRL.

VERONICA
FLOWERS IN AXILLARY CLUSTERS. CAPSULE SPLITTING INTO 4 VALVES; PLANTS OF WET PLACES; USUALLY HAIRLESS. PERENNIALS

1250 Brooklime *Veronica beccabunga*
Hairless creeping perennial of wet places, rooting at the nodes, and with thick rounded to oblong, stalked leaves. Flowers pale to dark blue, 5–7mm across, in spike-like clusters, from axils of upper leaves. May–Sep. Ditches, streams, marshes. Throughout area covered, except IS.

1251 Blue Water Speedwell
Veronica anagallis-aquatica
Distinguished from **1250** by its larger lanceolate, slightly toothed, stalkless upper leaves. Flowers blue with violet veins, 5–10mm across, in long spike-like clusters from axils of upper leaves. Calyx-lobes erect in fruit (down curved in fruit in **1250**). Jun–Aug. Wet places, riversides, streams. Throughout area covered. **279**

1252 Pink Water Speedwell *Veronica catenata*
Like **1251** but leaves linear to linear–lanceolate, dark green, all stalkless. Flowers usually pink with reddish veins 3–5mm across, flower-stalks spreading (flower-stalks more or less erect in **1251**). Bracts lanceolate, longer than flower-stalks at flowering. Jun–Aug. In or beside still or slow-flowing waters. B, GB, DK, F, D, IRL, NL, S.

1250

VERONICA
FLOWERS IN AXILLARY CLUSTERS; CAPSULE SPLITTING INTO 2 VALVES; PLANTS SELDOM OF WET PLACES; USUALLY HAIRY; PERENNIALS

1253 Large Speedwell *Veronica austriaca*
Usually distinguished by its leaves which are twice cut into linear lobes, but leaves very variable and may be entire. Stem up to 1m, usually erect. Flowers bright blue, 1–1·3cm across, usually in long dense spike-like clusters from the axils of the upper leaves. May–Jun. Calcareous grassland, sand-dunes. B, F, D, NL.

1254 *Veronica prostrata*
Flowering stems up to 25cm or more; non-flowering
stems short, creeping. Leaves linear–oblong to ovate
with wedge-shaped or cut-off base, toothed to nearly
entire, with margin inrolled. Flowers blue, 6–11mm or
more across; calyx hairless, with linear–oblong unequal
lobes. Apr–Jun. Dry grasslands, stony places. B, F, D, NL.

1255 Germander Speedwell *Veronica chamaedrys*
Hairy ascending perennial 7–25cm, with oblong to ovate,
toothed, sparsely hairy or nearly hairless leaves. Flowers
bright blue, c. 1cm across, in long spike-like paired
clusters from the axils of leaves. Calyx-lobes 4, sparsely
hairy. Apr–Jul. Grasslands, woods, hedges. Throughout
area covered; int IS. **285**

1256 Heath Speedwell *Veronica officinalis*
Stems rough-hairy, procumbent or ascending, 10–50cm.
Leaves ovate to elliptic, saw-toothed, softly hairy,
short-stalked. Flowers dull blue-lilac, c. 8mm across, in
dense erect stalked spike-like clusters from axils of
middle leaves. Calyx-lobes 4, oblong, unequal. Capsule
hairy. A variable species. Jun–Aug. Woods, hedges, dry
grassland, rocks. Throughout area covered.

1256

1257 Wood Speedwell *Veronica montana*
Softly hairy perennial with spreading stems 12–50cm.
Leaves broadly ovate, coarsely toothed, relatively
long-stalked; to 1·5cm. Flowers pale blue-lilac, in lax
few-flowered spike-like clusters. Corolla to 1cm across;
calyx with 4 elliptic blunt nearly equal lobes. Apr–Jul.
Damp deciduous woods. B, GB, DK, F, D, IRL, NL, S.

1258 Marsh Speedwell *Veronica scutellata*
Usually a hairless perennial up to 60cm, with narrow,
oblong, entire or obscurely toothed, stalkless leaves.
Flowers pink or lilac, in long spike-like clusters on
slender stalks, arising alternately from the axils of leaves.
Corolla 5–6mm across; calyx with 4 nearly equal elliptic
lobes; flower-stalks longer than bracts. Fruit deeply
notched. Jun–Aug. Marshes, wet places. Throughout
area covered.

VERONICA
FLOWERS SOLITARY IN LEAF AXILS, OR IN TERMINAL CLUSTERS;
ANNUALS

1259 Green Field Speedwell *Veronica agrestis*
Hairy spreading annual, 5–30cm. Leaves ovate,
rounded–toothed, shortly stalked, mostly alternate.
Flowers usually whitish with blue or pink upper lobe,
3–6mm across, short-stalked, solitary in axils of leaves.
Capsule 2-lobed, sparingly glandular-hairy. Mar–Nov.
Cultivated fields. Throughout area covered, except IS.

1259

383

1260 Grey Field Speedwell *Veronica polita*
Like **1259**, but leaves greyish, more regularly toothed, the
lower leaves wider than long (longer than wide in **1259**).
Flowers blue; calyx-lobes broadly ovate, overlapping
near base (not overlapping in **1259**). Capsule with long
glandular hairs and short curled hairs. Mar–Nov.
Cultivated ground. Throughout area covered, except IS.

1261 *Veronica opaca*
Like **1259** but leaves very shallowly rounded-toothed, the
lower often wider than long. Flowers deep blue, 3–4mm;
calyx-lobes oblong–lanceolate to spoon-shaped.
Mar–Jul. Waste places, cultivated ground. B, DK, SF, F, D,
NL, N, S.

1262 Common Field Speedwell *Veronica persica*
Hairy spreading annual 10–60cm, with alternate broadly
ovate short-stalked leaves. Flowers blue with darker
veins and lower petal pale, 8–12mm across, solitary in
leaf-axils on stalks longer than the leaves and recurved in
fruit. Calyx-lobes ovate–lanceolate. Capsule 2-lobed with
very divergent lobes, strongly keeled, glandular-hairy.
Feb–Dec. Cultivated ground. Native of S-W. Africa.
Naturalized throughout area covered.

1263 Ivy-leaved Speedwell *Veronica hederifolia*
Hairy spreading annual 10–60cm, with leaves rounded in
outline with 3–7 lobes, the terminal larger. Flowers pale
blue with white centre, 6–9mm across, solitary in leaf
axils on stalks shorter or as long as leaves. Calyx-lobes
with spreading hairs. Capsule shallowly 4-lobed,
hairless. Mar–Aug. Arable fields, walls, woodland
clearings. Throughout area covered, except IS. **285**

1264 Breckland Speedwell *Veronica praecox*
Glandular-hairy annual 5–20cm, with ovate, deeply
toothed, short-stalked leaves. Flowers blue, c. 3mm
across, solitary in leaf-axils, forming a narrow terminal
spike-like cluster occupying most of the stem. Calyx
4-lobed. Capsule obovate flat, glandular-hairy. Mar–May.

1264

Cultivated fields, stony hills. B, DK, F, GB, D, NL, S.

1265 Fringed Speedwell *Veronica triphyllos*
Differs from **1264** in having most leaves with 3–7 oblong
lobes, and lower bracts similarly lobed. Glandular-hairy
erect annual, branched from the base, up to 20cm.
Flowers deep blue, 3–4mm across, in a lax terminal
spike-like cluster. Mar–May. Cultivated fields, waste
places, dry grasslands. B, GB, DK, F, D, NL, S.

1266 Wall Speedwell *Veronica arvensis*
Hairy erect or spreading annual, with simple or
much-branched stem 9–40cm. Leaves triangular–ovate
with cut-off or weakly heart-shaped base, coarsely
toothed, the lower short-stalked. Flowers pale blue,

1267

2–3mm across, in a spike-like cluster, with bracts longer than flower-stalks. Calyx-lobes lanceolate. Apr–Oct. Cultivated ground, walls, sand-dunes, open places. Throughout area covered; int IS.

1267 Spring Speedwell *Veronica verna*
Differs from **1266**; upper stem-leaves pinnately lobed with narrow lobes. Stem simple or branched from base, hairy and with glandular hairs above. Flowers blue, c. 3mm, in spike-like clusters. Lower bracts pinnately-lobed. Capsule kidney-shaped, glandular-hairy. Apr–Jun. Fields, dry places. Throughout area covered, except IS, IRL.

1268 American Speedwell *Veronica peregrina*
Hairless erect, simple or branched annual, 5–25cm. Leaves oblong to spoon-shaped, entire or obscurely toothed, lower leaves narrowed to base with short leaf-stalk, upper stalkless. Flowers whitish, 2–3mm across, in spike-like clusters. Bracts lanceolate, longer than the nearly stalkless flowers. Capsule obovate, shallowly notched. Apr–Jul. Cultivated ground, damp waste places, streamsides. Native of W. & S. America. Int B, GB, F, D, IRL, NL, N, S.

VERONICA
FLOWERS SOLITARY IN LEAF AXILS, OR IN TERMINAL CLUSTERS; PERENNIALS

1269 Thyme-leaved Speedwell *Veronica serpyllifolia*
Stems spread at base and terminally erect, 5–20cm. Leaves ovate, shiny, entire or obscurely toothed, short-stalked. Flowers white or pale blue with dark blue veins, 6–8mm across, in long lax terminal clusters. Bracts longer than flower-stalks. Calyx-lobes 4, slightly unequal. Capsule hairy. Apr–Oct. Sparse grassland, lawns, bare places, heaths. Throughout area covered.

1270 Alpine Speedwell *Veronica alpina*
Perennial with ascending stems 5–15cm, with oval to elliptic, stalkless, almost hairless leaves. Flowers deep blue, c. 7mm across, in a dense cluster which elongates in fruit; flower-stalks shorter than bracts. Calyx-lobes hairy on margin. Capsule elliptic, hairless. Jul–Aug. Arctic heaths, mountains. GB, SF, F, D, IS, N, S.

1271 Rock Speedwell *Veronica fruticans*
Distinguished by its woody-based stem and deep blue flowers with reddish centres. Stems ascending, 5–15cm, with obovate to narrowly oblong, usually entire, nearly stalkless leaves. Flowers large 1·1–1·5cm across, in short more or less head-like clusters, elongating in fruit. Capsule ovate, densely and finely hairy like the calyx. Jul–Aug. Rocks, stony grassland. GB, SF, F, D, IS, N, S.

1271

1272 Slender Speedwell *Veronica filiformis*
Hairy perennial with slender spreading stems up to
20cm, rooting at the nodes, often forming mats. Leaves
kidney-shaped, rounded-toothed. Flowers pale blue-
lilac, solitary in leaf-axils, 1–1·5cm across, long-stalked;
calyx-lobes oblong blunt. Capsule rarely formed. Apr–
Jun. Damp grasslands, lawns, cultivated ground. Native of
Caucasus and N. Anatolia. Int B, GB, DK, F, D, IRL, NL, S.
285

1273 Spiked Speedwell *Veronica spicata*
Downy perennial with erect stems 20–60cm. Lower
leaves narrowly elliptic, short-stalked, often in a rosette,
upper leaves narrower, stalkless. Flowers bright blue,
4–8mm across, with narrowly ovate flat lower lobes, in
long dense leafless terminal spike up to 30cm long.
Calyx-lobes blunt, hairy. Capsule hairless. Jul–Oct. Dry
grassland, rocks. GB, DK, SF, F, D, N, S; int NL. **286**

1275

1274 *Veronica longifolia*
Robust erect perennial to 120cm. Leaves long,
lanceolate to narrowly lanceolate, pointed, acutely
double-toothed, opposite or in whorls of 2–4. Flowers
lilac to pale blue, in a very dense spike-like cluster up to
25cm long. Capsule ovoid to rounded, hairless. Jun–Aug.
River-banks, woods, damp places. B, DK, SF, F, D, NL, N, S.

1275 Cornish Moneywort *Sibthorpia europaea*
Slender creeping mat-forming perennial, rooting at the
nodes, up to 40cm. Leaves rounded or kidney-shaped,
with 7–13 blunt lobes, hairy, long-stalked. Flowers tiny,
white tinged pink, to 2·5mm across, in axils of leaves.
Jun–Oct. Damp shady places on acid soils. GB, F, IRL.

MELAMPYRUM
INFLORESCENCE DENSE, NOT TURNED TO ONE SIDE; BRACTS DENSELY
OVERLAPPING AND CONCEALING AXIS

1276 Crested Cow-wheat *Melampyrum cristatum*
Annual 15–50cm, with narrowly lanceolate, entire or
toothed, stalkless leaves. Flowers yellow, in dense
4-sided spikes, with broad-based yellowish-green or
often reddish-purple toothed bracts, with down-turned
lanceolate apices, densely overlapping. Corolla
12–16mm, lower-lip purple-tinged, throat closed.
Jun–Sep. Dry grassy and rocky places, wood verges. B,
DK, SF, F, D, N, S; int GB.

1277 Field Cow-wheat *Melampyrum arvense*
Distinguished from **1276** by its cylindrical spike of larger
purplish-pink flowers 2–2·5cm, with yellow throat.
Lower-lip of corolla with up-turned margin. Stem to
50cm, with lanceolate entire or toothed leaves. Bracts
white to purplish, ovate–lanceolate and pinnately lobed.

apex not down-turned. May–Sep. Cornfields, waysides.
B, DK, SF, F, D, NL, S; int GB. **264**

MELAMPYRUM
INFLORESCENCE LAX, TURNED TO ONE SIDE; BRACTS SCARCELY
OVERLAPPING AND NOT CONCEALING AXIS

1278 Common Cow-wheat *Melampyrum pratense*
Very variable branched annual up to 60cm, with linear to
ovate leaves. Flowers bright yellow to whitish, rarely with
tube and upper lip purple-tinged, throat closed, 1–1·8cm.
Bracts green, ovate to narrowly lanceolate, entire or
toothed. May–Sep. Woods, grassland, heaths.
Throughout area covered, except IS.

1279 Small Cow-wheat *Melampyrum sylvaticum*
Like **1278** but flowers golden-yellow, smaller 8–10mm,
the lower lip often purple-spotted, and throat of corolla
open. Stems to 40cm, with lanceolate entire leaves.
Bracts green, entire or with 1–2 teeth at base. Jun–Aug.
Woods. Throughout area covered, except B, NL.

1280 *Melampyrum nemorosum*
Stems up to 50cm, with narrow lanceolate to ovate,
entire, stalked leaves. Flowers bright yellow, 1·5–2cm,
throat closed; calyx densely hairy. Bracts usually
violet-blue, sometimes green, purple or whitish towards
apex, deeply toothed, hairy at base. Calyx densely hairy.
May–Sep. Heaths, woods. DK, SF, D, S. **230**

1281 Eyebright *Euphrasia officinalis*
Branched, sometimes glandular-hairy annual, 2–40cm,
with ovate leaves with 3–6 acute teeth on each side.
Flowers white with violet upper lip or violet overall, usually with a yellow spot on lower lip, 8–14mm, solitary in
axils of upper leaves. Corolla with upper lip with out-
curved or reflexed lobes, the lower lip 3-lobed, notched
at apex. Stamens 4. A variable aggregate of many micro-
species. Jun–Oct. Pastures, moorlands, sand-dunes.
Throughout area covered, except IS.

1282 Red Bartsia *Odontites verna*
Distinguished by its reddish-pink, 2-lipped flowers in a
lax one-sided spike, with reddish bracts. Annual to 50cm,
with 4-angled simple or branched stem. Leaves
lanceolate, toothed to nearly entire. Flowers 8–10mm,
with upper lip entire and lower lip 3-lobed; stamens 4,
protruding. Capsule oblong, hairy. A very variable
species. Jun–Sep. Meadows, roadsides, disturbed
ground. Throughout area covered, except IS. **251**

1283 Yellow Odontites *Odontites lutea*
Annual with numerous erect branches with adpressed

curled hairs, up to 40cm. Leaves linear blunt, entire or shortly toothed. Flowers bright yellow, in a lax inflorescence; bracts linear–lanceolate. Corolla 5–8mm, 2-lipped, the lower lip downturned, hairy; anthers long protruding. Calyx-teeth triangular. Capsule hairy. Jul–Sep. Dry grassy places. F, D.

1284 *Odontites jaubertiana*
Differs from **1283** in having linear–entire leaves, and lower bracts longer than lower flowers. Flowers cream or yellow, sometimes tinged pink; anthers not protruding. A downy annual, up to 50cm. Aug–Oct. Fields, wood verges, rocks, banks. F.

1285 Alpine Bartsia *Bartsia alpina*
Glandular-hairy perennial with simple erect stems up to 30cm. Leaves ovate with heart-shaped base, bluntly toothed, and bracts like leaves but dull purple and increasing in size upwards in inflorescence. Flowers dark purple, 1·5–2cm, 2-lipped, the upper lip entire, lower lip 3-lobed, glandular-hairy. Jun–Aug. Damp places, mountain meadows, heaths. GB, SF, F, D, IS, N, S.

1286 Yellow Bartsia *Parentucellia viscosa*
Glandular hairy erect annual up to 50cm, or more. Leaves oblong to lanceolate, coarsely toothed. Flowers yellow, sometimes white, 2-lipped, with 3-lobed lower lip and longer hooded upper lip, in a terminal spike-like cluster, with bracts like leaves. Corolla 1·6–2·5cm; calyx-teeth linear nearly as long as calyx-tube. Capsule oblong, hairy. Jun–Sep. Damp grassy or sandy places. GB, F, IRL; int B, DK, NL. **221**

1285

PEDICULARIS
FLOWERS PREDOMINANTLY YELLOW OR RED-BROWN

1287 Moor King *Pedicularis sceptrum-carolinum*
Tall erect hairless, often reddish perennial up to 80cm, or more. Basal leaves in a rosette, lanceolate pinnately lobed with ovate blunt toothed lobes, stem leaves few. Flowers pale yellow with red margin to lower-lip, to 3·2cm, lips convergent, upper sickle-shaped, hairy, lower with 2 hairy ridges. Jul. Fens, wet woods, river-banks. DK, SF, D, N, S. **269**

1288 Leafy Lousewort *Pedicularis foliosa*
Hairy erect leafy perennial up to 50cm. Leaves broadly lanceolate, 2–3-times pinnately lobed, hairless above, hairy beneath, alternate. Flowers pale yellow, up to 2·5cm, in dense leafy spike. Corolla with tube longer than calyx, upper-lip nearly straight, blunt, with cobwebby hairs. Calyx papery, teeth unequal. Jun–Aug. Meadows, stream-sides, scrub. F, D. **202**

1289 *Pedicularis oederi*
Distinguished by its yellow flowers with crimson apex to upper-lip, hairless, up to 2cm, and corolla-tube longer than hairy calyx. Stem up to 15cm, with few or no stem-leaves. Leaves lanceolate, pinnately lobed with ovate, deeply toothed lobes, hairless. Flowers in a dense spike-like cluster, becoming lax; bracts lanceolate, deeply toothed, hairy, shorter than flowers. Jun–Jul. Damp grassland, tundra. F, D, N, S.

1290 *Pedicularis flammea*
Like **1289** but flowers smaller, up to 12mm, yellow with most of upper-lip dark red; calyx hairy, often red-spotted. Capsule at least twice as long as calyx (c. 1½ times as long in **1289**). Erect leafy perennial up to 10cm. Jul. Damp places. IS, N, S.

1291 *Pedicularis lapponica*
Usually perennial up to 25cm, with linear–lanceolate hairless leaves, with shallow toothed lobes. Flowers very pale yellow, fragrant, in a rounded cluster; bracts longer than calyx. Calyx papery, split to nearly half-way to base on lower side, hairless. Corolla 14–16mm, beak short, lower-lip shorter than upper. Capsule curved. Jul. Heaths, dry tundra. SF, N, S. **202**

PEDICULARIS
FLOWERS PREDOMINATELY PINK OR PURPLE

1292 Marsh Lousewort *Pedicularis palustris*
Usually a biennial with branched hairless or sparsely hairy stem, up to 70cm. Leaves linear to broadly lanceolate, pinnately lobed with oblong toothed or lobed segments, hairless. Flowers usually reddish-pink, 1·5–2·5cm, in lax spike-like cluster, often interrupted below, with leaf-like bracts, the uppermost 3-lobed. Calyx 2-lipped, inflated in fruit. May–Sep. Damp meadows, fens, marshes, wet heaths. Throughout area covered, except IS. **264**

1293 Lousewort *Pedicularis sylvatica*
Perennial or biennial with erect central unbranched stem up to 25cm, and longer lateral spreading and ascending branched stems. Leaves lanceolate, twice pinnately lobed. Flowers pink or red, 1·5–2·5cm, in short lax spike-like clusters. Calyx papery, usually hairless, inflated in fruit, scarcely 2-lipped, teeth unequal, leaf-like, lobed. Apr–Jul. Moors, damp heaths, bogs, woods. Throughout area covered, except SF, IS. **265**

1294 *Pedicularis hirsuta*
Erect leafy perennial 2–10cm, woolly-hairy above. Leaves linear to lanceolate, pinnately lobed with shallow toothed lobes. Flowers bright pink, upper lip straight blunt, lower

lip nearly as long, in a woolly-hairy rounded cluster.
Calyx woolly-haired, with toothed lobes. Jun. Tundra,
seashores, river-banks. SF, N, S.

1295 Yellow Rattle *Rhinanthus minor*
Annual 10–50cm, with oblong to linear, toothed, stalkless
leaves. Flowers yellow, to 1·5cm, 2-lipped, upper lip
helmet-shaped, lower lip 3-lobed often with 2 purple
teeth, in lax leafy spike, with triangular hairless bracts.
Calyx inflated in fruit, hairless. A variable species.
May–Sep. Grassy places, sand-dunes, cornfields.
Throughout area covered. 221

1296 *Rhinanthus groenlandicus*
Distinguished from **1295** by its leaves and bracts which
are deeply toothed with spreading teeth (teeth directed
towards apex in **1295**). Flowers yellow. Stem up to 30cm,
stout, hairy on opposite sides. Leaves rather fleshy,
coarsely toothed, bright greenish-yellow. Jul. Meadows.
SF, IS, N, S.

1297 Narrow-leaved Yellow Rattle
Rhinanthus angustifolius
Simple or branched perennial up to 60cm. Leaves linear
to ovate–lanceolate, toothed. Flowers pale yellow, to
2cm; corolla tube slightly curved; calyx hairless; bracts
longer than calyx, toothed. Variable species. May–Sep.
Meadows. Throughout area covered, except IRL, IS.

1297

1298 Greater Yellow Rattle
Rhinanthus alectorolophus
Simple or branched annual up to 80cm, with lanceolate
to ovate sharply-toothed leaves. Flowers yellow up to c.
2cm; corolla-tube slightly curved and with closed throat,
and spreading teeth on upper-lip. Calyx with long white
hairs. Bracts rhombic-triangular, with similar sized teeth,
pale green. May–Sep. Meadows, sand-dunes. B, F, NL.

1299 Toothwort *Lathraea squamaria*
White or cream parasitic plant, tinged lilac-pink above,
with stout erect stem 10–30cm. Scale-leaves rounded
entire, clasping stem, crowded below. Flowers pale pink,
14–17mm, 2-lipped, the lips equal, upper entire, the lower
flat, in a dense one-sided spike-like cluster. Calyx c. 1cm.
Apr–May. Parasitic on trees and shrubs, mainly elm and
hazel. Woods, hedges. B, GB, DK, SF, F, D, IRL, N.

1300 Purple Toothwort *Lathraea clandestina*
Flowers purple, 4–5cm, in short flat-topped inflorescence of 4–8 flowers, on stalks to 3cm rising
from below-ground rhizome. Corolla 2-lipped, the upper
hooded, longer than lower-lip; calyx violet. Scale-leaves
and bracts kidney-shaped. Mar–May. Parasitic on roots
of willow, alder and poplar. B, F; int GB. 251

1299

GLOBULARIA FAMILY

Globulariaceae

Perennial herbs or small shrubs. Leaves simple, alternate. Flowers bilaterally symmatrical, 5-merous, in dense clusters surrounded by an involucre. Stamens 4. Fruit dry, 1-seeded.

1301 Globularia *Globularia vulgaris*
Perennial with lanceolate to elliptic, 3-toothed leaves, long-stalked in a basal rosette, stem leaves narrower. Flowers blue, in globular heads c. 2·5cm across, on stem 5–20cm. Bracts of involucre, numerous, lanceolate-pointed. Corolla 2-lipped, upper lip short 2-lobed, lower 3-lobed longer; stamens and style longer than corolla. Apr–Jun. Grassland, stony slopes, rocks. F, S. **251**

BROOMRAPE FAMILY

Orobanchaceae

Perennial, parasitic herbs, growing on the roots of other plants. Leaves alternate, scale-like. Flowers in terminal spike or raceme. Corolla 5-lobed. Stamens 4. Fruit a capsule with many very small seeds.

OROBANCHE
EACH FLOWER SUBTENDED BY 2 BRACTEOLES AND 1 BRACT

1302

1302 Yarrow Broomrape *Orobanche ramosa*
Yellowish-white perennial up to 30cm, usually with a few branches at base. Flowers whitish at base and blue or violet towards apex, 1–2cm, glandular-hairy; corolla tubular with inflated base, upper-lip 2-lobed, lower 3-lobed with rounded or elliptic, entire or toothed lobes. Very variable species. Jul–Sep. Parasitic on hemp, potato, tomato and other plants. F; int B, GB, D, NL.

1303 Purple Broomrape *Orobanche purpurea*
Distinguished from **1302** by its larger bluish-violet flowers with deep violet veins, 1·8–2·5cm or more. Stem to 60cm or more, enlarged at base; leaves narrow lanceolate. Inflorescence dense, to 20cm long; corolla narrowly bell-shaped, lobes of lower lip narrowly ovate with rounded or fine point. Jun–Jul. Parasitic on yarrow and other Compositae. B, GB, DK, F, D, NL, S.

OROBANCHE
STIGMA PURPLE, ORANGE OR DARK RED, AT OPENING OF FLOWERS. FLOWERS EACH WITHOUT BRACTEOLES, SUBTENDED BY ONE BRACT

1304 Thyme Broomrape *Orobanche alba*
Stem usually reddish-purple, glandular-hairy, up to 35cm or more, with lanceolate leaves. Flowers reddish-purple, yellowish or white, 1·5–2·5cm, fragrant. Corolla broadly cylindrical, slightly curved, upper lip 2-lobed or entire, lower lip with middle lobe much longer than lateral lobes, glandular hairy. Stamen filaments glandular-hairy. Apr–Aug. Parasitic on thyme and other Labiatae, in grassland and open woods. B, GB, F, D, IRL, S. **235**

1305 Thistle Broomrape *Orobanche reticulata*
Like **1304**, but taller and more robust, with flowers scarcely fragrant, and lower lip of corolla with equal lobes, hairless. Calyx with indistinct veins (with 1–3 conspicuous veins in **1304**). Stamen filaments hairless or sparsely hairy below; stigma lobes dark purple. Jun–Aug. Parasitic on thistles, scabious and related species. GB, DK, F, D, NL, S.

1306

1306 Common Broomrape *Orobanche minor*
Stem 10–80cm, yellow tinged red, glandular-hairy.
Leaves sparse, ovate to lanceolate, glandular-hairy.
Flowers pale yellow, tinged dull violet at apex, 1–1·5cm,
upper-lip notched or 2-lobed, lower-lip with 3 equal
lobes, or middle lobe largest. Filaments of stamens hairy
below. May–Jul. Parasitic on many species, especially
Leguminosae and Compositae. B, GB, F, D, NL; int DK,
IRL, S.

1307 *Orobanche amethystea*
Differs from **1306** in having longer bracts 1–2·2cm, and
stamens inserted 3·5mm above base of corolla (bracts
2–3mm and stamens inserted 2–3mm above base of
corolla in **1306**). Flowers white or cream, usually tinged
violet, pink or brown at apex, 1·5–2·5cm; upper-lip deeply
2-lobed, lobes of lower-lip more or less equal Jun–Jul.
Parasitic on various species. GB, F, D.

1308 Ox-tongue Broomrape *Orobanche loricata*
Differs from **1306** in having bracts 1–2·2cm, and stamens
inserted 3–5mm above base of corolla. Corolla white or
pale yellow, tinged or veined violet, 1·4–2·2cm. Jun–Jul.
Parasitic on species of wormwood and ox-tongue, also
on carrot and *Orlaya*. B, GB, DK, F, D, NL.

1309 Bedstraw Broomrape
Orobanche caryophyllacea
Distinguished by its pink or pale yellow purple-tinged
flowers, 2–3·2cm. Corolla narrowly bell-shaped, curved,
upper lip notched, lower lip with 3 equal glandular-hairy
lobes. Spike of flowers usually lax, glandular-hairy,
flowers fragrant; calyx 1–1·7cm. Filaments of stamens
hairy; stigma purple. Stem yellowish or purplish up to
50cm; leaves narrow–triangular. Jun–Jul. Parasitic on
bedstraws. B, GB, F, D, NL, N. **251**

OROBANCHE

STIGMA YELLOW OR WHITE, AT OPENING OF FLOWERS; FLOWERS WITHOUT
BRACTEOLES, SUBTENDED BY ONE BRACT

1310 Ivy Broomrape *Orobanche hederae*
Glandular-hairy, yellow to reddish-purple perennial with
stem to 60cm, conspicuously swollen at base. Flowers
cream tinged reddish-purple at apex, 1–2·2cm;
corolla-tube enlarged below, narrowed at mouth, lips
spreading, upper-lip entire or notched, lower-lip 3-lobed
with middle lobe larger, not bristly hairy. Flowering spike
10–40cm long, glandular-hairy; bracts lanceolate-
pointed. May–Jul. Parasitic on ivy. B, GB, F, D, IRL, NL.
235

1311 Knapweed Broomrape *Orobanche elatior*
Stem glandular-hairy, up to 70cm, with triangular to

lance-shaped leaves and yellow flowers tinged pink, in a dense spike 6–20cm. Corolla 1·8–2·5cm, narrowly bell-shaped, glandular-hairy, upper lip curved, shallowly 2-lobed, lower lip with more or less equal lobes, hairless. Jun–Jul. Parasitic on Compositae and meadow rue. GB, DK, F, D, S.

1312 Greater Broomrape *Orobanche rapum-genistae*
Stem stout up to 80cm, pale yellow, strongly swollen at base, and with numerous scale-leaves and a dense spike of yellow or reddish foetid-smelling flowers. Corolla bell-shaped, glandular-hairy, 2–2·5cm, slightly curved; upper lip almost entire, lower 3-lobed, the mid-lobe much larger, hairy. May–Jul. Parasitic on shrubs such as broom and gorse in Leguminosae. B, GB, F, D, IRL, NL.

1313 *Orobanche gracilis*
Distinguished by its fragrant flowers, which are yellow outside with red veins and reddish towards apex, and shining dark red within. Corolla broadly tubular, slightly curved, upper lip notched, lobes of lower lip nearly equal, bristly-hairy. Stem up to 60cm, yellow or reddish, somewhat swollen at base; flowering-spike 3–20cm, glandular-hairy, lax below. Jun–Jul. Parasitic on Leguminosae. F, D.

1312

BUTTERWORT FAMILY

Lentibulariaceae

Perennial herbs, notable for their insectivorous habit. Leaves alternate or basal. Corolla 2-lipped, with spur. Stamens 2. Fruit a capsule, with many very small seeds. Plants of wet places.

1314 Common Butterwort *Pinguicula vulgaris*
Leaves in a basal rosette, oblong to ovate–oblong with margin incurved and sticky glands on upper surface. Flowers violet, usually with a white throat, lobes of upper and lower lip oblong, spreading not overlapping; spur 3–6mm or more, straight. Flowers solitary, on leafless stem up to 18cm. May–Jul. Bogs, wet heaths, wet rocks, damp grassland. Throughout area covered.

1315 Large-flowered Butterwort
Pinguicula grandiflora
Distinguished by its larger flowers 2·5–3·5cm, which are purple. Lobes of upper- and lower-lip rounded, overlapping and somewhat undulate; spur 1–1·2cm, straight. Flower-stems glandular-hairy, up to 15cm; leaves oblong, in a rosette. Apr–Jun. Bogs, wet rocks. F, IRL; int GB.

1316

1316 Pale Butterwort *Pinguicula lusitanica*
Distinguished by its smaller pinkish to pale lilac flowers with yellow throat, 7–9mm, with lips nearly equal with rounded notched lobes; spur 2–4mm, down-curved. Flower-stems very slender up to 15cm; leaves oblong–ovate with strongly incurved margin, in a rosette. May–Jul. Bogs, wet heaths. GB, F, IRL.

1317 *Pinguicula villosa*
Flower small 6–9mm, pale violet with yellow stripes in throat, upper and lower lips unequal, broadly wedge-shaped; spur 2–3mm, straight. Plant usually 1-flowered, on stem to 6cm, with long glandular hairs. Leaves elliptic, with margin strongly incurved, in a rosette. Jul. Peat-bogs. SF, N, S.

1318 Alpine Butterwort *Pinguicula alpina*
Distinguished by its white flowers, 1–1·6cm with one or more yellow spots in throat. Corolla-lobes unequal, upper-lip with triangular lobes, lower-lip with obovate lobes; spur short conical, 2–3mm, curved, yellowish. Leaves elliptic to oblong, pale greenish-yellow, with incurved margin in a rosette; flowering stems to 11cm. May–Jul. Bogs, wet places, in mountains. †GB, SF, F, D, N, S.

1319 Greater Bladderwort *Utricularia vulgaris*
Floating or submerged aquatic perennial with slender stems up to 1 m. Leaves 2-lobed from base, lobes ovate, pinnately divided into thread-like segments with small bladders which catch minute animals. Flowers deep yellow, 12–18mm, borne on an erect leafless stem above water. Corolla with upper-lip about as long as base of lower-lip; spur broadly conical at base, with narrow apex. Jun–Aug. Still waters. Throughout area covered, except IS.

1320 Bladderwort *Utricularia australis*
Like 1319 but lower-lip of corolla flat (margin deflexed in 1319). Flower stalks 3–5 times as long as bracts (2–3 times as long as bracts in 1319). Flowers lemon-yellow, upper-lip longer than swollen basal part of lower-lip; spur narrow conical and gradually tapering. Jul–Aug. Still waters. Throughout area covered, except IS.

1321 Intermediate Bladderwort *Utricularia intermedia*
Differs from 1319 in having two kinds of stems, some with rounded crowded leaves without bladders, and others much reduced, colourless leaves with bladders. Flowers yellow 1–1·5cm, and slender spur with a conical base. Jul–Sep. Shallow waters, pools in bogs. Throughout area covered, except IS.

1322 Lesser Bladderwort *Utricularia minor*
Like 1321 with stems of two kinds, one bearing green, much-divided leaves with few bladders, and colourless stems with bladders and much reduced leaves often buried in the mud. Flowers pale yellow with very short blunt spur. Jun–Sep. Ponds, ditches, pools in bogs. Throughout area covered.

1321

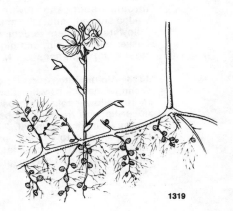

1319

PLANTAIN FAMILY

Plantaginaceae

Perennial herbs. Leaves mostly basal. Flowers small, greenish, usually in dense spikes. Sepals persistent. Petals papery. Stamens long, conspicuous. Fruit a several-seeded capsule opening by a lid, or 1-seeded and indehiscent.

PLANTAGO
LEAVES OVAL OR ELLIPTIC, LESS THAN 3 TIMES AS LONG AS BROAD

1323 Greater Plantain *Plantago major*
Perennial with rosette of ovate to elliptic stalked leaves each with 5–9 parallel veins, more or less hairless. Flowering stem as long or longer than leaves and with a long dense terminal spike of tiny greenish flowers. Sepals with narrow papery margins; corolla-tube hairless, with blunt lobes; stamens much longer. Fruits usually with less than 12 seeds. Jun–Oct. Waste places, paths, lawns. Throughout area covered; naturalized in IS. Ssp. *intermedia* has leaves with 3–5 parallel veins, shortly hairy, usually smaller. Fruits with more than 12 seeds. Cultivated and open ground. **191**

1324 Hoary Plantain *Plantago media*
Differs from **1323**, in having narrower short-stalked leaves which are greyish downy-hairy. Flowering stems much longer than leaves which are in a basal rosette. Flowering spikes with whitish flowers with much longer pinkish-lilac stamens. May–Aug. Grassland. Throughout area covered, except IS; int IRL. **251**

PLANTAGO
LEAVES LINEAR OR LANCEOLATE, ENTIRE OR 1–2-PINNATELY LOBED

1325 Sea Plantain *Plantago maritima*
Distinguished by its rosette of fleshy, lanceolate, slightly toothed, 5–7-veined leaves, stalkless or with stalks as long as blade. Flowering stems 10–40cm, twice as long as leaves, strongly grooved, hairy, bearing a short ovoid–oblong dark spike of flowers. Stamens little longer than corolla; anthers pale yellow. A very variable species. Apr–Oct. Salt-marshes, grassy places near sea, and on mountains. Throughout area covered. **202**

1326 Ribwort Plantain *Plantago lanceolata*
Distinguished by its rosette of lanceolate, slightly toothed, 5–7-veined leaves, stalkless or with stalk shorter than blade. Flowering stems 10–50cm, twice as long as leaves, strongly grooved, hairy, bearing a dense short

ovoid–oblong dark flower spike. Stamens little longer than corolla; anthers pale yellow. A very variable species. Apr–Oct. Grassy and waste places. Throughout area covered. **179**

1327 Branched Plantain *Plantago arenaria*
Distinguished by its much-branched hairy flowering stems up to 50cm, bearing terminal ovoid spikes of pale brown flowers. Downy annual with broadly linear leaves not in a rosette, but with leafy shoots at base. May–Aug. Dry places, sand-dunes. F, D; int B, NL.

1328 Buckshorn Plantain *Plantago coronopus*
Readily distinguished by its pinnately lobed leaves in a basal rosette, leaves less often linear and deeply toothed. Flowering stems numerous, shorter or longer than leaves, spreading or ascending; flowers yellow-brown, in long spikes. Sepals unequal; corolla-tube hairy; anthers yellow. A very variable species. May–Oct. Dry places, sands, especially on coast. B, GB, DK, F, D, IRL, NL, S.

1329 Shoreweed *Littorella uniflora*
Low hairless perennial with rooting runners, often forming dense grass-like mats in shallow water. Leaves in a basal tuft, cylindrical but flat on one side. Male flowers whitish, solitary, 5–6mm, on a slender stalk; stamens with very long filaments; female flowers stalkless, at base of stalks of male flowers. Jun–Aug. Shallow fresh water, pond margins. Throughout area covered.

1327

1329

HONEYSUCKLE FAMILY

Caprifoliaceae

1330

Usually shrubs or climbers. Leaves opposite. Flowers mostly 5-merous. Petals forming long tube. Fruit a berry or nutlet.

1330 Dwarf Elder *Sambucus ebulus*
Foetid perennial with stout erect stem up to 2m. Leaves pinnate with 7–9 lanceolately pointed sharply toothed leaflets. Flowers white or pinkish, in a large flat-topped inflorescence 5–16cm across. Petals 5; stamens 5, longer than petals. Fruit a black berry. Jul–Aug. Wood clearings, by rivers, waste places. B, F, D, NL; int GB, DK, IRL, S.

1331 Twinflower *Linnaea borealis*
Small slender creeping undershrub, with evergreen ovate to roundish, toothed, short-stalked leaves. Flowers white or pinkish, two drooping, on slender leafless stems to 8cm. Corolla bell-shaped, 5–9mm, with 5 broad lobes, red-striped and hairy within. Stamens 4. Jun–Aug. Coniferous woods, shady rocks, moss tundra. GB, DK, SF, F, D, NL, N, S. **252**

MOSCHATEL FAMILY

Adoxaceae

Rhizomatous perennial herbs. Flowers in terminal head, 1 terminal and 4 lateral. Fruit a small drupe. One genus, with one species only.

1332 Moschatel *Adoxa moschatellina*
Low delicate hairless perennial up to 10cm, with 3-lobed long-stalked leaves, the lobes further divided into rounded lobes. Flowers greenish, 4–6 in a compact rounded terminal head 6–8mm across. Uppermost flowers with 4-lobed corolla and 4 stamens, lateral flowers 5-lobed with 5 stamens. Berry green. Mar–May. Shady places, woods, mountains. Throughout area covered, except IS. **191**

VALERIAN FAMILY

Valerianaceae

Annual or perennial herbs. Flowers in dense, terminal clusters, small, often somewhat bilaterally symmetrical, funnel-shaped. Calyx sometimes forming feathery dispersal organ for fruit. Stamens 1–3. Fruit 1-seeded, indehiscent.

VALERIANELLA
CALYX WELL-DEVELOPED

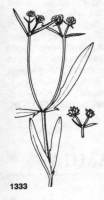

1333 Narrow-fruited Cornsalad *Valerianella dentata*
Erect branched annual up to 30cm or more, with ovate to spoon-shaped blunt lower stem-leaves; middle stem-leaves narrower, uppermost oblong and coarsely toothed or lobed at base. Flowers pale lilac, in terminal flat-topped branched inflorescence. Corolla tubular, 5-lobed; calyx with unequal teeth shorter than fruit; stamens 3. Jun–Jul. Cornfields. Throughout area covered, except SF, IS.

1334 Broad-fruited Cornsalad *Valerianella rimosa*
Like **1333** but calyx in fruit minutely toothed and c. a third as broad as the ovoid fruit (calyx half as broad as ovoid fruit in **1333**). Annual with stem rough on angles; upper leaves and bracts linear. Flower-cluster rather lax. Jun–Aug. Cornfields. B, GB, DK, F, D, IRL, NL.

1333

1335 Hairy-fruited Cornsalad *Valerianella eriocarpa*
Differs from **1334** in having flowers in very dense clusters; calyx in fruit deeply 5–6 toothed, strongly veined. Fruit with fertile cell many times larger than sterile cells. Jun–Jul. Dry banks, walls. B, GB, F, D.

VALERIANELLA
CALYX ABSENT OR REDUCED TO MINUTE TEETH OR A NARROW RIM

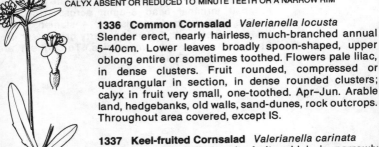

1336 Common Cornsalad *Valerianella locusta*
Slender erect, nearly hairless, much-branched annual 5–40cm. Lower leaves broadly spoon-shaped, upper oblong entire or sometimes toothed. Flowers pale lilac, in dense clusters. Fruit rounded, compressed or quadrangular in section, in dense rounded clusters; calyx in fruit very small, one-toothed. Apr–Jun. Arable land, hedgebanks, old walls, sand-dunes, rock outcrops. Throughout area covered, except IS.

1337 Keel-fruited Cornsalad *Valerianella carinata*
Like **1335**, but differing in fruit, which is narrowly oblong–ovoid, 4-winged; calyx reduced to an indistinct

tooth above the fertile part of the fruit. Apr–Jun. Arable land, banks, old walls, rock outcrops. B, GB, F, D, IRL, NL.

1338 Common Valerian *Valeriana officinalis*
Perennial with usually solitary robust stem up to 150cm. Leaves usually pinnate or pinnately lobed, with linear or elliptic leaflets or lobes. Flowers white or pink, with short tube and 5 spreading blunt lobes; stamens longer. Inflorescence branched, with numerous flowers in dense clusters. Calyx inrolled in flower, enlarging into a hairy pappus in fruit. Very variable species. Jun–Aug. Grassland, woods, scrub. Throughout area covered. **179**

1339 Marsh Valerian *Valeriana dioica*
Differs from **1338** in being smaller, up to 50cm, having lower leaves ovate entire, but upper leaves pinnately lobed, and creeping runners. Flowers pink or occasionally white, male or female in a branched inflorescence with dense rounded terminal clusters. Fruit elliptic, hairless. May–Jun. Marshes, fens, wet places. B, GB, DK, F, D, NL, N, S.

1340 Red Valerian *Centranthus ruber*
Rather blue-green, hairless perennial up to 80cm. Leaves ovate–lanceolate, the upper clasping stem, entire or with a few blunt teeth, hairless. Flowers red, pink or white, 5mm across, in a branched cluster forming an oblong inflorescence. Corolla with long slender tube with 5 blunt lobes, and a shorter slender curved spur. Stamens protruding from corolla. May–Aug. Walls, rocks, cliffs, waste places. F; nat B, GB, IRL. **265**

1339

SCABIOUS FAMILY

Dipsacaceae

Biennial or perennial herbs. Leaves opposite or whorled. Inflorescence a head of flowers surrounded by involucre of bracts. Flowers bilaterally symmetrical; petals fused in curved tube. Stamens 2 or 4, protruding. Fruit 1-seeded, indehiscent, often crowned by persistent calyx.

1341 Teasel *Dipsacus fullonum*
Robust biennial with prickly stem 0·5–2m. Basal leaves ovate to elliptic, usually undivided, toothed or entire; stem-leaves lanceolate, opposite and fused at the base. Flowers rose-purple, in an ovoid head 3–9cm long, surrounded by linear upcurved spiny involucral bracts equal to or longer than the flower-head. Jul–Aug. Grassy, often damp places. B, GB, F, D, IRL, NL; int DK.

1342 Fuller's Teasel *Dipsacus sativus*
Like **1341**, but scales of receptacle equalling the florets and with rigid spine (receptacle scales longer than florets and with straight upcurved spine in **1341**). Usually taller, with short erect prickles on angles of stem. Stem-leaves linear–lanceolate, opposite and fused at base. Involucral bracts spreading. Jul–Aug. Escape from cultivation; int GB, F, D.

1343 Small Teasel *Dipsacus pilosus*
Distinguished by its globular heads of whitish flowers, with white, narrowly triangular bristly-hairy involucral bracts, shorter than the flower head. Basal leaves in a rosette, ovate; stem-leaves narrower with a pair of unequal basal leaflets, short-stalked. Jul–Sep. Damp woods, scrub, streamsides. B, GB, DK, F, D, NL.

1343

1344 Yellow-flowered Teasel *Dipsacus strigosus*
Differs from **1343** in having pale yellow flowers in a head 2·5–4cm long (head 1·5–2cm long in **1343**). Larger biennial to 2m. Receptacle-scales 1·5–2cm (receptacle-scales 1–1·2cm in **1343**). Jul–Aug. Native of S. Russia. Int GB, DK, S.

1345 *Dipsacus laciniatus*
Distinguished by its pinnately lobed stem-leaves, with blunt spreading lobes. Flowers pale pink, in ovoid–cylindrical head, with involucral bracts curved upwards, not longer than the flower head; receptacle-scales with hairy margin. Jul–Aug. Meadows; streamsides, waste places. F, D. **180**

1346 Devilsbit Scabious *Succisa pratensis*
Erect perennial up to 80cm, with elliptic to obovate entire, usually stalked, basal leaves in a rosette. Stem-

leaves shorter, narrower. Flowers dark blue-purple, rarely white or pink, in long-stalked heads up to 2·5cm across; heads either female or bisexual. Involucral bracts lanceolate, hairy; flowers 4-lobed, receptacle scales purple-tipped. Jun–Oct. Marshes, fens, grasslands, damp woods. Throughout area covered. **280**

1347 Field Scabious *Knautia arvensis*
Perennial or biennial with flowering stems up to 1m, or more. Lower leaves oblanceolate usually entire, sometimes lobed; stem-leaves deeply lobed, with narrow lateral lobes and elliptic terminal lobe. Flowers bluish-lilac, the outer larger than the inner, in flat head 3–4cm across. Involucral bracts in two rows, shorter than the florets. Corolla 4-lobed; calyx with 8 teeth with hairy margins. A very variable species. Jul–Sep. Grasslands, dry pastures, banks, woods. Throughout area covered; int IS.

1348 Wood Scabious *Knautia dipsacifolia*
Like **1347** but leaves undivided, oblong–lanceolate, the upper toothed and with clasping base. Flowers lilac, in heads to 4cm across, on stems up to 1·5m. Jun–Sep. Wood verges, tall herb communities, in mountains. B, F, D.

1349 Small Scabious *Scabiosa columbaria*
Branched perennial, 10–60cm, with ovate to lanceolate, simple or lobed basal leaves; stem-leaves 1–2-pinnately lobed with linear to lanceolate hairy lobes. Flowers bluish-lilac, in flat-topped head to 4cm across; involucral bracts narrowly lanceolate, shorter than florets. Corolla 5-lobed. Variable species. Jul–Nov. Calcareous grassland, woods, moorlands. B, GB, DK, F, D, NL, S.

1349

1350 Yellow Scabious *Scabiosa ochroleuca*
Distinguished by its pale yellow flowers in heads 2·5cm across, with outer florets larger than inner, and involucral bracts shorter than florets. Calyx bristly-hairy, reddish-brown. Plant up to 80cm; leaves ovate–lanceolate, toothed, upper stem leaves pinnately lobed with a larger terminal lobe. Dry meadows, stony ground. D; int F. **202**

1351 *Scabiosa canescens*
Distinguished by its entire lanceolate lower stem leaves, and by its anthers which are bright purple. Flowers blue or lilac, with much larger marginal florets, in heads 2·5cm across; involucral bracts ovate–lanceolate, about half as long as florets. Upper stem-leaves pinnately lobed with linear lobes. Jul–Sep. Sunny banks, rocks, open woods, scrub. B, DK, F, D, S. **279**

BELLFLOWER FAMILY

Campanulaceae

Annual or perennial herbs, usually containing latex. Leaves alternate, simple. Flowers bell-shaped or with only a short tube, often blue. Style 1; stigmas 2–5. Fruit a capsule, with numerous seeds, dehiscing by pores or valves.

CAMPANULA
CALYX WITH 5 LOBES AND 5 ALTERNATE SHORTER TEETH

1352 Canterbury Bell *Campanula medium*
Stout erect rough hairy biennial up to 60cm. Basal leaves ovate–oblong, stalked; upper leaves lanceolate, stalkless, all toothed. Flowers blue-lilac to whitish, in a lax terminal inflorescence. Corolla bell-shaped, enlarged at base, 3–4cm long. Calyx with large downcurved teeth between lobes. May–Aug. Rocks, stony places, woods. F; int GB, D.

1353 Bearded Bellflower *Campanula barbata*
Hairy perennial with stout rhizome and erect stems 10–30cm. Basal leaves lanceolate to oblong in a rosette, rough-hairy; stem-leaves strap-shaped. Flowers pale blue, bell-shaped, conspicuously hairy within, 2–3cm, usually nodding, few in lax one-sided inflorescence. Calyx with ovate reflexed teeth between lobes. Jun–Aug. Grassland and scrub in mountains. F, D, N. **286**

CAMPANULA
CALYX 5-LOBED WITHOUT SMALLER TEETH BETWEEN LOBES; FLOWERS STALKLESS, CLUSTERED INTO A DENSE HEAD OR SPIKE

1354 Clustered Bellflower *Campanula glomerata*
Usually a hairy perennial with erect reddish stem 15–80cm. Lower leaves ovate–lanceolate, rounded toothed, and with rounded base, long-stalked; upper stem-leaves stalkless. Flowers violet, usually 2·5cm, sometimes larger, numerous in a dense head or cluster. Calyx-teeth lanceolate; corolla with lobes a third as long as tube. A very variable species. Jun–Oct. Grassland. B, GB, DK, SF, F, D, NL, S; int N. **280**

1355 *Campanula cervicaria*
Like **1354** but with smaller pale blue flowers, 1·3–1·6cm, in a dense head. Stem up to 70cm, grooved. Lower leaves gradually narrowed at base or abruptly contracted into a winged leaf-stalk. Calyx-lobes ovate blunt; style longer than corolla. Jun–Aug. Meadows, woods. B, DK, SF, F, D, N, S.

CAMPANULA

1356 Harebell *Campanula rotundifolia*
Slender hairless perennial 10–50cm, with basal leaves
heart-shaped rounded, toothed and stalked; stem leaves
lanceolate to linear, remotely toothed, uppermost entire,
stalkless. Flowers blue or violet, 1·2–2cm or more, in a lax
branched inflorescence. Calyx-teeth linear to
narrowly triangular. A very variable species. Jun–Sep.
Dry grassland, heaths, rocky ground, sand-dunes. A
variable species. Throughout area covered.

1357 *Campanula cochlearifolia*
Perennial with creeping rhizome and stems up to 20cm,
bearing 1 or few blue-violet flowers. Basal leaves
heart-shaped or rounded, toothed, stalked; stem-leaves
elliptic to lanceolate, remotely toothed. Flowers
drooping in bud; corolla 13–16mm; calyx-teeth linear to
narrowly triangular. Jun–Aug. Rocks, screes, stony
ground, mainly in mountains. F, D; int GB.

1356

1358 *Campanula rhomboidalis*
Perennial with slender rhizome, and erect angular stem
up to 40cm, bearing few blue flowers. Flower buds erect.
Basal leaves rounded, toothed, absent at flowering;
stem-leaves ovate to broadly lanceolate, bluntly toothed.
Calyx-teeth linear; corolla 1·6–2·2cm. Capsule pendant.
Jun–Aug. Mountain meadows. F; int B, D, NL.

1359 *Campanula giesekiana*
Perennial with slender creeping rhizome, and stems up
to 10cm or more. Basal leaves rounded to bluntly
heart-shaped; stem leaves linear to linear–lanceolate, all
stalked. Flowers solitary or few; corolla 12–20mm,
broadly bell-shaped; calyx-teeth linear to narrowly
triangular. Flower buds erect. Capsule pendent. Dry
grassland, stony and gravelly places. ?SF, N, ?S.

1357

1360 *Campanula baumgartenii*
Perennial with slender branched rhizome, and erect
stems up to 50cm or more, angular, hairy below, and leafy
to inflorescence. Basal leaves rounded to
kidney-shaped, rounded-toothed; stem leaves
lanceolate to narrow lanceolate finely toothed or entire.
Inflorescence branched, many-flowered. Corolla
14–18mm or more; calyx-teeth linear to bristle-like. Jul.
Scrub, woods, dry grassland. F, D.

1361 Creeping Bellflower *Campanula rapunculoides*
Erect perennial up to 1m, with rounded stem, and
spreading roots with numerous adventitious buds. Basal
leaves heart-shaped, toothed, long-stalked; uppermost

leaves lanceolate, toothed, stalkless. Distinguished by its calyx-teeth which are down-curved in flower and its nodding flowers in a branched inflorescence. Corolla bluish-violet, funnel-shaped, 2–3cm with long spreading lobes, bristly-hairy. Jun–Sep. Fields, grassy places, open woods. B, DK, SF, F, D, NL, N, S; int GB, IRL. 280

CAMPANULA
FLOWERS STALKED, SOLITARY OR IN LAX CLUSTER; BASAL AND STEM-LEAVES DIFFERING LITTLE IN SHAPE

1363

1362 Spreading Bellflower *Campanula patula*
Hairless or hairy erect perennial 30–70cm. Basal leaves ovate–oblong, short-stalked; stem-leaves narrower, stalkless. Flowers violet to pale blue, in a lax cluster, rarely solitary. Corolla 2–2·5cm, broadly bell-shaped, narrowed at base, lobed to halfway; calyx teeth narrowly lanceolate pointed, spreading. May–Jul. Meadows, woods, waysides. B, GB, SF, F, D, NL; int DK, N, S.

1363 Rampion Bellflower *Campanula rapunculus*
Erect perennial to 1m, with turnip-shaped root. Leaves obovate to lanceolate, the upper narrower. Flowers white or pale blue, narrowly funnel-shaped, 1–2cm, few in a narrow branched cluster. Corolla little longer than long bristle-like calyx-teeth. May–Sep. Meadows, waste places, woodland edges. B, F, D, NL; int GB, DK, S.

1364 Peach-leaved Bellflower *Campanula persicifolia*
Hairless perennial with erect unbranched stem up to 70cm. Leaves lanceolate to obovate, rounded–toothed, stalked; stem leaves narrower, stalkless. Flowers blue-violet, broadly bell-shaped, with broad triangular lobes, 3–4cm, stalked, terminal and axillary. Calyx-teeth half as long as corolla. May–Aug. Woods, scrub. B, DK, SF, F, D, NL, N, S; int GB. **280**

1365 Giant Bellflower *Campanula latifolia*
Stout erect, softly or sparsely hairy perennial, 50–120cm, with blunt-angled stem. Leaves ovate pointed, irregularly double-toothed, lower stalked, upper stalkless. Flowers blue, purple or white, 4–5·5cm, with lobes slightly shorter than corolla-tube, hairy within, in a terminal leafy spike. Calyx with short 5-ribbed tube and erect teeth to 2·5cm long. Jul–Aug. Woods, hedgebanks. GB, DK, SF, F, D, N, S; int B, NL. **280**

1366 Nettle-leaved Bellflower *Campanula trachelium*
Differs from **1364** in having stem sharply angled with reddish bristly hairs, and basal leaves broadly ovate. Flowers bluish-violet or pale blue, 3–5cm, hairy within, in a leafy, shortly branched cluster. Calyx-tube bristly-hairy. Simple or branched perennial up to 1m. Jul–Sep. Woods, hedgebanks. Throughout area covered, except IS. **280**

1367

1367 *Campanula uniflora*
Readily distinguished by its solitary nodding flowers, borne on erect hairless unbranched stems up to 15cm. Lower leaves oblanceolate blunt, hairless, middle leaves lanceolate, upper leaves narrower. Flowers blue, funnel-shaped, up to 9mm; calyx-teeth pointed, erect. Capsule club-shaped, dark blue becoming blackish. Jul–Aug. Stony places, arctic heaths. SF, IS, N, S.

1368 **Venus's Looking Glass** *Legousia hybrida*
Bristly hairy annual up to 35cm, with oblong to narrow–obovate leaves with strongly undulate margin, the lower stalked, upper stalkless. Flowers purplish to lilac, in small terminal clusters. Corolla 8–15mm, half as long as narrow calyx-lobes. Capsule cylindrical, up to 3cm, with erect lobes. May–Aug. Arable fields, cultivated ground. B, GB, F, D, NL. **280**

1369 **Large Venus's Looking Glass**
Legousia speculum-veneris
Like **1368**, but flowers violet, as long or longer than calyx-lobes, which are spreading or recurved in fruit. Flowers c. 2cm across, numerous in a large branched cluster. Capsule to 1·5cm. May–Jul. Cornfields, waste ground. B, F, D, NL. **280**

1370 **Spiked Rampion** *Phyteuma spicatum*
Hairless perennial with simple erect leafy stem 30–80cm. Basal and lower stem-leaves ovate with heart-shaped base, toothed, long-stalked; upper leaves lanceolate to linear, stalkless. Flowers yellowish-white, in a terminal cylindrical spike up to 8cm. Corolla c. 1cm, cylindrical, curved in bud, with narrow lobes in full flower. Stigmas 2. May–Sep. Woods, thickets, mountain meadows. B, GB, DK, F, D, NL, N; int SF, S. **286**

1371 *Phyteuma nigrum*
Differs from **1370** in having middle and upper leaves, with much reduced blade, and lower stem-leaves narrowed to base. Flowers bluish-violet, rarely blue or white, in an ovoid, then cylindrical spike. Stigmas usually 3. Hairless perennial up to 60cm, with upper third of stem more or less leafless. May–Jul. Damp mountain meadows, open woods. B, F, D.

1372 **Round-headed Rampion** *Phyteuma orbiculare*
Flowers blue to blue-violet, rarely white, in a globular inflorescence c. 1–2·5cm across. Erect perennial 10–50cm, with basal leaves linear–lanceolate to elliptic, toothed, stalked, the upper leaves nearly stalkless, toothed or entire. Corolla strongly curved in bud, 1–1·5cm, with narrow spreading or reflexed lobes in flower; styles 3. A variable species. May–Jul. Calcareous grasslands, mountain pastures. B, GB, F, D. **286**

BELLFLOWER
FAMILY

1373

1374

1377

1373 Ivy-leaved Bellflower *Wahlenbergia hederacea*
Slender creeping perennial up to 30cm. Leaves
kidney-shaped/rounded, angled or obscurely lobed,
stalked, more or less opposite. Flowers pale blue,
bell-shaped to 1cm, nodding and solitary, on long
slender stalks from axils of upper leaves. Lobes of corolla
ovate pointed, equalling or shorter than corolla-tube;
calyx-lobes awl-shaped. Jul–Aug. Damp places, moors,
heaths, by streams. B, GB, F, D, IRL.

1374 Sheepsbit *Jasione montana*
Hairy annual or biennial, with erect or ascending stems
5–50cm, branched from the base, and without stolons.
Leaves broadly linear to lanceolate, with undulate
margin, entire or toothed. Flowers blue, rarely white, in a
globular head surrounded by ovate to triangular
involucral bracts usually shorter than the flowers.
Corolla c. 5mm, with 5 narrow lobes. A very variable
species. Jun–Aug. Grassy places, heaths, cliffs, banks.
Throughout area covered, except IS.

1375 Perennial Sheepsbit *Jasione laevis*
Distinguished from **1374** in having creeping stolons
terminating in rosettes of leaves (stolons absent in **1374**).
Flower heads blue, globular, surrounded by deeply
toothed involucral bracts. Perennial with leaves not
undulate, nearly entire. Jul–Sep. Grassland, open woods,
waysides, rocks. B, F, D; int SF.

1376 Water Lobelia *Lobelia dortmanna*
Submerged aquatic plant with basal rosette of oblong
blunt cylindrical leaves, and erect almost leafless stems
up to 60cm, bearing above water a few-flowered
spike-like cluster of pale lilac drooping flowers. Corolla
up to 2cm, pale blue, with 2 narrow short curved upper
lobes and 3 longer broader lower lobes; corolla-tube as
long as lobes. Calyx-teeth oblong blunt. Jul–Aug. Still
acid waters. Throughout area covered, except IS. **181**

1377 Heath Lobelia *Lobelia urens*
Nearly hairless terrestrial perennial with leafy stem up to
60cm. Leaves narrowly lanceolate to broadly oblong,
remotely toothed, stalkless. Flowers blue or purple,
stalkless, in a many-flowered terminal, often branched
cluster. Corolla tubular, 1–1·5cm, 2-lipped, upper lip
2-lobed, the lower 3-lobed. Aug–Sep. Damp grassy
places, woods. B, GB, F.

DAISY FAMILY

Compositae

Annual, biennial or perennial herbs and shrubs, often containing latex. Flowers (florets) small, 5-merous, aggregated into a head surrounded by an involucre of bracts. Florets may be all regular (tubular or disc-florets); all with one strap-shaped longer petal (ligulate or ray-florets); or a mixture of both types, the disc-florets in the centre of the head. Stamens 5, united in a tube. Stigma 1, bifid. Fruit an achene, crowned by persistent calyx (pappus), which acts as a wind-dispersal mechanism. The largest family of flowering plants, often colonizing open ground.

1378 Hemp Agrimony *Eupatorium cannabinum*
Erect densely leafy perennial 50–180cm, with reddish stems. Leaves palmately 3- to 5-lobed, the lobes elliptic and coarsely toothed. Flower heads pink, oblong, 2–5mm across, many clustered into a dense flat-topped inflorescence. Tubular florets only present. Fruit black; pappus hairs numerous. Jul–Sep. Marshes, fens, moist woods. Throughout area covered, except IS. **252**

1379 Goldenrod *Solidago virgaurea*
Erect perennial 15–100cm. Leaves ovate to lanceolate, usually toothed, stalked, the upper stem-leaves narrower, entire, stalkless, hairless above and usually hairy beneath. Flower heads bright yellow 7–8mm long, in branched clusters. Ray-florets 6–12, 4–9mm long; involucre greenish. A very variable species. Jun–Oct. Woods, heaths, grassy and rocky places. Throughout area, except IS. **221**

1380

1380 Canadian Goldenrod *Solidago canadensis*
Tall downy perennial up to 150cm or more, with numerous lanceolate sharply toothed 3-veined leaves. Flower heads yellow, with 10–17 short ray-florets, in a broad pyramidal inflorescence with spreading branches. Aug–Oct. Waste places; cultivated in gardens. Native of N. America. Int B, GB, DK, F, D, IRL, NL, N.

1381 *Solidago gigantea*
Like **1380** but stems hairless, often blue-green; involucre of flower heads 3·2–5mm long (involucre 2–2·8mm long in **1380**); ray-florets longer than involucre. Stem to 2·5m; leaves hairless. Aug–Oct. Cultivated and sometimes naturalized. Native of N. America. Int B, GB, DK, F, D, IRL, NL, S.

1382 *Solidago graminifolia*
Distinguished by its linear–lanceolate 3- to 5-veined entire leaves, hairless except on the veins beneath.

Flower heads golden-yellow, with ray-florets not longer than disk-florets, in a flat-topped inflorescence. Jul–Oct. Cultivated, and sometimes naturalized. Native of N. America. Int GB, F, D.

1383 Daisy *Bellis perennis*
Hairy perennial with basal rosette of leaves and erect leafless stems bearing a terminal flower head 1–3cm across. Leaves spoon-shaped, bluntly toothed. Ray-florets white, strap-shaped, 4–8mm long, often reddish-purple beneath, disk-florets yellow; involucral bracts oblong. Very variable species. Feb–Dec. Pastures, roadsides, grassy places, sand-dunes. Throughout area covered; int SF, IS. **181**

1384 Sea Aster *Aster tripolium*
Hairless maritime annual to perennial 20–80cm, with many blue or lilac flower heads in a branched cluster. Leaves fleshy, oblong–lanceolate, usually entire. Flower heads 1–3cm across, with 10–30 strap-shaped ray-florets, or ray-florets often absent; disk-florets yellow. Jul–Oct. Saline meadows, salt-marshes, sea-cliffs. Throughout area covered, except IS. **281**

1385 Michaelmas Daisy *Aster novi-belgii*
Erect nearly hairless perennial up to 120cm, with broad to narrowly lanceolate remotely toothed leaves with lobed bases. Flower heads with blue-violet ray-florets and yellow disk-florets, in often branched clusters. Involucral bracts in several rows, the outer green, as long as inner, lax with recurved apex. Aug–Nov. Waste places, streamsides. Native of N. America. Int B, GB, DK, F, D, IRL, NL, N, S.

1385

1386 Hairy Michaelmas Daisy *Aster novae-angliae*
Distinguished fron **1385** by its stem which is glandular-hairy above, and its flower heads with usually reddish ray-florets, in a branched flat-topped cluster. Involuctral bracts glandular-hairy, the inner bristle-like, the outer lax or recurved. Perennial up to 2m. Sep–Nov. Waste ground, river-banks. Native of N. America. Int B, GB, F, D, NL.

1387 *Aster × salignus*
Distinguished from **1385** by leaves not or scarcely lobed at base, and outer involucral bracts tapering almost from base, and not so lax or so leafy. Ray-florets at first white, then light blue-violet. Aug–Nov. River-banks, railway embankments, waste places. Garden origin; int B, GB, DK, SF, F, D, NL, N, S.

1386

1388 Alpine Aster *Aster alpinus*
Erect or ascending perennial up to 20cm or more, with spoon-shaped to nearly elliptic leaves, the basal and lower stem-leaves narrowed to a wide leaf-stalk. Flower

heads usually solitary, 3–5cm across; ray-florets 20–40, blue-violet, rarely pink or white, sometimes absent; disk-florets yellow. Involucral bracts in 2 indistinct rows, hairy, or hairless with hairy or fringed margin. Jul–Aug. Mountain meadows, stony grassland, rocks. F, D. **252**

1389 Goldilocks *Aster linosyris*
Distinguished by absence of ray-florets, and its golden-yellow disk-florets in numerous small flower heads in a dense flat-topped inflorescence. Perennial with slender very leafy stems up to 70cm. Leaves linear, stalkless, rough-margined. Flower heads 8–10mm across; involucral bracts in several rows, the outer rows with curved apices, the inner with papery margin. Aug–Sep. Dry sandy grassland, wood verges, cliffs. B, GB, F, D, S; int NL.

1389

ERIGERON
RAY-FLORETS ERECT, LITTLE LONGER THAN DISK-FLORETS

1390 Blue Fleabane *Erigeron acer*
Usually annual or biennial, with grey-hairy stems up to 60cm or more. Leaves lanceolate, the lower stalked, usually entire. Flower heads with pale violet ray-florets little longer than the yellowish tubular disk-florets; heads 6–13mm across in flat-topped or elongated inflorescence. Involucral bracts linear, with brown centre and papery margin. A very variable species. Jun–Sep. Dry and stony places, sand-dunes, walls. Throughout area covered, except IS. **252**

ERIGERON
RAY-FLORETS SPREADING, MUCH LONGER THAN DISK-FLORETS; FLOWER HEAD SOLITARY OR SEVERAL

1391 *Erigeron uniflorus*
Low perennial up to 15cm, with solitary flower head 1–1·5cm across, with white or pale lilac ray-florets and yellow disk-florets. Involucral bracts white-woolly and lilac-tipped. Basal leaves spoon-shaped, narrowed to leaf-stalk; stem leaves few. Jul–Sep. Snow patches, stony slopes, alpine pastures. SF, F, D, IS, N, S.

1392 Alpine Fleabane *Erigeron borealis*
Flower heads usually solitary, rarely 2–3, c. 1·8cm across. Ray-florets purple, many, spreading, much longer than disk-florets; involucral bracts usually densely hairy. Flowering stem up to 20cm; leaves mostly basal in a rosette, narrow oblanceolate with a long winged leaf-stalk; stem-leaves narrower, stalkless leaves very hairy. Jul–Aug. Rock ledges, meadows, stony ground. GB, SF, IS, N, S.

1392

1393 *Erigeron humilis*
Differs from **1392** by the involucral bracts with purple hairs (hairs long, white in **1392**), and flowering stems scarcely longer than the basal rosette of leaves. Flower heads solitary, with white or purplish ray-florets. Basal leaves spoon-shaped, narrowly stalked stem leaves 1–4. Jul–Aug. Tundra, damp stony hillsides. SF, IS, N, S.

ERIGERON
RAY FLORETS SPREADING, MUCH LONGER THAN DISK FLORETS; FLOWER HEADS AT LEAST 6

1394 *Erigeron annuus*
Annual or perennial with erect leafy stems up to 80cm. Basal leaves ovate, stalked, lower stem-leaves ovate–lanceolate, entire or toothed, upper leaves narrower. Flower heads white or pale blue, with ray-florets 6–8mm, in flat-topped cluster. Variable species. Jun–Oct. Waste places. Native of N. America. Int B, DK, F, D.

1395 Mexican Fleabane
Erigeron karvinskianus (=*E. mucronatus*)
Differs from **1394** in having spreading or ascending stems, with lower leaves usually 3-lobed. Flower heads with white or lilac ray-florets which are purple beneath, in a lax leafy flat-topped cluster. Jun–Aug. Naturalized locally on rocks and walls. Native of Mexico. Int GB, F.

1395

1396 Canadian Fleabane *Conyza canadensis*
Erect annual 20–150cm, with lanceolate, finely toothed or entire, hairy leaves, the upper leaves linear, stalkless. Flower heads whitish, with ray-florets scarcely longer than disk-florets, numerous, 3–5mm across, in a long branched inflorescence. Involucral bracts linear, hairless, with broad papery margin. Aug–Oct. Waste places, cultivated ground, sand-dunes. Native of N. America. Int throughout area covered, except IS.

1397 Common Cudweed *Filago vulgaris*
Greyish-white annual up to 35cm, regularly branched above the middle. Leaves narrowly lanceolate; margin undulate with white hairs. Flower heads cylindrical, 5mm long, 10–30 in dense globular clusters not overtopped by subtending leaves. Involucral bracts lanceolate with awn-like points, yellowish usually tinged red. Florets yellow, all tubular. Aug–Sep. Dry open places, fields, grassland, sand-dunes. Throughout area covered, except SF, IRL, IS, N. **230**

1398 Red-tipped Cudweed *Filago lutescens*
Distinguished from **1397** by its clusters of flower heads overtopped by one or more subtending leaves. Stem to 25cm; leaves oblong–lanceolate to spoon-shaped, with yellowish hairs. Flower heads weakly 4-angled;

1399

1402

involucral bracts reddish-purple before flowering. Jun–Sep. Sandy fields, riversides, open woods. B, GB, DK, F, D, S.

1399 Broad-leaved Cudweed *Filago pyramidata*
Greyish-white annual; stem up to 30cm or more, with linear–oblong to spoon-shaped leaves. Distinguished from **1398** by its involucral bracts 4–6 in each vertical row, keeled and straw-like, softly hairy, with recurved apices. Flower heads pyramidal, sharply 5-angled, in a cluster of 5–20. Variable species. Jul–Sep. B, GB, F, D, NL.

1400 *Logfia arvensis*
Erect white-woolly annual up to 40cm, with short lateral branches above, and lanceolate leaves. Flower heads 4–5mm, 2–7 in small clusters in a branched inflorescence topped by uppermost leaves. Involucral bracts linear, with woolly hairs, spreading in a star in fruit. Jul–Sep. Fields, sand. B, DK, SF, F, D, NL, N, S; int GB.

1401 Small Cudweed *Logfia minima*
Differs from **1400** in having forked branches with flower clusters both terminal and in axils of branches, and clusters longer than the subtending leaves. Greyish annual up to 15cm, or more, with flat oblong to linear leaves 4–10mm. Jun–Aug. Fields, open woods, sand-dunes. Throughout area covered, except SF, IS.

1402 Narrow-leaved Cudweed *Logfia gallica*
Like **1401** but leaves linear pointed, 1·5–2·5cm, often with incurved margin. Clusters of flower heads much shorter than subtending leaves. Middle involucral bracts strongly pouched at base. Variable species. Jul–Sep. Sandy and clay soils, uncultivated ground. B, GB, F, D.

1403 *Logfia neglecta*
Distinguished by its broadly cylindrical flower heads, with brownish involucral bracts, all similar. Stem up to 15cm, usually branched from the base, leaves linear-lanceolate. Flower heads in clusters of 2–6, terminal and overtopped by subtending leaves or in angles of branches. Involucral bracts more or less equal, linear–lanceolate blunt. Jul–Oct. Fields. B, F.

1404 Heath Cudweed *Omalotheca sylvatica*
Greyish woolly-hairy perennial, densely leafy above, up to 50cm or more, with non-flowering rosettes. Leaves lanceolate to linear, 1-veined, woolly-haired beneath, nearly hairless above, decreasing in size up stem. Flower heads c. 6mm, solitary or in small clusters in axils of upper leaves, in a long interrupted leafy spike. Florets pale brown; involucral bracts with broad papery margin and central green stripe. Jul–Sep. Heaths, acid grassland, wood clearings. Throughout area covered.

1405 Highland Cudweed *Omalotheca norvegica*
Like **1404** but leaves lanceolate, 3-veined. Flowers in a short compact spike about one quarter the length of the stem (spike about half length of stem in **1404**); involucral bracts dark brown. Jul–Aug. Woods, heaths, acid grasslands. GB, SF, F, D, IS, N, S. **203**

1406 Dwarf Cudweed *Omalotheca supina*
Differs from **1405** in having an inflorescence with up to 10 flower heads (flower heads 10–150 in **1404**, **1405**). Spreading, densely tufted perennial with numerous non-flowering shoots. Leaves linear–lanceolate, 1-veined, greyish-woolly. Flower heads broadly bell-shaped, 7–8mm wide, short-stalked; involucral bracts in 2 rows, soon spreading in a star. Jul. Snow-patches, wet places in mountains. GB, SF, F, D, IS, N, S.

1406

1407 Marsh Cudweed *Filaginella uliginosa*
Annual, with flower heads in dense clusters overtopped by uppermost leaves. Stem up to 20cm, branched from near base, densely woolly-hairy. Leaves narrowly oblong to spoon-shaped, woolly-hairy. Flower heads 3–4mm, 3–10 in dense rounded clusters. Florets yellowish; involucral bracts oblong to linear, papery, pale brown, woolly below and darker and hairless towards apex. Very variable species. Jul–Aug. Damp places, fields, waysides, heaths. Throughout area covered.

1408 Jersey Cudweed *Gnaphalium luteo-album*
White woolly-haired annual, branched from the base, up to 40cm. Stem-leaves oblong to linear, white-hairy above and below. Flower heads 4–12, in small dense globular clusters, not overtopped by uppermost leaves. Florets c. 3mm, yellowish, reddish above. Jun–Sep. Damp, usually sandy, places. B, GB, DK, F, D, NL, S.

1409 Cape Cudweed *Gnaphalium undulatum*
Differs from **1408** in having leaves green and rough above and white-woolly beneath. Robust annual up to 80cm, with erect branched stem; leaves oblong–lanceolate with blade running down stem. Flower heads white to yellow, in large lax flat-topped clusters; involucral bracts white. Jun–Sep. Roadsides, waste places. Native of S. Africa. Int F.

1408

1410 Everlasting *Helichrysum arenarium*
Perennial with greyish-white erect or ascending stems up to 30cm or more. Leaves white-woolly, the uppermost stem leaves linear, the lower obovate–oblong, 1-veined, stalked; non-flowering shoots with spoon-shaped leaves. Flower heads 6–7mm across, many in dense terminal cluster 2–5cm across without ray-florets; disk-florets yellow. Involucral bracts shining yellow or orange. Jun–Aug. Dry grassland, sand-dunes, pinewoods. B, DK, F, D, NL, S.

1411 Mountain Everlasting *Antennaria dioica*
Mat-forming woolly-hairy perennial with rooting runners and numerous rosettes of leaves. Flowering stems erect leafy, 5–20cm, bearing a dense terminal cluster of whitish or pinkish flower heads. Basal leaves spoon-shaped, woolly-hairy below, hairless or nearly so on upper surface; upper stem leaves short, green, with a fine point. Flower heads usually 2–8 and stalkless. Involucral bracts in several rows, with upper part whitish or pink and petal-like in male flowers, narrow pinkish in female flowers. May–Jul. Heaths, dry grassland, sandy and stony places. Throughout area covered, except IS. **181**

1412 *Antennaria alpina*
Differs from **1411** in having upper half of involucral bracts lanceolate, dark greenish-brown, not petal-like. Stems up to 15cm; leaves woolly beneath; upper stem leaves with papery apex. Flower heads 3–5 in cluster. Jul. Mountain rocks, heaths. SF, N, S. **182**

1413 *Antennaria porsildii*
Differs from **1412** in having basal leaves nearly hairless, not woolly-hairy beneath. Perennial with flowering stems not more than 10cm; stems and stem-leaves somewhat woolly-hairy. Jul. Damp mountain heaths. SF, N, S.

1414 Pearly Everlasting *Anaphalis margaritacea*
Woolly-hairy perennial up to 1m, with linear to lanceolate pointed leaves with inrolled margins. Flower heads yellowish, 9–12mm across, numerous in crowded terminal flat-topped clusters; male florets tubular, female florets thread-like. Involucral bracts oblong blunt, pearly-white. Aug. Waste places, damp woods, river banks. Native of N. America, N-E. Asia. Int GB, DK, F, D, NL, N, S.

1414

INULA
RAY-FLORETS WITH STRAP-SHAPED LOBE NOT MORE THAN 12MM

1415 Ploughman's Spikenard *Inula conyza*
Erect hairy perennial 30–120cm. Lower leaves elliptic to oblong–lanceolate, finely toothed, hairy, the upper stalkless with wedge-shaped base. Flower heads yellowish, c. 1cm across, numerous in a terminal flat-topped cluster. Marginal florets with a short strap-shaped lobe, or tubular, shorter than the inner papery, often purple, involucral bracts. Involucral bracts triangular with recurved apex, inner linear. Jul–Sep. Dry calcareous slopes, cliffs, open woods. B, GB, DK, F, D, NL. **230**

1416 German Fleabane *Inula germanica*
Distinguished from **1415** by its upper leaves which clasp

the stem. Flower heads yellow, 7–11mm across, with strap-shaped marginal florets 8–11mm. Outer involucral bracts with recurved apex, inner linear. Jul–Aug. D.

INULA
RAY-FLORETS WITH STRAP-SHAPED LOBE MORE THAN 1·5CM

1417 Elecampane *Inula helenium*
Stout erect hairy perennial up to 1·5m, with large elliptic, toothed, stalked lower leaves; stem-leaves ovate, heart-shaped at base, clasping stem. Flower heads large, 6–8cm across, solitary or 1–3, with numerous slender yellow ray-florets 3–4cm long. Involucral bracts broadly ovate, leaf-like, softly hairy, the inner bracts oblong, papery. Jul–Aug. Fields, waysides, waste places. Native of W. & C. Asia. Introduced throughout area covered, except IS. **221**

1418 Irish Fleabane *Inula salicina*
Erect hairless or sparsely hairy perennial up to 75cm, with leaves prominently net-veined. Lower leaves linear–lanceolate to ovate, the upper stalkless with heart-shaped base clasping stem. Flower heads golden-yellow, 2·5–3cm across, usually solitary. Ray–florets with lobe 1·5–2·5cm; outer involucral bracts lanceolate with spreading apex, the inner linear. Jul–Sep. Damp grassy places, fens. B, DK, SF, F, D, IRL, NL, N, S. **231**

1419 *Inula britannica*
Distinguished from **1418** by its narrowly lanceolate leaves, softly-hairy below, and outer involucral bracts linear, hairy. Stem up to 75cm; lower leaves elliptic–ovate, stalked, upper stalkless and slightly clasping stem. Flower heads golden-yellow, 2–4cm across, usually solitary. Ray-florets with lobe 1·5–2·5cm. Outer involucral bracts longer than inner. Jul–Sep. Meadows, woods. B, DK, F, D, NL, N, S; int SF. **221**

1420 Golden Samphire *Inula crithmoides*
Small hairless shrub with fleshy stems, branched above, up to 1m. Leaves fleshy, linear to oblanceolate mostly entire, those of main stem 3-toothed at apex. Flower heads golden-yellow, c. 2–5cm across, few in a branched flat-topped cluster. Ray-florets numerous spreading, 1·4–2·5cm; involucral bracts linear–lanceolate, hairless, not spreading. Jul–Oct. Salt-marshes, shingle beaches, coastal cliffs. GB, F, IRL.

1420

1421 *Inula ensifolia*
Linear–lanceolate entire leaves with 3 to 7 prominent parallel veins. Flower heads yellow, with lobes of ray-florets 1·5–2·2cm. Involucral bracts silvery hairy at base. Jun–Aug. Native of E. & E-C. Europe. int S. **221**

1422

1424

1422 Hairy Fleabane *Inula hirta*
Distinguished by the lower surface of leaves and involucral bracts which are densely hairy. Erect perennial up to 50cm, with leaves prominently net-veined on both surfaces, hairy, the upper stalkless. Lobes of ray-florets 1·5–3cm; outer involucral bracts linear to lanceolate, about as long as inner. May–Aug. Wood clearings and margins, dry hills. F, D.

1423 Common Fleabane *Pulicaria dysenterica*
Perennial with stolons, and sparsely hairy erect stems up to 60cm, branched above. Basal leaves oblong, middle and upper stem-leaves oblong to lanceolate with heart-shaped clasping base, remotely toothed, grey-woolly beneath. Flower heads golden-yellow, 1·5–3cm across, numerous in a lax flat-topped inflorescence. Ray-florets numerous, linear, twice as long as linear glandular-hairy involucral bracts. Jul–Sep. Marshes, wet meadows, ditches. Throughout area covered, except SF, IS, N. **222**

1424 Small Fleabane *Pulicaria vulgaris*
Differs from **1423** in having stem-leaves without heart-shaped base. Flower heads c. 1cm across; ray-florets pale yellow, erect, little longer than disk-florets. Annual up to 30cm, with upper stem-leaves stalkless with rounded base. Aug–Sep. Damp fields, river-banks, ditches. B, GB, F, D, NL, S.

BIDENS
LOWER LEAVES SIMPLE OR LOBED

1425 Nodding Bur-marigold *Bidens cernua*
Hairless or somewhat hairy annual up to 90cm, with narrowly lanceolate, coarsely toothed, stalkless leaves. Flower heads yellow, solitary, 1·5–2·5cm across, nodding. Ray-florets with lobe often present, disk-florets many. Outer involucral bracts 5–8, leaf-like, the inner much shorter, ovate and papery with dark lines. Fruit 4-angled, with 4 barbed bristles. Jul–Oct. Damp places, ponds, streamsides. Throughout area covered, except IS. **230**

1426 Trifid Bur-marigold *Bidens tripartita*
Hairy or hairless branched annual up to 60cm or more, with leaves usually 3-lobed, the lobes ovate–lanceolate with short winged leaf-stalk. Flower heads 1–2·5cm across, with 5–8 leaf-like yellow-brown outer involucral bracts, inner bracts ovate, brownish. Fruit wedge-shaped, with deflexed marginal hairs, and 3–4 barbed bristles. Jul–Sep. Damp places, ditches, ponds and lake margins, waste places. Throughout area covered, except IS. **222**

417

1427 *Bidens connata*
Like **1426** but leaves usually unlobed, and lower leaves
sometimes with 1–2 pairs of decurrent lobes. Fruit with
4–5 bristles, the central fruits strongly 4-angled. Jul–Oct.
Margins of canals. Native of N. America. Int B, F, NL.

1428 *Bidens radiata*
Like **1426**, but outer involucral bracts 10–12 (5–8 in **1426**).
Fruit 3–4mm long, with 2 bristles. Aug–Oct. Damp places.
DK, SF, F, D, S.

BIDENS
LOWER LEAVES PINNATE WITH STALKED LEAFLETS

1429 Beggarticks *Bidens frondosa*
Leaves pinnate with 1–2 pairs of lanceolate toothed
stalked leaflets, the upper 3-lobed. Flower heads
orange-yellow, solitary, long-stalked, erect, 1·5–2cm
across. Ray-florets usually absent. Fruit blackish, with 2
barbed bristles. Jun–Oct. Wet places, waste ground.
Native of America. Int B, GB, F, D, NL.

1430 Cone Flower *Rudbeckia laciniata*
Tall hairy perennial 1–3m, with lower leaves twice
pinnately lobed; middle leaves deeply 2- to 3-lobed,
upper ovate and stalkless, all entire or toothed. Flower
heads yellow, 7–12cm across, with cone-like centre
bearing the yellow-green disk-florets. Ray-florets with
lobes 3–6cm, soon down-turned. Jun–Oct. Damp woods,
waste places, river-banks. Native of N. America. Int B, F,
D, NL.

1431 Jerusalem Artichoke *Helianthus tuberosus*
Tall perennial 2–3m, usually branched above, with
tuberous rhizomes, forming clumps. Leaves ovate
pointed, coarsely toothed, rough above and white
hairy beneath, leaf-stalk winged. Flower heads yellow
4–8cm across; ray-florets with lobe 3–4cm; involucral
bracts lanceolate long-pointed, spreading. Sep–Nov.
Cultivated and waste ground. N. America. Int GB, D, NL.

1432 Gallant Soldiers *Galinsoga parviflora*
Annual with branched hairless stems 10–50cm, with
ovate acute, short-stalked, toothed leaves. Flower heads
more or less globular, 3–5mm, with usually 5 short white
ray-florets, and few yellow tubular disk-florets. Involucral
bracts broadly ovate; receptacle scales 3-lobed.
Jun–Oct. Cultivated ground, waste places. S. America.
Int B, GB, DK, SF, F, D, NL, N, S; casual in IRL.

1433 Shaggy Soldiers *Galinsoga ciliata*
Differs from **1432** in having white-hairy stem, and flower
stalks with long spreading glandular hairs. Receptacle

1434

scales entire. Jun–Oct. Cultivated ground, waste places. Native from Mexico to Chile. Int B, GB, DK, SF, F, D, NL, N, S; casual in IRL.

1434 Corn Chamomile *Anthemis arvensis*
Aromatic, hairy branched annual up to 80cm, with 2- to 3-pinnately lobed leaves with pointed lobes. Flower heads with white ray-florets and yellow disk-florets, 2–3cm across. Receptacle conical, with receptacle scales fine-pointed and 10-ribbed. Involucral bracts oblong blunt with papery margin, hairy. May–Oct. Cultivated ground, waste places. Throughout area covered.

1435 Stinking Chamomile *Anthemis cotula*
Like **1434** but an almost hairless, foetid annual up to 60cm. Leaves 1–3-pinnate, with linear pointed more or less hairless segments. Flower heads with white ray-florets and yellow disk-florets, 1·2–2·5cm across; involucre hemispherical with oblong bracts, pale brown with papery margins. Jul–Sep. Arable fields, waste places. Throughout area covered, except IS; int SF. **181**

1436 Yellow Chamomile *Anthemis tinctoria*
Distinguished by its solitary long-stalked yellow flower heads. Grey woolly-haired biennial or perennial, branched above, up to 60cm. Leaves 2-pinnate, downy beneath, segments comb-like. Flower heads 2·5–4cm across, with ray-florets with lobe 8–15mm; disk-florets tubular. Outer involucral bracts triangular pointed, inner oblong, brown. Variable species. Jul–Aug. Waste places, dry grassland. B, DK, F, D, NL, N, S; int GB, SF. **222**

1437 Yarrow *Achillea millefolium*
Erect aromatic perennial 10–100cm, with leaves linear in outline, 2–3 times pinnately-cut with linear segments, basal leaves long-stalked, upper stalkless. Flower heads 3–6mm across, many in a flat-topped inflorescence. Ray–florets usually 5, white or pink with lobes 1–2mm, disk-florets white or cream. Involucral bracts oblong with brown or blackish margin. A very variable species. Jun–Nov. Meadows, dry grassland, marshes, sand-dunes. Throughout area covered. **181**

1438 Sneezewort *Achillea ptarmica*
Differs from **1437** in its entire broadly linear toothed leaves and larger flower heads 1·2–1·8cm across, few, in a lax flat-topped cluster. Ray-florets white, lobes 4–6mm long; involucral bracts hairy, with papery margins. Jul–Sep. Wet meadows, ditches, marshes. Throughout area covered; int IS. **182**

1439 Chamomile *Chamaemelum nobile*
Aromatic, hairy spreading perennial up to 30cm. Leaves oblong in outline, 2–3 times pinnately lobed, with linear

419

pointed segments. Flower heads 1·8–2·5cm across with white spreading ray-florets and yellow disk-florets, long-stalked. Involucral bracts oblong, papery, shiny, white-margined, sparsely hairy. Jun–Sep. Damp grassland, roadsides. GB, F, IRL; int B, D. **182**

1440 Sea Mayweed *Matricaria maritima*
Biennial or perennial with spreading to erect stems, branched above, to 80cm. Leaves 2–3-times pinnately lobed, segments short, fleshy. Flower heads 3–5cm across, with white ray-florets to 2cm, and yellow disk-florets. Involucral bracts oblong, with brown papery margins. Variable species. Jun–Oct. Waste places, seashores, sand-dunes, coastal shingle. Throughout area covered. **182**

1441 Scentless Mayweed *Matricaria perforata*
Annual with erect or ascending branched stems up to 80cm. Leaves 2–3-pinnate, with slender, not fleshy segments. Flower heads 3–4·5cm across, with white ray-florets 1–1·8cm, and with yellow disk-florets. Fruit with well separated ribs (ribs touching or slightly separated in **1440**). Apr–Oct. Disturbed ground, cultivated fields, waste places. Throughout area covered, except IS.

1441

1442 Scented Mayweed *Chamomilla recutita*
Aromatic annual with erect or ascending hairless stems, much branched above, up to 60cm. Leaves irregularly 2- to 3-pinnately lobed with linear bristle-pointed segments. Flower heads with white ray-florets, soon down-turned and a globular cluster of yellow disk-florets. Involucral bracts with pale-edged margins. Jun–Jul. Waste places, fields. Throughout area covered, except IRL, IS.

1443 Pineappleweed *Chamomilla suaveolens*
Strongly aromatic annual 5–45cm, rather fleshy, branched above with rigid branches. Distinguished by its globular greenish-yellow flower heads 5–9mm across, enlarging as they mature. Ray-florets absent, disk-florets 4-lobed; involucral bracts with colourless margin. Leaves 2–3-times divided into numerous linear segments, hairless. Jun–Sep. Roadsides, cultivated ground, trampled places, farmyards. Probably native in N-E. Asia. Introduced throughout area covered. **191**

1442

1444 Cottonweed *Otanthus maritimus*
Densely white-woolly, many-stemmed, maritime perennial to 50cm, with small fleshy oblong to lanceolate alternate leaves. Flower heads globular, yellow, 6–9mm, several in a flat-topped inflorescence. Ray-florets absent; disk-florets tubular; involucral bracts numerous, ovate, the outer with hairy apex, the inner hairless. Aug–Sep. Sandy sea-shores. †GB, F, IRL. **222**

1445 Corn Marigold *Chrysanthemum segetum*
Hairless, somewhat fleshy, blue-green annual, with simple or branched stem up to 60cm. Leaves oblong, the lower and middle stem-leaves deeply toothed, the upper nearly entire and clasping stem at base. Flower heads solitary, 3·5–6·5cm across, with golden-yellow ray-florets and disk-florets. Involucral bracts ovate, hairless, yellowish-green with pale brown papery margin. May–Aug. Cultivated ground, waste places. Native of S-W. Asia. Int B, GB, DK, F, D, IRL, NL, N, S. **222**

1446 Tansy *Tanacetum vulgare*
Aromatic perennial with erect leafy stems 50–150cm, branched above. Leaves oblong in outline, pinnate with c. 12 pairs of lanceolate, deeply pinnately-cut, toothed, dark green, gland-dotted and fragrant leaflets. Flower heads golden-yellow, 7–12mm across, numerous in dense flat-topped inflorescence. Ray-florets absent; outer disk-florets tubular, 3-toothed, inner 5-toothed. Involucral bracts pale green with papery margin, hairless. Jul–Sep. Waste places, roadsides, hedgerows. Throughout area covered; int IRL. **222**

1447 Feverfew *Tanacetum parthenium*
Erect, strongly aromatic perennial up to 80cm, with ridged stem, distinguished by its broad white ray-florets and yellow disk-florets. Leaves pinnately lobed, with 3–7 oblong to ovate, entire or lobed segments, greenish-yellow. Flower heads 1·2–2·2cm across, long-stalked, in a flat-topped inflorescence. Involucral bracts oblong, downy, with pale papery margin. Jun–Aug. Waste places, hedgerows, rocky places. Native of E. Europe. Int B, GB, DK, F, D, IRL, NL, S. **182**

1448

1448 *Tanacetum corymbosum*
Differs from **1447** in having narrow white ray-florets 1–2cm long, and stem-leaves stalkless, shining, with 7–15 oblong segments further divided into linear toothed lobes. Erect perennial to 1·2m. Jun–Aug. Open woods, scrub, meadows. F, D; int DK, S.

1449 Ox-eye Daisy *Leucanthemum vulgare*
Perennial with usually simple stems up to 1m. Basal leaves ovate to spoon-shaped, long-stalked, toothed; stem leaves oblong, entire or lobed, the upper stalkless, half-clasping stem. Flower heads usually 2·5–6cm across and solitary, with white spreading ray-florets and yellow disk-florets. Involucral bracts with brown or black papery margin. A very variable species. Jun–Oct. Grassland, waysides. Throughout area covered; int IS. **182**

1450 Buttonweed *Cotula coronopifolia*
Hairless aromatic annual with spreading or ascending stem up to 30cm, with linear, entire or toothed leaves with whitish sheathing base. Flower heads 5–10mm across,

stalked, terminal and axillary. Ray-florets with abortive corolla and short style; disk-florets yellow. Involucral bracts rounded, purplish, with papery margin. Jul–Aug. Damp, often saline places. Native of S. Africa. Int GB, DK, F, D, IRL, N.

ARTEMISIA
ULTIMATE SEGMENTS OF LEAVES AT LEAST 2MM BROAD

1451 Mugwort *Artemisia vulgaris*
Tufted perennial with much-branched leafy stems up to 1·5m. Leaves pinnately lobed with segments lanceolate or sometimes deeply lobed, hairless above, white-woolly beneath. Flower heads ovoid, reddish-brown, 3–4mm long, numerous in a much-branched cluster. Involucral bracts greyish-hairy. Jul–Sep. Dry waste places, hedgerows, river-banks. Throughout area covered, except IS. **203**

1452 Chinese Mugwort *Artemisia verlotiorum*
Like **1451** but not tufted and with long rhizomes. Segments of upper stem-leaves linear entire. Flower heads globular; involucral bracts linear, nearly hairless. Oct–Nov. Roadsides, waste places. Native of S-W. China. Int B, GB, F, D.

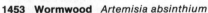

1453 Wormwood *Artemisia absinthium*
Aromatic perennial with grooved and angled silky–hairy stems up to 90cm. Leaves 2–3-times pinnately lobed, stalked, the lobes lanceolate to linear, blunt, silky–hairy. Flower heads yellowish, 3–4mm across, hemispherical, nodding, numerous in a branched inflorescence. Involucral bracts oblong, green, silky-haired, with wide papery margins. Jul–Aug. Waste places. Throughout area covered, except IS; int IRL.

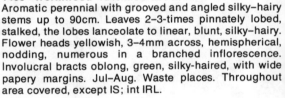

1454 *Artemisia stellerana*
Densely white-woolly, not aromatic, perennial up to 60cm. Lower leaves pinnately lobed to deeply toothed, stalked; upper leaves stalkless, sometimes entire. Flower heads yellow, broadly bell-shaped, erect or recurved, crowded into a branched cluster. Involucral bracts oblong to ovate, blunt, with papery margins. Native of N-E. Asia. Int GB, DK, S.

ARTEMISIA
ULTIMATE SEGMENTS OF LEAVES LESS THAN 2MM BROAD

1455 Sea Wormwood *Artemisia maritima*
Strongly aromatic, grey-woolly perennial with non-flowering rosettes and erect downy flowering stems up to 60cm, branched above. Leaves twice-pinnate with linear segments, woolly-haired above and below, lower leaves

stalked, upper stalkless, uppermost often entire. Flower heads yellowish or reddish, ovoid 1–2mm across, numerous in branched leafy cluster. Involucral bracts oblong, downy, the inner with papery margins. Aug–Sep. Salt-marshes, coastal cliffs. B, GB, DK, F, D, IRL, NL, N, S.

1456 Norwegian Mugwort *Artemisia norvegica*
Hairy aromatic, low-tufted perennial, with sparsely leafy flowering stems 5–20cm. Leaves twice-pinnate, with entire or sometimes toothed blunt or acute segments, stalked, stem-leaves stalkless, all silky-haired. Flower heads usually solitary, c. 1cm across, long-stalked, nodding. Flowers yellow, shaggy-haired; involucral bracts with wide brown papery margins. Jul–Sep. Sandy, gravelly or dry peaty places in mountains. GB, N.

1456

1457 *Artemisia rupestris*
Small shrub with numerous spreading non-flowering shoots, and ascending flowering stems 7–45cm. Leaves 1–2-pinnately lobed, the lobes linear. Flower heads hemispherical, nodding, in a lax branched inflorescence. Involucral bracts oblong, green, the inner brown with long hairy margins. Jul–Sep. Open rocky ground. S.

1458 Field Wormwood *Artemisia campestris*
Scentless perennial with creeping woody rootstock, with tufts of non-flowering shoots and flowering stems up to 80cm or more, branched above. Leaves silvery-hairy when young; basal leaves 2–3-pinnately lobed, stalked, the upper less divided, the uppermost linear. Flower heads yellow or red, ovate, 3–4mm across, numerous in a long branched cluster. Involucral bracts hairless, with wide papery margins. Aug–Sep. Dry places, poor grassland, sand-dunes. Throughout area covered, except IRL, IS.

1458

1459 Coltsfoot *Tussilago farfara*
Flower heads yellow, 2–3cm across, terminal on stout stems 4–15cm, with purplish scales, many appearing before the leaves. Leaves all basal, rounded with heart-shaped base and shallowly indented margin, blade up to 20cm across or more, white-hairy beneath, leaf-stalk grooved. Flower heads with ray-florets in many rows; disk-florets few; involucral bracts linear–lanceolate blunt, with papery margins, numerous. Feb–Apr. Waste places, river-banks, disturbed ground, waysides. Throughout area covered. **223**

PETASITES
LEAVES REGULARLY LOBED, LOBES TOOTHED

1460 Butterbur *Petasites hybridus*
Flower heads pale lilac-pink or yellowish, male and female florets on different heads. Male flower heads

6–21, with larger involucre 5·5–8·5mm; female flower heads 32–130, with smaller involucre up to 6mm. Involucral bracts purplish, with few hairs at base. Female flower heads elongating in fruit. Leaves appearing after flowering, heart-shaped/rounded, up to 60cm across, irregularly lobed, greyish beneath at maturity. Mar–May. Wet meadows, river-banks, copses. B, GB, F, D, IRL, NL; int DK, SF, N, S. **252**

1461 White Butterbur *Petasites albus*
Differs from **1460** in having whitish flower heads with involucral bracts glandular-hairy. Leaves smaller, up to 30cm across, and white-woolly beneath at maturity. Mar–May. Damp places, roadsides, mainly in mountains. DK, F, D, N, S; int GB, IRL. **203**

PETASITES
LEAVES WITHOUT REGULAR, TOOTHED LOBES

1462

1462 Winter Heliotrope *Petasites fragrans*
Distinguished by its lilac, vanilla-scented flower spikes, appearing at the same time as the leaves. Flowering stems up to 25cm, with a short lax inflorescence; bracts narrowly pointed. Leaves up to 20cm across, blade rounded with deeply heart-shaped base, equally toothed. Flower heads with florets with short lobe to 5·5mm; marginal florets female. Nov–Mar. Stream-sides, waste places, banks. Native of Mediterranean region. Int B, GB, DK, F, IRL.

1463 Giant Butterbur *Petasites japonicus*
Flowering spikes appearing before leaves; flower heads whitish in a dense flat-topped cluster, with scale leaves on stem below. Leaves large, with rounded/heart-shaped, sharply toothed, nearly hairless blade up to 1m across, with leaf-stalks up to 2m. Mar. Stream-sides, banks. Native of Japan. Int GB, DK, NL.

1464 *Petasites frigidus*
Flower heads whitish-yellow or reddish with outer florets of flower head with lobes; involucral bracts purplish or green, hairy. Leaves triangular to heart-shaped, hairy beneath, margin coarsely toothed or lobed. Inflorescence either male or female, 5–9 flower heads in male plant; 8–12 flower heads in female plant; flowering stems with scale leaves, the lower sheathing at base. Jun–Jul. Wet places, streamsides, bogs. SF, N, S.

1465 *Petasites spurius*
Differs from **1464** in having marginal florets tubular and involucral bracts hairless except at apex. Flower heads yellowish; involucral bracts pale green. Leaves triangular, with 2–3 pointed lobes on each side at base. Apr–May. Sandy sea-shores, river-banks. DK, D, S.

1466 Purple Coltsfoot *Homogyne alpina*
Low creeping perennial with leaves mostly basal, and
stems 10–40cm, each terminating in a purplish-red
flower head 1–1·5cm across. Leaves rounded with
heart-shaped base, toothed, thinly hairy on veins
beneath and purplish, long-stalked. Flower heads with
outer row of florets with short lobes, the inner florets
tubular; involucral bracts linear–lanceolate, purplish,
woolly-haired. May–Aug. Damp shady places in
mountains. F, D, GB. **252**

1467 Arnica *Arnica montana*
Aromatic perennial with rhizomes, and stems up to 60cm.
Basal leaves in a rosette of ovate pointed, glandular-hairy
leaves; stem-leaves narrower, opposite. Flower heads
golden-yellow 5–8cm across, usually solitary, with outer
row of strap-shaped florets 2–3cm long and toothed at
apex, and inner disk-florets. Involucral bracts lanceolate.
Jun–Aug. Acid grasslands, upland pastures in
mountains. B, DK, F, D, NL, N, S. **223**

1468 *Arnica angustifolia*
Like **1467** but leaves narrower, only 0·5–2cm wide (2–4cm
wide in **1467**), and stem-leaves scattered up stem, not
crowded near base. Stems up to 45cm, with usually
solitary flower heads 3·5–4·5cm across, borne on
glandular-hairy stems without bracts. Jul. Calcareous
meadows. SF, N, S.

1469 Leopardsbane *Doronicum pardalianches*
Often patch-forming perennial, with stems 30–90cm.
Basal leaves rounded to heart-shaped, toothed, hairy,
long-stalked; lower stem-leaves ovate, heart-shaped at
base, stalked; middle stem-leaves fiddle-shaped, uppermost broadly lanceolate and clasping stem. Flower
heads 3–6cm, usually several in a terminal branched
cluster, with glandular hairy flower-stalks. Ray florets
with lobe c. 2·5cm long. May–Jul. Woods, shady places.
B, F, D, NL; int GB. **223**

1470 Green Leopardsbane *Doronicum plantagineum*
Differs from **1469** in having narrower ovate–elliptic basal
leaves narrowed to a long leaf-stalk (basal leaves with
heart-shaped base in **1469**), and uppermost leaves
elliptic to lanceolate, stalkless. Flower heads yellow
3–5cm across, usually solitary. Jun–Jul. Woods,
pastures, heaths. F; int GB, NL.

1470

SENECIO
RAY-FLORETS ABSENT OR INCONSPICUOUS WITH NARROW
DOWN-ROLLED LOBES

1471 Groundsel *Senecio vulgaris*
Somewhat fleshy annual up to 40cm, with irregularly

branched stem. Leaves oblanceolate in outline, with
coarse blunt lobes, the lower stalked; middle and upper
leaves oblong with clasping base. Flower heads yellow
4–5mm across, numerous in a dense cluster. Ray-florets
usually absent; involucral bracts usually hairless
5–8mm, with shorter outer black-tipped bracts. Feb–Dec
Waste places, cultivated ground, coastal sands and
shingle. Throughout area covered. **223**

1472 Sticky Groundsel *Senecio viscosus*
Foetid sticky annual, with glandular branched stems
20–60cm. Leaves dark green, obovate in outline
pinnately lobed with lobes further toothed or lobed
narrowed to a short stalk, densely glandular-hairy
Flower heads many, 6–12mm across, in branched
clusters. Ray-florets yellow with short down-rolled lobes
involucre conical with bracts 8–11mm, densely
glandular, and with 3–4 shorter outer bracts. Fruits
hairless. Jun–Oct. Waste ground, open woods
sea-shores. B, GB, F, D, NL; int DK, SF, IRL, N, S.

1473 Heath Groundsel *Senecio sylvaticus*
Erect annual up to 70cm, with grooved hairy stem
glandular-hairy above, but not sticky. Leaves irregularly
pinnately lobed, the lower leaves oblanceolate in outline
the middle and upper leaves oblong in outline and
clasping stem. Flower heads many, 4–6mm across, in a
large flat-topped cluster. Ray-florets with very short
down-rolled lobes; involucral bracts glandular-hairy, to
1cm, the outer bracts 1–2mm. Fruits hairy. Jun–Sep
Wood verges, heaths, disturbed ground. Throughout
area covered, except IS.

SENECIO
RAY FLORETS CONSPICUOUS AND SPREADING; USUALLY PERENNIALS

1474 Broad-leaved Ragwort *Senecio fluviatilis*
Perennial with long creeping stolons and flowering
stems up to 2m, erect, hairy, branched above. Leaves
elliptic, with margin with cartilaginous teeth, hairless
stalkless. Flower heads yellow, 1·5–3cm across, many in
a branched flat-topped inflorescence. Ray-florets 6–8
spreading with lobes 8–12mm. Involucre 5–8mm, with
3–5 basal bracts half as long. Jul–Sep. Stream-sides
fens, damp meadows. F, D, NL; int GB, DK, IRL.

1475 Alpine Ragwort *Senecio nemorensis*
Differs from **1474** in having leaves with outer margin of
teeth straight or concave (outer margin of teeth convex in
1474), and basal bracts of flower heads about as long as
inner bracts. Perennial up to 2m, with lanceolate
fine-toothed, hairless leaves. Flower heads 2–3·5cm
across, many; ray-florets yellow, with 5–6 spreading
lobes 12–15mm long. Involucral bracts hairless or

1474

sparsely hairy, often black-tipped. Jul–Aug. Damp meadows, woods. B, F, D, NL; int S.

1476 Fen Ragwort *Senecio paludosus*
Perennial with erect cottony stems 1–2m, and with creeping rootstock. Leaves narrowly elliptic, sharply toothed, basal leaves narrowed to a short broad base, upper stalkless, all cottony-hairy beneath. Flower heads 3–4cm across, with 12–20 bright yellow spreading ray-florets. Involucre bell-shaped, inner bracts lanceolate, the outer basal bracts half as long as inner. May–Jul. Ditches, fens. B, GB, F, D, NL, S.

1477 Field Fleawort *Senecio integrifolius*
Perennial 10–70cm, basal leaves rounded or oblong–elliptic, entire or toothed, stalked, more or less pressed to ground; lower stem-leaves lanceolate, upper linear, clasping stem. Flower heads 1·5–2·5cm, solitary or up to 15 in branched cluster. Ray-florets to 2cm, yellow or golden-yellow. Involucre 5–8mm, bracts green. May–Jul. Dry grassy places, cliffs. GB, DK, F, D, N, S.

1477

1478 *Senecio helenitis*
Like **1477**, but basal leaves not pressed to ground, usually withered at flowering; leaf-stalks longer than blade; stem-leaves many. Flower heads yellow, 2–2·5cm across. Mar–Jun. Woods, meadows. B, F, D.

1479 Marsh Fleawort *Senecio congestus*
Annual or perennial with erect stems up to 2m; stems hollow, hairy, leafy throughout. Leaves narrowly lanceolate, entire or coarsely toothed, usually undulate, upper stem leaves clasping stem. Flower heads 2–3cm across, in a dense or lax cluster. Ray-florets c. 21, yellow; involucre with soft woolly hairs, without basal bracts. Jun–Jul. Meadows, marshes. B, †GB, DK, F, D, NL, S.

1479

SENECIO
SOME OR ALL LEAVES DEEPLY LOBED

1480 Common Ragwort *Senecio jacobaea*
Biennial or perennial 30–150cm, with branched inflorescence. Leaves 1–2-pinnately lobed, with lobes at right angles to axis, usually with sparse soft star-shaped hairs beneath. Flower heads 1·5–2cm across, numerous in a rather dense flat-topped cluster. Ray-florets yellow, 12–15; involucral bracts narrowly ovate, 3 times as long as the 2–5 basal bracts. Jul–Oct. Waste ground, waysides, wood verges, pastures, sand-dunes. Throughout area covered, except IS; int SF. **223**

1481 Marsh Ragwort *Senecio aquaticus*
Differs from **1480**, in being biennial and with stems

branched below, up to 80cm. Basal leaves persistent, often entire; upper leaves with lobes directed forward. Flower heads 1·2–3cm across, in lax cluster. Jul–Aug. Marshes, wet meadows, ditches. Throughout area covered, except SF, IS. **223**

1482 Hoary Ragwort *Senecio erucifolius*
Perennial 30–120cm, with stolons and leaf rosettes, and with flowering stems branched above. Basal and lower leaves pinnately lobed, stalked; upper leaves pinnate with linear lateral lobes and narrow terminal lobe, with soft woolly hairs beneath. Flower heads 1·2–1·5cm across, numerous in a narrow flat-topped cluster. Ray-florets yellow, 12–15; involucre woolly-hairy, with 4–6 outer bracts half as long as the inner bracts. Aug–Oct. Calcareous grassland, dry waysides. B, GB, DK, F, D, IRL, NL, S.

1483 Oxford Ragwort *Senecio squalidus*
Annual or perennial with erect branched stems 20–60cm. Lower leaves usually deeply pinnately lobed, with winged leaf-stalks, upper leaves narrowly lobed and clasping stem. Flower heads 1·5–2·5cm across, few in a lax irregular flat-topped cluster. Ray-florets c. 13, bright yellow; involucral bracts lanceolate, black-tipped, with 5–13 shorter outer bracts. Leaves very variable. May–Nov. Waste ground, rocky ground, walls, waysides. Native of mountains of S. Europe. D; int GB, DK, F, IRL. **224**

1484 Spring Groundsel *Senecio vernalis*
Annual up to 50cm, with young stems woolly-hairy. Basal leaves oblong in outline with wide toothed mid-rib, pinnately lobed with ovate toothed lobes, the middle and upper leaves clasping stem with enlarged toothed base. Flower heads 2–2·5cm across, in a lax cluster. Ray-florets c. 13, 1cm long, yellow; involucral bracts hairless, outer bracts several, usually black-tipped. May–Nov. Arable fields, by paths. Native of E. & E-C. Europe. Int B, GB, DK, F, D, NL, N, S. **224**

1486

1485 Marigold *Calendula arvensis*
Much-branched annual 5–25cm, with oblong leaves. Flower heads 1·2cm across (sometimes to 3·5cm) with ray-florets orange or yellow, longer than involucral bracts. Disk-florets orange or yellow, sometimes brownish or violet-purple. Fruiting heads with outer row of incurved beaked achenes. A variable species. Apr–Oct. Cultivated and waste ground, vineyards. F, D. **224**

1486 Garden Marigold *Calendula officinalis*
Like **1485** but flower heads larger, 4–7cm across, with ray-florets at least twice as long as involucral bracts. Florets yellow or orange, disk-florets sometimes

brownish. Annual to perennial 10–50cm. May–Oct. Waste
ground, usually near the sea. Origin unknown. Escaping
from gardens; frequent casual in GB.

1487 Carline Thistle *Carlina vulgaris*
Spiny biennial up to 30cm. Leaves oblong to narrowly
ovate with undulate spiny-toothed margin, the lower
leaves tapering into a short leaf-stalk. Flower heads
yellow-brown, 1·5–2·5cm across, solitary or in terminal
groups of 2–3. Florets all similar, 5-lobed. Outer
involucral bracts lanceolate with spiny margin, shorter
than inner straw-coloured bracts. Achenes hairy.
Jul–Oct. Calcareous grassland, by paths, open woods,
sand-dunes. Throughout area covered, except IS. **203**

1488 Stemless Carline Thistle *Carlina acaulis*
Distinguished by its single stalkless flower head
2·5–5cm across, surrounded by a rosette of pinnately
lobed spiny leaves. Florets white or purplish-brown;
outer involucral bracts 3–5cm, the inner nearly as long,
silvery-white or pale pink. Stems may be up to 60cm,
simple or branched, with up to 6 flower heads. May–Sep.
Grassy and rocky places in mountains. F, D. **253**

1489 Globe Thistle *Echinops sphaerocephalus*
Thistle-like white-woolly perennial up to 2m, with
lanceolate, pinnately lobed leaves clasping stem at base,
the lobes broadly triangular, spiny-margined, white-
woolly beneath. Flower heads in globular cluster 3–
6cm across, pale blue, spiny. Involucre 1·5–2·5cm with
many long-pointed bracts, the outer shorter. Florets all
tubular, few in each flower head. Achenes densely hairy.
Jun–Sep. Bare stony places. F; int B, D, S.

1490

1490 Great Burdock *Arctium lappa*
Finely hairy or nearly hairless biennial up to 1·5m, each
main branch terminating in a flat-topped inflorescence.
Basal leaves heart-shaped, to 50cm, with solid leaf-stalk.
Flower heads globular in bud, on stalks up to 10cm,
hemispherical and widely open in fruit, up to 4cm across.
Florets purple or white, tubular; involucral bracts with
rigid spreading hooked apices. Jul–Sep. Waste places,
waysides. Throughout area covered, except IS.

1491 Woolly Burdock *Arctium tomentosum*
Like **1490** with branches with long-stalked, flat-topped
flower clusters, but involucre in fruit smaller, 1·5–2·5cm
broad, and with dense woolly hairs; outer involucral
bracts hooked, the inner straight. Perennial up to 1·5m,
with large narrowly heart-shaped leaves, white-woolly
below, with solid leaf-stalk. Jul–Aug. Waste places,
river-banks, track-sides. B, DK, SF, F, D, NL, N, S; int GB.

1492 Lesser Burdock *Arctium minus*
Differs from **1490** in having main branch of inflorescence

429

elongate, with shorter lateral branches, usually with solitary short-stalked flower heads. Flower heads globular, 1·5–2·5cm across in fruit, green or purple-tinged, with dense cobweb-like hairs when young. Flowers longer than hooked involucral bracts. Leaf-stalks hollow. Jun–Sep. Waste places, waysides, wood margins. Throughout area covered, except IS.

1493 Arctium pubens
Differs from **1492** in having larger involucre in fruit up to 3–3·5cm across, and florets about as long as involucral bracts. Perennial up to 1·5m; leaf-stalks hollow. Flowers in a long branched inflorescence. Jul–Sep. Roadsides, uncultivated ground, waste places. B, GB, DK, F, NL.

1494 Wood Burdock *Arctium nemorosum*
Differs from **1493** in having involucre green or tinged dark purple, and stalks of flower heads less than 1cm (involucre straw-coloured, and stalks of flower heads 1–4cm in **1493**). Perennial to 2·5m, with leaves broadly heart-shaped, with hollow leaf-stalks. Inflorescence elongated, branched, often terminating in 3 flower heads; involucre 3–3·5cm across in fruit, usually with sparse cobwebby-hairs. Jul–Sep. Damp wood clearings. Throughout area covered, except NL, IS.

1495 Alpine Sawwort *Saussurea alpina*
Slender perennial with erect leafy stem 10–50cm. Leaves ovate to broadly lanceolate with wedge-shaped base, gradually narrowed to a winged leaf-stalk, greyish-hairy beneath. Flower heads ovoid, 1·5–2cm long, in a compact flat-topped cluster. Tubular florets only present, purple, longer than the purplish hairy outer involucral bracts. A variable species. Aug–Sep. Mountain and maritime cliffs. GB, SF, F, D, IRL, N, S. **287**

1496 Musk Thistle *Carduus nutans*
Distinguished by solitary, red-purple, drooping globular flower head 2–5cm across. Biennial with erect spiny-winged cobwebby hairy stem, 1–1·5m. Basal leaves elliptic, narrowed to base, wavy-margined; stem-leaves oblong–lanceolate, deeply pinnately lobed; triangular lobes have spiny margins, and blade running down stem. Florets 2-lipped, to 2·5cm; involucre cottony-hairy, often purplish, outer bracts strongly reflexed, inner erect, all spine-tipped. May–Aug. Pastures, disturbed ground, waste places. B, GB, F, D, NL; int DK, S. **281**

1497 Welted Thistle *Carduus acanthoides*
Biennial with erect cottony stem with narrow undulate spiny wings, up to 1·5m. Leaves oblong–lanceolate, with 6–8 pairs of palmate lobes, the lobules with apical spines. Flower heads pale red, globular, 2–2·5cm across, solitary or in small clusters. Florets 1·6–1·8cm; outer involucral bracts spreading or slightly deflexed, long-pointed, inner

1497

1498

bracts blunt, spine-tipped, hairy. Jun–Sep. Waysides, waste places. B, GB, DK, F, D, IRL, NL, S; int N.

1498 *Carduus crispus*
Like **1497** but with distinctly winged spiny stems. Leaves lanceolate to oblanceolate, with 6–8 pairs of short spiny lobes, or rounded teeth. Flower heads globular, 1·5–2·5cm, in a cluster of 2–4, on narrowly winged stalks. Florets 1·2–1·5cm; involucral bracts with outer overlapping, recurved at apex, the inner larger. Jun–Oct. Fields, river-banks, wet woods. B, DK, SF, F, D, NL, N, S.

1499 Great Marsh Thistle *Carduus personata*
Perennial up to 1·2m, with narrowly winged stem with tiny spines. Leaves of two kinds, the basal oblanceolate to lanceolate, with 4–6 pairs of lobes; the stem-leaves lanceolate, toothed, the teeth with an apical spine. Flower heads purple, 1·5–2·5cm, mostly stalkless and in clusters. Florets 1·4–1·6cm long; involucral bracts curled, S-shaped; outer bracts half as long as middle bracts, inner bracts linear bristle-like. Jul–Aug. Stream-sides, meadows, woods, in the mountains. F, D.

1500 Slender Thistle *Carduus tenuiflorus*
Annual or biennial with spiny winged hairy stem up to 75cm, branched above. Leaves oblanceolate, with 6–8 pairs of broadly triangular lobes with spiny margins, cottony-hairy beneath. Flower heads pale red-purple, rarely white, cylindrical 5–10mm across, stalkless, in dense terminal clusters of 3–10 or more. Involucral bracts ovate–lanceolate pointed, with papery margins and with out-curved spine, hairless; inner bracts papery, equalling florets. Jun–Aug. Waysides, waste places, especially near the sea. B, GB, F, IRL, NL; int N, S. **253**

CIRSIUM
FLOWER HEADS USUALLY WHITISH OR YELLOW; SEVERAL

1501 Cabbage Thistle *Cirsium oleraceum*
Distinctive leafy perennial to 1·5m, with terminal clusters of pale yellow flower heads, surrounded by 2–10 large, longer ovate, spiny leaves. Flower heads 1·5–2·4cm, with close-pressed involucral bracts; florets tubular, 1·8–2·5cm. Leaves elliptic–lanceolate, pinnately lobed or toothed, with weak hairy spines, blade hairless. Jul–Sep. Meadows, woods, stream-banks. B, DK, F, D, NL, N, S; int SF. **203**

CIRSIUM
FLOWERS HEADS PURPLE, VIOLET OR REDDISH; USUALLY SOLITARY OR 2–3

1502 Spear Thistle *Cirsium vulgare*
Perennial 30–150cm, or more, stems with interrupted

wings. Leaves pinnately lobed, all prickly, hairy, the stem leaves stalkless with blade running down stem and with a long narrow terminal lobe. Flower heads usually long-stalked, in a branched cluster, the heads 3–5cm across, with involucral bracts sparsely hairy or nearly hairless, each bract with a spine. Jul–Oct. Fields, waste places. Throughout area covered, except IS. 265

1503 Woolly Thistle *Cirsium eriophorum*
Differs from **1502** in having woolly-hairy stems which are not winged, and involucre of flower head with dense cobwebby hairs. Stout biennial up to 150cm or more, with pinnate leaves with lanceolate lobes, each with apical spines, woolly-hairy beneath. Flower heads purple, with globular involucre up to 5cm across, few in a lax cluster. Florets 2·5–4·4cm; outer involucral bracts spreading or recurved. Very variable species. Jun–Sep. Grassland, scrub, roadsides. B, GB, F, D, NL.

1504 Meadow Thistle *Cirsium dissectum*
Perennial with stolons, and erect cottony–hairy unwinged stem up to 80cm, usually with few small bract-like leaves above the middle. Basal leaves elliptic-lanceolate, toothed or shallow-lobed, long-stalked; stem leaves few, clasping stem, all leaves white-cottony beneath, and margins with soft prickles. Flower heads red-purple, solitary, 2·5–3cm across; involucral bracts purple, cottony–hairy, the outer spine-tipped. Jun–Aug. Fens, bogs, damp grassy places. B, GB, F, D, IRL, NL; int N. 253

1504

1505 Tuberous Thistle *Cirsium tuberosum*
Like **1504**, but leaves deeply pinnately lobed, each lobe with 2–5 oblong to elliptic toothed segments, green beneath. Stolons absent, roots swollen spindle-shaped. Flower heads solitary; florets purple, to 2cm; involucre 1·5–2cm across. Involucral bracts erect, the outer blunt. Jul–Sep. Calcareous pastures. GB, F, D; int B. 265

1506 Dwarf Thistle *Cirsium acaule*
Usually a stemless perennial with solitary, or sometimes 2–3 purple flower heads surrounded by a rosette of spiny leaves. Leaves oblong–lanceolate, pinnately lobed. Flower heads 2–5cm across, with purplish erect blunt involucral bracts. Jun–Sep. Dry grassland. B, GB, DK, F, D, NL, N, S. 265

1507 Melancholy Thistle *Cirsium helenioides*
Erect perennial up to 1m or more, with simple or sparsely branched stem, usually leafless towards apex. Leaves lanceolate to broadly oblong, entire or pinnately lobed, green above and white-woolly beneath; lobes narrowly triangular, toothed, with soft spines; upper leaves clasping stem. Flower heads purple, usually solitary;

florets 2·5–3cm; involucral bracts with weak spine, the outer bracts acute, the inner blunt. Jul–Aug. Wet meadows, stream-sides, upland scrub. GB, DK, SF, F, D, IRL, N, S; int IS.

CIRSIUM
FLOWER HEADS PURPLISH, USUALLY CLUSTERED

1508

1508 Marsh Thistle *Cirsium palustre*
Erect biennial with winged spiny stem up to 1·5m. Leaves lanceolate in outline, with spiny triangular to oblong lobes, hairy above, slightly cottony beneath. Flower heads dark red-purple or occasionally white, 1·5–2cm, crowded into leafy clusters at the ends of stem and branches. Involucre ovoid, with purplish erect bracts, weakly spiny. Jul–Sep. Marshes, wet grassland, moorlands, woods. Throughout area covered, except IS.

1509 Creeping Thistle *Cirsium arvense*
Erect perennial with much-branched, leafy, unwinged stems up to 1·5m, and with far-creeping runners with leafy shoots. Leaves lanceolate to oblong, entire or pinnately lobed with triangular spiny lobes, hairless or with cobwebby hairs. Flower heads 1–5, pale purple, 1·5–3cm long, shortly stalked, at apex of branches. Involucral bracts dark violet, erect, the outer blunt. Florets 5-lobed, with long corolla-tube. Very variable species. Jun–Sep. Arable fields, pastures, waste places, wood clearings. Throughout area covered; int IS. **281**

1510 Cotton Thistle *Onopordum acanthium*
Tall spiny white-woolly biennial 1–3m, with broadly winged spiny stems. Leaves elliptical to broadly lanceolate, with wavy, toothed margins, or with 6–8 pairs of triangular lobes with strongly spiny margins, all stalkless. Flower heads globular, 3–6cm across, usually solitary, with purple or rarely white florets up to 2·5cm long. Involucral bracts narrowly lanceolate, with stiff yellow apical spine, cottony-hairy. Jul–Sep. Fields, roadsides, waste places. B, F, D, NL; int GB, DK, S.

1511 Sawwort *Serratula tinctoria*
Perennial with erect leafy stem, branched above, 10–100cm. Leaves ovate–lanceolate, coarsely bristly-toothed or deeply pinnately lobed, upper leaves stalkless. Flower heads purple, rarely white, narrow ovoid, 1·5–2cm long, in a lax or compact cluster. Involucral bracts adpressed, often purple-tinted, the outer acute and with downy margin, the inner long-pointed. A very variable species. Jul–Aug. Water meadows, open woods, heaths, mountain meadows. Throughout area covered, except SF, IS. **253**

CENTAUREA
INVOLUCRAL BRACTS WITH A TERMINAL SPINE

1512

1512 Yellow Star-thistle *Centaurea solstitialis*
Erect annual to perennial, much branched below, with
broadly winged greyish-woolly stems up to 1m. Leaves
deeply pinnately lobed with distant, toothed or entire
lobes, upper leaves linear–lanceolate more or less entire
with blade running down stem, all cottony-hairy. Flower
heads pale yellow, 1–2cm, solitary, stalked. Outer
involucral bracts with palmate spiny apex, the terminal
spine spreading, yellow. Jul–Sep. Cultivated and waste
ground. S. Europe, F; int GB, D.

1513 Red Star-thistle *Centaurea calcitrapa*
Stems spreading or ascending, branched from the base,
up to 1m. Lower leaves pinnately lobed, with widely
spaced lanceolate toothed lobes, upper leaves with
narrower lobes, uppermost leaves lanceolate. Flower
heads pink or purple, with involucre ovoid, 6–8mm, and
bracts ovate, leathery, with long thickened terminal spine
and smaller spines at base. Variable species. Jul–Oct.
Waste places, waysides. F; int B, GB, D, NL. **253**

CENTAUREA
INVOLUCRAL BRACTS TERMINATING IN A PAPERY FRINGED BORDER

1514 Cornflower *Centaurea cyanus*
Distinguished by its solitary blue flower heads, with outer
florets, 5-lobed, much larger than the red-purple central
florets. Annual with grooved cottony stem to 90cm,
usually much-branched. Lower leaves pinnately lobed
with distant narrow lobes, the upper leaves mostly
linear–lanceolate, all greyish-hairy. Flower heads
1·5–3cm across; involucral bracts with fringed margin.
Jun–Aug. Cornfields, cultivated grounds, waste places.
S-E. Europe. Int throughout area covered, except IS. **281**

1515 Perennial Cornflower *Centaurea montana*
Perennial up to 80cm, with erect, broadly winged stem,
and with ovate to broadly lanceolate, usually entire
leaves, densely white-felted beneath. Flower heads
solitary, with large deep blue marginal florets and violet
central florets. Involucral bracts with dark brown fringed
margins. May–Jul. Woods, scrub, meadows in the
mountains. B, F, D; int SF. **281**

1516 Greater Knapweed *Centaurea scabiosa*
Perennial with hairy stems, usually branched above,
up to 1m. Basal leaves usually deeply lobed, or entire,
lobes oblong-lanceolate often further lobed; stem
leaves stalkless, deeply lobed. Flower heads red-
purple, solitary, 3–5cm across with larger stalked
marginal florets. Involucral bracts with dark brown

horseshoe-shaped toothed margin. Jul–Sep. Dry
grasslands, roadsides, hedgebanks, cliffs. Throughout
area covered, except IS. **265**

CENTAUREA
INVOLUCRAL BRACTS WITH AN ENLARGED PAPERY APPENDAGE AT APEX

1517 Common Knapweed *Centaurea nigra*
Perennial up to 1m, with branches thickened below
flower heads. Lower leaves ovate to lanceolate, entire,
toothed or lobed, upper leaves lanceolate. Flower heads
red-purple, 2–4cm across, solitary or clustered; outer
florets usually not larger than inner. Involucre globular,
bracts produced into long comb-like black appendage.
Fruit with a pappus of short bristly hairs. Jun–Sep. Grasslands, cliffs. B, GB, F, D, IRL, NL, N, S; int DK. **266**

1518 *Centaurea debeauxii*
Differs from **1517** in having involucre 9–14mm across and
appendages of involucral bracts brown and not recurved
at apex (involucre 1·5–2cm across, appendages of
bracts, black or blackish-brown, somewhat recurved at
apex in **1517**). Greyish-hairy perennial up to 80cm, the
upper leaves mostly entire. Flower heads solitary, with
pinkish-orange florets, the outer erect or spreading.
Jun–Sep. Woods, meadows, waysides, usually on
calcareous soils. B, GB, F, D, NL.

1518

1519 *Centaurea phrygia*
Perennial up to 80cm, with ovate finely toothed leaves,
the lower stalked, the upper clasping stem. Flower heads
pink to purple, 1·5–2cm across; involucral bracts with
pale brown to black appendage with a long erect or
recurved feathery point fringed with teeth. Jul–Aug.
Grasslands, open woods. DK, SF, D, N; int S.

1520 Brown Knapweed *Centaurea jacea*
Distinguished by its inner involucral bracts which have
rounded papery pale brown appendages with darker
brown centre, blunt, the outer bracts toothed or
comb-like. Perennial up to 1·2m, with erect or ascending, sparingly branched, angled stems. Basal leaves
ovate to broadly lanceolate, toothed or pinnately lobed,
stem leaves oblong–lanceolate, entire or toothed,
stalkless. Flower heads purple, rarely white, 3–6cm
across, in a flat-topped cluster. Marginal florets
red-violet, longer than inner. Jun–Oct. Grassland. B, DK,
SF, F, D, NL, N, S; int GB.

1520

1521 *Centaurea decipiens*
Distinguished by its involucral bracts which have pale
brown appendages with 9–10 narrow lobes on each
side. Erect perennial up to 60cm, simple or branched,
with 5–6 green or greyish-woolly leaves, the lower

elliptic–oblanceolate, entire, toothed or lobed,
long-stalked, upper leaves elliptic to lanceolate pointed.
Flower heads purple, solitary, the outer florets not
spreading. Aug–Oct. Pastures. B, DK, F, D, NL, N.

1522 Centaurea microptilon
Differs from **1521** in having involucral bracts with
lanceolate usually recurved appendages, with 7–8
narrow lobes on each side (appendages
ovate–triangular, erect in **1521**). Erect much-branched
perennial up to 1 m, with lower leaves lanceolate, toothed
or lobed, the upper linear to lanceolate, entire or lobed.
Flower heads solitary, purple or pink, with outer florets
spreading. Involucre ovoid, 1–1·3 cm long. Jun–Sep.
Roadsides, pastures, wood verges. B, F, NL.

1523 Chicory Cichorium intybus
Stiffly branched perennial up to 1·2 m, with furrowed
stem. Basal leaves pinnately lobed with backward
projecting lobes, upper stem-leaves broadly lanceolate,
entire or toothed. Flower heads blue, rarely white or pink,
3–5 cm across, with large ray-florets, solitary or in
stalkless clusters of 2–3, in axils of upper leaves.
Involucre with 8 lanceolate outer bracts and 5 narrower
and longer inner bracts. Jul–Oct. Waste places, dry
waysides, field verges. Throughout area covered, except
IS; int SF, IRL, N. **286**

1524 Lamb's Succory Arnoseris minima
Annual with leaves all basal in a rosette, and many
slightly branched stems bearing solitary yellow flower
heads 7–11 mm across. Stem below flower head
conspicuously thickened. Leaves spoon-shaped to
oblanceolate, toothed, narrowed to a short leaf-stalk.
Flowering stems 5–30 cm. Ray-florets only present, 1½
times as long as involucre; involucral bracts many,
narrowly triangular pointed, prominent keel. Jun–Aug.
Arable land on sandy soil. B, GB, DK, F, D, NL, S.

1524

1525 Smooth Catsear Hypochoeris glabra
Usually annual, with basal rosette of nearly hairless
shining leaves, and sparsely branched stems 10–40 cm,
with few scales or narrow leaves. Leaves oblanceolate to
spoon-shaped, toothed to shallowly lobed. Flower heads
0·5–1·5 cm across, with yellow ray-florets not longer than
the involucre, which has lanceolate pointed bracts in
several rows. Jun–Oct. Grassy fields, heaths,
sand-dunes. Throughout area covered, except SF, IS.

1526 Catsear Hypochoeris radicata
Like **1525**, but leaves bristly-hairy, and flower heads
larger yellow, with ray-florets longer than involucre.
Perennial with rosette of broadly oblong–lanceolate,
toothed or lobed leaves. Flowering stem 20–60 cm,

usually branched and with scales below flower heads. Flower heads 2·5–4cm across; involucral bracts lanceolate pointed, bristly-hairy on mid-rib. Jun–Sep. Grassland, sand-dunes, waysides. Throughout area covered, except SF, IS. **224**

1527 Spotted Catsear *Hypochoeris maculata*
Distinguished by its leaves which are spotted purplish-black, and its larger flower heads 4·5–6cm across. Perennial up to 75cm, or more, simple or sparingly branched, bristly-hairy. Leaves obovate-oblong, entire or deeply toothed, hairless or bristly-haired; stem leaves few or absent, but stem with scales above. Flower heads pale yellow; florets twice as long as involucre; involucral bracts bristly hairy, with woolly margin. Jun–Aug. Calcareous pastures, cliffs, open woodlands. B, GB, DK, SF, F, D, NL, N, S. **224**

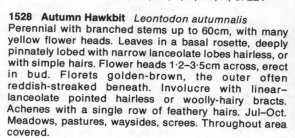

1528 Autumn Hawkbit *Leontodon autumnalis*
Perennial with branched stems up to 60cm, with many yellow flower heads. Leaves in a basal rosette, deeply pinnately lobed with narrow lanceolate lobes hairless, or with simple hairs. Flower heads 1·2–3·5cm across, erect in bud. Florets golden-brown, the outer often reddish-streaked beneath. Involucre with linear-lanceolate pointed hairless or woolly-hairy bracts. Achenes with a single row of feathery hairs. Jul–Oct. Meadows, pastures, waysides, screes. Throughout area covered.

1528

1529 Rough Hawkbit *Leontodon hispidus*
Differs from **1528** in having leaves with forked hairs, and achenes with 2 rows of hairs, the outer feathery, the inner simple. Flower head solitary, borne on unbranched stem, golden-yellow, 2·5–4cm across, with outer florets orange or reddish beneath; flower head drooping in bud. Involucre hairless or with bristly hairs. A very variable species. Jun–Oct. Meadows, water-meadows, in mountains. Throughout area covered, except IS. **224**

1530 Lesser Hawkbit *Leontodon taraxacoides*
Usually perennial with one or many unbranched stems up to 25cm. Leaves in a basal rosette, narrowly oblanceolate, shallow-lobed, hairless or with dense forked hairs. Flower heads golden-yellow, 1·2–2cm across, the outer florets grey-violet beneath; involucre with rigid hairs. Achenes of 2 kinds, the outer shortly beaked, the inner with 2 rows of hairs. Jun–Oct. Dry grassy places, sand-dunes. B, GB, F, D, IRL, NL; int DK, S.

1531 Hawkweed Oxtongue *Picris hieracioides*
Biennial or perennial; branched stems with rigid hairs, up to 1m. Lower leaves lanceolate to ovate, entire or toothed, long-stalked, upper smaller, stalkless, more or less clasping stem, all leaves bristly hairy. Flower heads

bright yellow, 2–3·5cm across, few to numerous, stalked. Involucre ovoid, with outer bracts short and narrow, spreading or recurved, with blackish hairs; the inner lanceolate, twice as long as the outer, hairy. Jul–Oct. Grassland, fields, waysides. Throughout area covered, except IRL, IS, N. **225**

1532 Bristly Oxtongue *Picris echioides*
Differs from **1531**: 2–5 large ovate/heart-shaped leaf-like bristly-hairy outer involucral bracts, and achenes with long beaks (beak very short or absent in **1531**). Annual or biennial, with furrowed, forked, hairy stem up to 90cm. Flower heads yellow, 2–2·5cm across, crowded on short stalks in an irregular flat-topped cluster. Florets twice as long as involucre. Jun–Nov. Field verges, waste places, roadsides. F; int B, GB, D, IRL, NL. **230**

1533 Viper's Grass *Scorzonera humilis*
Perennial with stout rootstock, with one or few simple erect woolly-hairy stems up to 50cm, or more. Basal leaves linear to broadly elliptic, entire, gradually narrowed to a broad leaf-stalk, upper stem-leaves scale-like. Flower heads pale yellow or rarely white, 2·5–3cm across, usually solitary; florets 1½–2 times as long as involucre. Involucre woolly below, outer bracts ovate. May–Jun. Poor grassland, heaths, pinewoods. Throughout area covered, except IRL, IS.

1533

1534 Purple Viper's Grass *Scorzonera purpurea*
Distinguished by solitary pale violet flower head, and linear, keeled, grass-like leaves. Hairless perennial to 45cm. Flower heads with florets up to twice as long as involucre. May–Jun. Grassy and rocky places in mountains. F, D.

1535 Goatsbeard *Tragopogon pratensis*
Erect annual to perennial, up to 70cm, with narrowly lanceolate long-pointed entire, hairless leaves; upper leaves clasping stem, and with a cylindrical rootstock. Flower heads yellow, 3–5cm across, solitary, florets strap-shaped, usually shorter than involucre. Involucral bracts 8, lanceolate pointed, up to 3cm long. May–Aug. Dry grassland, waste places, roadsides. Throughout area covered, except IS. **225**

1536 *Tragopogon dubius*
Like **1535**, but stems distinctly inflated below flower heads (not inflated in **1535**). Annual or biennial up to 60cm, unbranched, with linear–lanceolate leaves clasping stem. Flower heads pale yellow, 4–6cm across, with ray-florets shorter than the 8–12 involucral bracts. May–Jul. Dry woods, grassland, rural communities. F, D; int B.

1537 Salsify *Tragapogon porrifolius*
Lilac to violet flower heads, with florets about as long as

involucral bracts, which are 3–5cm. Perennial up to
120cm, with broadly linear hairless leaves. Flower-stalks
inflated below flower heads. Apr–Jun. Grassy places,
roadsides. Native of Mediterranean region. F; int B, GB,
DK, D, IRL, NL, S. **253**

1538 Prickly Sow-thistle *Sonchus asper*
Annual or biennial up to 120cm, hairless below,
glandular-hairy above. Lower leaves spoon-shaped,
entire to pinnately lobed, the upper entire, or more
deeply lobed with triangular to linear toothed lobes and
rounded basal lobes. Flower heads golden-yellow
2–2·5cm across, in a terminal stalked cluster. Achenes
3-ribbed. Jun–Aug. Cultivated ground, waste places,
grassland. Throughout area covered, except IS. **225**

1539 Smooth Sow-thistle *Sonchus oleraceus*
Like **1538**, but stem-leaves with pointed basal lobes, and
achenes rough. Stem to 150cm, 5-angled, hollow. Leaves
dull green, not spiny, hairless, very variable. Flower
heads not in a cluster, 2–2·5cm across, with yellow
ray-florets, the outer purple-tinged. Involucral bracts
usually hairless, with outer bracts broadly lanceolate.
Jun–Aug. Cultivated ground, waste places, waysides.
Throughout area covered, except IS. **203**

1540 Perennial Sow-thistle *Sonchus arvensis*
Perennial with creeping underground roots, and erect
stems up to 150cm, with stems furrowed below. Basal
leaves oblong to lanceolate and narrowed to a winged
stalk, pinnately lobed, the lobes spine-toothed; stem-
leaves similar, stalkless with rounded clasping base.
Flower heads golden-yellow, 4–5cm across, in a lax
cluster, with many oblong–lanceolate blunt involucral
bracts. Bracts and flower-stems usually densely covered
with yellowish hairs. Achenes 5-ribbed on each face.
Jul–Oct. Stream-sides, sea-shores, arable fields.
Throughout area covered, except IS.

1540

1541 Marsh Sow-thistle *Sonchus palustris*
Tall perennial up to 3m, with upper part of stem and
inflorescence densely dark glandular-hairy. Basal leaves
pinnately lobed; stem-leaves lanceolate, with long acute
narrow basal lobes clasping stem. Flower heads yellow,
to 4cm across, stalked, in a dense terminal cluster;
involucre up to 1·5cm, outer bracts ovate pointed,
shorter than florets. Jul–Sep. Marshes, fens, stream-
sides. B, GB, DK, F, D, NL, N, S. **225**

LACTUCA
FLOWER HEADS BLUE-LILAC

1542 Blue Lettuce *Lactuca perennis*
Erect hairless perennial up to 80cm, branched above.

Leaves pinnately lobed, with lanceolate entire or toothed lobes, grey-green, the upper stalkless. Flower heads blue or lilac, 2cm across, in a lax cluster. Involucral bracts with white margin. Achenes black, with beak to 1·5cm. May–Jun. Dry grassland, rocky outcrops, walls. B, F, D. **281**

1543 *Lactuca tatarica*
Flower heads blue-lilac, few in a branched cluster. Perennial up to 80cm, branched above and with underground stolons. Lower leaves with backward-directed lobes, shortly stalked. Florets numerous; involucral bracts red-spotted. Achenes yellowish to black, with beak half as long as achene. Jul–Aug. Sea-shores, river-banks, open ground. Native of E. Europe. Int DK, SF, D, GB, NL, N, S.

1544 *Lactuca sibirica*
Differs from **1543** in having leaves usually without lobes and rhizomes without underground stolons. Flower heads large, with blue-lilac florets. Erect hairless perennial up to 1m, leaves lanceolate, entire or toothed, with heart-shaped base. Aug. Woods, scrub, river banks, gravel. SF, N, S.

1543

LACTUCA
FLOWER HEADS YELLOW

1545 **Least Lettuce** *Lactuca saligna*
Annual or biennial with erect hairless, whitish, branched stem up to 1m. Lower leaves entire, or pinnately lobed with widely spaced triangular lobes, upper leaves oblong–linear with arrow-shaped basal lobes. Flower heads pale yellow, often reddish beneath, c. 1cm across, numerous in a spike-like cluster. Involucre 1·5cm, with linear–lanceolate greenish bracts. Achenes ribbed, with beak 1½–3 times as long as achene. Jul–Aug. Grassy places, dry banks, often by sea. B, GB, F, D, NL.

1547

1546 **Prickly Lettuce** *Lactuca serriola*
Stiffly erect foetid annual or biennial 50–200cm, with prickly branches above. Leaves rigid, spiny on mid-rib and margin beneath, the lower leaves ovate–oblong usually deeply lobed, upper less lobed and held vertically. Flower heads pale yellow, 1–1·5cm across, many in a long branched pyramidal or spike-like cluster. Involucre narrowly cylindrical, with lanceolate hairless bracts. Achenes ribbed, with bristly apex and beak as long as achene. Jul–Sep. Roadsides, waste places, dry banks, sand-dunes. B, GB, DK, F, D, NL, S.

1547 **Great Lettuce** *Lactuca virosa*
Erect annual or biennial up to 2m, differing from **1546** in its blackish achenes, with beak as long as achene (achenes greyish in **1546**). Flower heads pale yellow, in a

DAISY
FAMILY

long branched pyramidal inflorescence. Leaves obovate–oblong entire and toothed, or pinnately lobed with wide lobes, spiny on the mid-rib beneath. Jul–Sep. Dry stony and sandy places. B, GB, F, D.

1548 Alpine Sow-thistle *Cicerbita alpina*
Tall erect perennial up to 2m, with dense reddish glandular hairs on upper part of stem, flower-stalks and involucre. Flower heads pale blue, numerous in a branched cluster. Lower leaves pinnately lobed, with broad triangular terminal lobes and few smaller triangular lateral lobes, and with a winged leaf-stalk; upper leaves smaller, less divided and with clasping base. Involucral bracts linear, with brownish glandular hairs. Jul–Sep. Scrub and tall herb communities in mountains. GB, SF, F, D, N, S. **281**

1549 Blue Sow-thistle *Cicerbita macrophylla*
Differs from **1548** in having terminal lobe of lower leaves heart-shaped (triangular in **1548**) and usually with a single pair of lateral lobes. Flower cluster wider, more or less flat-topped. Achenes narrow elliptic (linear in **1548**). Jul–Aug. Waysides, waste places. Native of Caucasus. Int GB, DK, SF, F, D, IRL, N, S.

1550 Wall Lettuce *Mycelis muralis*
Hairless perennial up to 1m, with a branched flat-topped inflorescence and many small pale yellow flower heads. Lower leaves deeply pinnately lobed, with much larger often 3-lobed terminal lobe, leaf-stalk winged; upper leaves smaller and less divided, stalkless and clasping stem. Ray-florets usually 5, spreading, 7–10mm across; involucre narrowly cylindrical to 1cm, with very small spreading lanceolate outer bracts, the inner linear. Achenes blackish. Jul–Aug. Woods, rocks, walls, waste places. Throughout area covered, except IS; int IRL.

1550

TARAXACUM
(VERY DIFFICULT GENUS WITH C. 1200 MICROSPECIES DESCRIBED IN EUROPE; ONLY SOME OF MAIN GROUPS DESCRIBED)

1552

1551 Broad-leaved Marsh Dandelion
Taraxacum spectabile group
Flower heads with bright deep yellow florets with red or purple stripe, 3·5–4·5cm across, borne on a stout often purplish stem, 3–30cm. Leaves entire or shallowly lobed, dull green, often dark-spotted, leaf-stalks narrow, often purplish. Involucre 1·5–2·5cm long, bracts ovate to lanceolate, sometimes purplish, the outer spreading or reflexed. Apr–Aug. Wet places. GB, DK, IRL, IS, N, S.

1552 Narrow-leaved Marsh Dandelion
Taraxacum palustre group
Flower heads with pale yellow florets, 2·5–5cm across,

441

borne on usually hairless, often purplish stem to 15cm.
Leaves linear to narrowly lanceolate, entire or lobed,
hairless or nearly so; leaf-stalks long narrow. Outer
involucral bracts ovate, up to 7mm, often violet or purple
with pale papery margin. Apr–Jun. Wet places, meadows.
Throughout area covered, except IS.

1553 *Taraxacum erythrospermum* group
Flower heads solitary, 1·5–3·5cm across, with short,
wide, pale yellow ray-florets with grey-brown or purple
stripe, on slender often purplish stem up to 15cm. Leaves
lobed, with narrow variable lobes and narrow green, red
or purplish leaf-stalks. Involucre 6–12mm, outer bracts
often blue-green and purplish with pale margin and with
a small horn-like apex. Achenes red, purple or violet, with
a slender white beak. Apr–Jun. Dry grassy places,
sand-dunes. Throughout area covered.

1554 Common Dandelion *Taraxacum officinale* group
Distinguished by its narrowly lanceolate to linear outer
involucral bracts which are spreading or recurved and
nearly half as long as inner bracts. Flower heads
2·5–7·5cm, with yellow florets with usually a brown stripe,
borne on stout hairy stems up to 40cm. Leaves entire to
deeply lobed, the lobes more or less triangular; leaf-stalk
often winged. Mar–Oct. Woods, meadows, disturbed
ground. Throughout area covered. **225**

1555 Skeleton Weed *Chondrilla juncea*
Greyish-green biennial or perennial, with usually solitary
stem up to 1m, much branched above. Lower
stem-leaves oblanceolate, deeply and irregularly
toothed, with winged leaf-stalk, upper leaves usually
small, linear, entire or finely toothed. Flower heads
yellow c. 1cm across, with 9–12 florets, numerous in
short-stalked clusters up stem. Involucre 9–12mm, with
linear–lanceolate, hairless or woolly-haired bracts.
Achenes with slender beak half as long as achene.
Jul–Sep. Dry open stony places. F, D.

1556 Nipplewort *Lapsana communis*
Hairy annual to 120cm, branched above, with numerous
small, pale yellow flower heads. Leaves ovate, toothed, or
pinnately lobed with large terminal lobe and small lateral
lobes, upper leaves stalkless, often lanceolate, entire.
Flower heads 1·5–2cm across, with ray-florets 8–15,
about 1½ times as long as involucre. Involucre ovoid, with
few short outer basal bracts and much longer
oblong–linear blunt inner bracts which are strongly
keeled in fruit. Jul–Oct. Waysides, hedges, wood verges,
waste places, cultivated land. Throughout area covered,
except IS. **225**

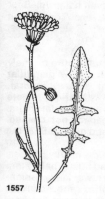

1557 Stinking Hawksbeard *Crepis foetida*
Usually annual with branched stem up to 50cm, smelling of bitter almonds when crushed. Leaves oblanceolate, toothed to twice pinnately lobed; upper leaves elliptic to linear and pinnately lobed, stalkless and clasping stem. Flower heads up to 2cm across, with yellow ray-florets, reddish-purple on outer surface; flower buds drooping. Involucre up to 1·6cm, outer bracts c. $\frac{1}{2}$ as long as inner; receptacle with linear scales. Achenes of two kinds, the outer shortly and coarsely beaked or beakless, the inner with a long slender beak. Jun–Aug. Waysides, waste places. B, GB, F, D.

1558 Beaked Hawksbeard *Crepis vesicaria*
Differs from **1557** in having flower heads erect in bud, and achenes all similar, 10-ribbed and gradually narrowed into a beak as long as achene; pappus longer than involucre. Usually a biennial up to 80cm. Flower heads yellow, 1·5–2·5cm across, in flat-topped cluster; involucre with outer bracts narrow, spreading, with papery margin, inner bracts lanceolate. May–Jul. Waysides, walls. B, F, D, NL; int GB, IRL. **226**

1559 Bristly Hawksbeard *Crepis setosa*
Distinguished by its flower heads and upper part of branches sparsely covered with long stiff bristly hairs. Annual or biennial up to 70cm. Flower heads pale yellow, 1–1·4cm across, erect in bud. Achenes with beak half as long as achene. Jul–Sep. Arable fields. F; int D.

1560 Narrow-leaved Hawksbeard
Crepis tectorum
Annual up to 1m, with basal leaves in a rosette, lanceolate to oblanceolate pointed, toothed or 1–2-pinnately lobed, upper leaves lanceolate or linear, stalkless. Flower heads, yellow, many; florets 10–18mm long; involucral bracts linear–lanceolate, the outer third as long as the inner, and with adpressed hairs on inner surface. Achenes cylindrical, 10-ribbed; pappus with stiff brownish hairs. May–Aug. Sandy ground, fields, walls. B, DK, SF, F, D, NL, N, S.

1561 Marsh Hawksbeard *Crepis paludosa*
Perennial up to 1m, with lower leaves dark green, oblanceolate, toothed, narrowed to a winged leaf-stalk, the middle leaves lanceolate, ovate to fiddle-shaped with a rounded ear-shaped clasping base; the uppermost linear, bract-like. Flower heads yellow, 1·5–2·5cm across, long-stalked, in a lax terminal flat-topped cluster.

443

Involucre bell-shaped, woolly-hairy and with black glandular hairs, outer bracts half as long as linear-lanceolate inner bracts. Achenes with stiff brownish hairs. Jul–Sep. Stream-sides, wet meadows, copses, fens. Throughout area covered.

1562 Northern Hawksbeard *Crepis mollis*
Distinguished by its elliptic to lanceolate entire or finely toothed leaves which are hairy with yellow glandular hairs. Flower heads yellow, 0·3cm across, several; involucre up to 1cm, with linear to linear–lanceolate bracts with black, yellow or brown glandular hairs. Achenes reddish-brown, spindle-shaped, not beaked. Jul–Aug. Stream-sides, mountain woodlands. GB, F, D.

1563 French Hawksbeard *Crepis nicaeensis*
Annual or biennial with strongly ribbed bristly-hairy stem up to 1m, branched above. Basal and lower leaves oblanceolate, with backward-directed lobes, short-stalked; middle and upper leaves lanceolate, deeply toothed, clasping stem with arrow-shaped lobes, all with yellow hairs. Flower heads 2·5cm across, on glandular-hairy stalks, in a flat-topped cluster. Involucral bracts woolly-haired, the outer $\frac{1}{3}$–$\frac{1}{2}$ as long as inner. Achenes golden-brown, spindle-shaped. Jun–Jul. Meadows, arable fields. Native of S. Europe. F; int GB, DK, D, S.

1564 Smooth Hawksbeard *Crepis capillaris*
Hairy annual or biennial usually with many stems 20–100cm. Basal leaves numerous, lanceolate to oblanceolate, either toothed or lobed with backward-pointing lobes, or 2-pinnately lobed, stem leaves similar, smaller. Flower heads yellow, 1·5–1·8cm across, many in a flat-topped cluster. Involucre with linear–lanceolate bracts, usually without glandular hairs, the outer $\frac{1}{3}$–$\frac{1}{2}$ as long as inner. Achenes brown, without beaks. Jun–Sep. Grasslands, heaths, waste places, walls. B, GB, F, D, IRL, NL; int DK, S. **226**

1565 Rough Hawksbeard *Crepis biennis*
Hairy biennial with erect stem up to 120cm, branched above. Basal leaves oblanceolate, toothed or pinnately lobed, with triangular terminal lobe and remote lateral lobes; upper stem-leaves lanceolate to linear, entire or pinnately lobed, stalkless, all rough-hairy. Flower heads yellow, 2–3·5cm across, in a simple or branched cluster; ray-florets golden-yellow, longer than involucre. Outer bracts of involucre spreading, without papery margin, inner bracts linear–lanceolate, downy within. Achenes reddish-brown, narrowed above. Jun–Jul. Pastures, waysides. B, GB, DK, F, D, NL, S; int SF, IRL, N.

1565

444

1566 *Crepis praemorsa*
Hairy perennial with stems up to 75cm, and leaves all
basal in a rosette. Leaves obovate to lanceolate, entire or
toothed, wavy margined, with pale hairs or nearly
hairless, stalked. Flower heads pale yellow, 2·5–3cm
across, few in a narrow elongate cluster. Involucre up to
1·2cm, with linear–lanceolate pointed often hairy bracts,
the outer $\frac{1}{3}$–$\frac{2}{3}$ as long as inner. Achenes pale brown,
spindle-shaped, 20-ribbed. May–Jul. Fields, open woods.
DK, SF, F, D, N, S.

HIERACIUM
(NUMEROUS MICROSPECIES HAVE BEEN RECORDED IN EUROPE BUT THEIR
IDENTIFICATION IS DIFFICULT)

1567 Few-leaved Hawkweed
Hieracium murorum group
Perennial with hairy stems up to 50cm, or more. Leaves
very variable, basal leaves elliptic to oblong, blunt or
acute, entire or deeply toothed, stem-leaves few or
absent. Flower heads yellow, 2–3cm across, few in a
terminal cluster borne on flower stalks with star-shaped
and glandular hairs. Ray-florets hairless or with
glandular hairs. Involucral bracts glandular-hairy and
with star-shaped hairs. May–Aug. Grassland, open
woods, disturbed ground. Throughout area covered.

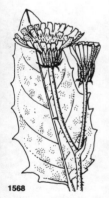

1568 Spotted Hawkweed *Hieracium maculatum* group
Distinguished by its leaves which are bright green with
dull dark brownish-purple blotches; stem-leaves usually
2–4, and involucre usually with small glandular hairs.
Flower heads yellow, c. 3cm across, 6–20 in a lax cluster,
with stalks densely glandular-hairy. Jun–Aug. Walls,
banks, rocks. B, GB, F, D, IRL, NL.

1569 Leafy Hawkweed *Hieracium umbellatum*
Distinguished by its numerous yellow flower heads in a
flat-topped cluster, and with numerous (15–50) leaves on
flowering stem. Stem up to 1m or more, hairy. Leaves
linear to lanceolate, with wedge-shaped base, entire or
toothed, often nearly hairless above, hairy beneath.
Flower heads 3·5–4cm across; involucral bracts usually
hairless, and with recurved apex. Jun–Nov. Grassy
places, open woods, sand-dunes. Throughout area
covered, except IS. **226**

1568

1570 Mouse-eared Hawkweed *Hieracium pilosella*
Distinguished by its long slender leafy stolons spreading
over the ground, and flower heads solitary borne on
densely hairy leafless stems up to 30cm or more. Leaves
in a rosette, oblanceolate to elliptic, entire, narrowed
below, with few or many pale hairs. Flowers 1·8–2·2cm
across, florets pale yellow, red-striped on outer surface;
involucral bracts with dense curled hairs. Very variable

species. May–Oct. Pastures, heaths, rocks, walls, dry
banks. Throughout area covered, except IS. **226**

1571 Alpine Hawkweed *Hieracium alpinum* group
Distinguished by its usually solitary yellow flower heads
2·5–3·5cm across, and leaves mostly in a basal rosette,
with up to 3 lanceolate, bract-like stem-leaves. Flowering
stems to 15cm, or more, with numerous dark hairs.
Leaves elliptic to oblong, entire or deeply toothed, with
winged leaf-stalk, densely hairy. Jul–Aug. Grassy and
rocky places in mountains. GB, SF, F, D, IS, N, S. **226**

WATER-PLANTAIN FAMILY

Alismataceae

Annual or perennial herbs, often aquatic. Leaves alternate or basal. Flowers 3-merous. Fruit a cluster of achenes.

1572 Arrowhead *Sagittaria sagittifolia*
Aquatic perennial up to 90cm, with linear submerged leaves and lanceolate to ovate floating leaves if present, and long-stalked arrow-shaped leaves above water. Flowers white with usually purple patch at base of petals, in a spike-like or branched inflorescence. Flowers c. 2cm across, one-sexed, the female flowers below, shorter-stalked. Stamens numerous with anthers usually purple. Fruiting-head globular, carpels numerous, spirally arranged. Jul–Aug. Shallow ponds, slow-flowing rivers, canals, ditches. Throughout area, except IS.

1572

1573 *Sagittaria natans*
Differs from **1572** in having mostly floating leaves, linear to oblong with base wedge-shaped to heart-shaped with 2 short lobes. Flowers white; anthers yellow. Carpels with short beak below apex (beak apical in **1572**). SF, S. **183**

1574 Lesser Water-plantain *Baldellia ranunculoides*
Flowering-stem 5–20cm, bearing an umbel of long-stalked pale purplish flowers, with a basal rosette of linear–lanceolate, long-stalked leaves. Flowers up to 1·5cm across, with 3 rounded petals up to 1cm, in 1–3 whorls each of 10–20 flowers; bracts small, papery. Fruiting heads spherical. May–Jul. Damp places, ponds, shallow lakes, fens, ditches. B, GB, DK, F, D, IRL, NL, N, S.

1575 Floating Water-plantain *Luronium natans*
Perennial with slender stems either creeping and rooting at the nodes or rising in the water. Lower leaves submerged, and reduced to leaf-stalks; floating and aerial leaves long-stalked with ovate to elliptic blades. Flowers white with yellow spots in middle, 1·2–1·5cm across, long-stalked in axils of floating or aerial leaves. Stamens 6. Fruits in a hemispherical head. May–Aug. Lakes, bogs, canals. B, GB, DK, F, D, NL, N, S.

1576 Water-plantain *Alisma plantago-aquatica*
Erect perennial with stout stem borne above water up to 1m. Leaves ovate to lanceolate with rounded or heart-shaped base, usually aerial. Flowers white or pale lilac, to 1cm across, long-stalked in umbels in an elongated cluster. Outer petals oblong, the inner rounded. Fruit with c. 20 carpels, in a more or less flat head. Jun–Aug. Slow flowing rivers, ponds, ditches, shallow waters. Throughout area covered, except IS.

1576

447

1577 Narrow-leaved Water-plantain
Alisma lanceolatum
Differs from **1576** in having lanceolate to elliptic leaves tapering to the leaf-stalk. Flowers pinkish-purple 6–8mm across; inner petals acute. Carpels with short beak arising near apex (beak long, arising near middle in **1576**). Jun–Sep. Slow rivers, ponds, ditches, shallow waters. Throughout area covered, except IS, N.

1578 Ribbon-leaved Water-plantain
Alisma gramineum
Leaves submerged or aerial, linear to elliptic and narrowed at base into leaf-stalk. Flowers white or purplish-white, 4–6mm across, in an inflorescence longer than the leaves. Petals 2·5–3·5mm; anthers nearly rounded; styles recurved. Aug–Sep. Shallow waters. B, GB, DK, F, D, NL.

1579 *Alisma wahlenbergii*
Differs from **1578** in inflorescence not longer than the leaves. Petals white, 1·5–3mm; anthers rounded; styles shorter than ovary, recurved. Leaves usually submerged, narrowly linear, sometimes narrowly elliptic. Jul–Aug. SF, S.

1580 Parnassia-leaved Water-plantain
Caldesia parnassifolia
Distinguished by its small ovate to elliptic blunt floating and aerial leaves with heart-shaped base, long-stalked. Plant 10–60cm. Flowers white, with petals 5–7mm, in whorls. Stamens 6; carpels 5–10 in a whorl, smooth but longitudinally-ribbed, swollen, beaked. Jul–Sep. Lakes, ditches by fresh waters. F, D.

1581 Starfruit *Damasonium alisma*
Aquatic annual up to 30cm, or more, with oblong–ovate blunt long-stalked floating leaves. Aerial leaves of sub-terrestrial plants, lanceolate to linear–lanceolate. Flowers white with yellow spots at base, c. 6mm across, in several whorls. Carpels usually 6, in a whorl, fused at base; fruits laterally compressed in a star-shaped cluster, with long beaks. Jun–Aug. Ditches, ponds. GB, F.

FLOWERING RUSH FAMILY

Butomaceae

Rhizomatous, aquatic perennial herbs. Flowers in umbellate terminal cluster. Flowers 6-merous. Fruits joined at the base.

1582 Flowering Rush *Butomus umbellatus*
Erect perennial growing in shallow water with stems up to 150cm, with a terminal umbel of many pinkish flowers with darker veins. Leaves linear, all basal, up to 1·5m, 3-angled, sheathing at base. Flowers 2·5–3cm across, many, long-stalked; perianth segments 6; stamens 9; carpels 6. Jun–Aug. Slow streams and rivers, ditches, reed-beds. Throughout area covered, except IS. **254**

FROGBIT FAMILY

Hydrocharitaceae

Aquatic perennial herbs. Flowers 3-merous (petals sometimes absent), subtended by large bracts. Stamens 1–9. Many species are submerged.

1583 Frogbit *Hydrocharis morsus-ranae*
Hairless floating perennial, with rounded to kidney-shaped floating leaves with heart-shaped base, 3–6cm across. Flowers white, c. 2cm across, with 3 broad ovate petals with yellow spots at base, and narrow outer green sepals. Flowers one-sexed, the male flowers 2–3, subtended by bracts; female flowers solitary. Jun–Aug. Ponds, ditches. Throughout area covered, except IS. **183**

1584 Water Soldier *Stratiotes aloides*
Underwater floating water plant, with 3-angled prickly-toothed, rigid, lanceolate pointed leaves in a large rosette, rising to surface at flowering. Flowers white, 3–4cm across, borne above water. Petals rounded, thick; sepals smaller, green. Male flowers several in axil of large bracts; female flowers solitary, stalkless. May–Aug. Still or slow-flowing waters, ponds. B, GB, DK, SF, D, NL, S; int F, IRL. **183**

1585 Canadian Waterweed *Elodea canadensis*

Underwater dark green herbaceous plant, with slender stems with numerous whorls of usually 3 oblong–lanceolate translucent finely toothed leaves each up to 1cm. Stems up to 3m, usually much less, brittle. Flowers either male or female, in tubular bract, greenish-purple, 5mm across, floating, on long stalk from leaf-axil. May–Oct. Slow-flowing waters. Native of N. America. Int throughout area covered, except IS.

1586 Esthwaite Waterweed *Elodea nuttallii*
Differs from **1585**: narrower pointed green leaves 1–1·5mm wide (leaves mostly blunt, 3–4mm wide in **1585**). Male flowers breaking free and rising to surface of water. Sepals of female flowers 1–1·8mm (sepals of female flowers 2–2·7mm *in* **1585**). Jun. Still or slow-moving waters. Native of N. America. Int B, GB, D, IRL, NL.

1585

1587 South American Waterweed
Elodea callitrichoides (=*E. ernstiae*)
Differs from **1586** by its longer leaves up to 2·5cm, gradually tapering to a pointed apex, and sepals of female flowers 3–3·5mm (leaves usually c. 1cm with rounded apex; sepals of female flowers up to 1·8mm in **1586**). Jul–Aug. Still and slow-flowing waters. S. America. Int GB, F.

1588 **Hydrilla** *Hydrilla verticillata*
Submerged aquatic plant with leaves in whorls of 3–8, linear, fringed with teeth, up to 2cm. Flowers tiny, long-stalked, with 3 white petals and sepals. Male flowers breaking free and rising to surface of water. Sepals of female flowers up to 3mm. Petals narrower than sepals, transparent with few red streaks. Jul–Aug. Still waters. Native of Asia, Africa and Australia. Int GB, IRL, D.

1589 **Tape-grass** *Vallisneria spiralis*
Submerged perennial with long ribbon-like leaves up to 1cm wide, with reddish dots and streaks, 3- to 5-veined, arising from basal stolons. Female flowers small up to 4mm, pinkish-white, solitary; male flowers very small, several in cluster with ovoid bract. Stalks of female flowers becoming spirally coiled after flowering; male flower breaking free and rising to surface. Jun–Oct. Fresh-waters. S. Europe. F; int B, GB, D, NL.

1588

RANNOCH RUSH FAMILY

Scheuchzeriaceae

Rhizomatous perennial herbs. Leaves alternate, linear, sheathing at the base. Perianth segments 6, sepal-like. Fruit an inflated carpel.

1590 **Rannoch Rush** *Scheuchzeria palustris*
Hairless perennial with linear leaves with sheathing base, up to 40cm, leaves equal or longer than flowering stem. Flowers greenish-yellow, with 6 narrow–lanceolate perianth segments 2–3mm, in a lax cluster, with leaf-like bracts. Stamens 6; carpels 3, inflated in fruit. Jun–Aug. Wet bogs. B, GB, DK, SF, F, D, NL, N, S.

1590

ARROWGRASS FAMILY

Juncaginaceae

Perennial herbs. Leaves basal, linear. Perianth-segments 2–6, sepal-like. Stamens 6. Fruits 6 (3 sometimes sterile).

1591 Sea Arrowgrass *Triglochin maritima*
Perennial 15–60cm, with short thick rhizome, and with linear fleshy leaves, sheathing at base, all basal. Flowers green, 3–4mm, short stalked, in a long spike borne on leafless stem. Fruit oblong–ovoid with rounded base, 3–4mm. May–Sep. Salt-marshes. Throughout area covered. **191**

1592 Marsh Arrowgrass *Triglochin palustris*
Differs from **1591** in fruit, club-shaped with narrow base. Perennial 20–70cm, with leaves narrower, up to 2mm wide (leaves up to 4mm wide in **1591**). Jun–Aug. Fresh-water marshes, wet meadows. Throughout area covered.

1592

PONDWEED FAMILY

Potamogetonaceae

Submerged or floating, aquatic perennial herbs. Leaves usually with stipules. Flowers 4-merous, green and inconspicuous, borne in pedunculate spikes. Fruit (1–)4 drupes or achenes.

POTAMOGETON
FLOATING LEAVES PRESENT

1593 Broad-leaved Pondweed *Potamogeton natans*
Floating leaves ovate to lanceolate, with wedge-shaped or nearly heart-shaped base, up to 12·5cm long, 7cm broad, with leaf-stalks with a flexible joint below blade, and stalk longer than the blade. Submerged leaves linear, up to 3mm wide. Flower spikes many-flowered, dense cylindrical. Nutlets 3–4mm. May–Sep. Lakes, ponds, ditches, rivers. Throughout area covered. **192**

1594 Bog Pondweed *Potamogeton polygonifolius*
Differs from **1593** in having smaller floating leaves up to 9×4cm, with leaf-stalk shorter or longer than blade and without a flexible joint below the blade. Submerged leaves longer, lanceolate, stalked, often disappearing early. Nutlets 2–2·5mm, red or reddish-brown. May–Oct. Acid waters, peat-bogs, small streams. Throughout area covered, except IS. **192**

1594

1595 Fen Pondweed *Potamogeton coloratus*
Differs from **1594** in having translucent floating leaves (leaves opaque in **1594**) and leaf-stalk not longer than blade; submerged leaves similar to floating leaves but narrower. Nutlets 1·5–1·75mm, greenish. Jun–Jul. Shallow ponds, pools in fens. B, GB, DK, F, D, IRL, NL, S.

1596 Loddon Pondweed *Potamogeton nodosus*
Floating leaves elliptic, to 15×6cm, with wedge-shaped to blunt base, opaque. Submerged leaves lanceolate to elliptic–lanceolate, shortly pointed, leathery; stipules large and conspicuous. Flowering spike 2–6cm, on stout stalk. Nutlets c. 3·5mm, acutely keeled, with short stout beak. Aug–Sep. Gravelly shallow waters, slow rivers. GB, F, D, NL.

1597 Various-leaved Pondweed
Potamogeton gramineus
Floating leaves, if present, elliptic to ovate–elliptic with wedge-shaped or rounded base, opaque, to 7×3cm, with longer leaf-stalk. Submerged leaves elliptic to oblong lanceolate, minutely toothed. Stipules broadly lanceolate, half as long as internodes. Stalk of flowering

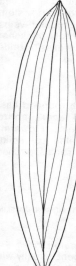

1596

453

spike thickened upwards. Fruiting spike cylindrical,
2·5–5cm; nutlets slightly 3-keeled, short, straight.
Jun–Sep. Lakes, ponds, canals, streams. Throughout
area covered.

1598 Red Pondweed *Potamogeton alpinus*
Plant often tinged red. Floating leaves, if present, elliptic
to oblanceolate with wedge-shaped base, to 8×2cm,
opaque, with leaf-stalks shorter than blade. Submerged
leaves lanceolate to elliptic–oblong, with rounded apex,
secondary veins horizontal (secondary veins ascending
in **1597**). Nutlets 2·5–3mm, with sharp dorsal keel, beak
fairly long, somewhat curved. Jun–Sep. Lakes, ditches,
streams. Throughout area covered.

POTAMOGETON
FLOATING LEAVES ABSENT (SEE ALSO **1597, 1598**)

1599 Shining Pondweed *Potamogeton lucens*
Leaves all submerged, oblong–lanceolate, up to 20cm
long, translucent and with finely toothed margin, stalked;
stipules large and conspicuous, leafy. Flowers in
cylindrical spikes, flowering stem thickened upwards.
Nutlets 3·5–4mm. Jun–Sep. Nutrient-rich lakes, ponds,
canals and streams. Throughout area covered, except IS.

1600 Perfoliate Pondweed *Potamogeton perfoliatus*
Readily distinguished by its broadly ovate to lanceolate
leaves with heart-shaped base surrounding stem,
translucent and with 5–7 strong longitudinal veins.
Flowering spikes cylindrical, stalks not thickened
upwards. Nutlets 3–3·5mm. Jun–Sep. Lakes, ponds,
streams, canals. Throughout area covered.

1601 Long-stalked Pondweed
Potamogeton praelongus

Leaves lanceolate to ovate–oblong with rounded base
and narrowing to a blunt hooded apex, entire,
translucent with 13–17 longitudinal veins. Flowering
stalks 15–40cm, bearing a dense cylindrical spike.
Nutlets 4–6mm. May–Aug. Lakes, rivers, canals, ditches.
Throughout area covered.

POTAMOGETON
FLOATING LEAVES ABSENT; LEAVES PARALLEL-SIDED, NOT MORE THAN 5MM
WIDE

1602 Flat-stalked Pondweed *Potamogeton friesii*
Leaves linear fine-pointed, thin translucent, usually with
5 veins. Flowering spike 0·7–1·5cm, in 3–4 remote whorls,
flowering-stalk flattened, somewhat thickened upwards.
Nutlets 2–3mm. Jun–Aug. Muddy lakes, ponds, canals.
Throughout area covered, except IS.

1603 Shetland Pondweed *Potamogeton rutilus*
Differs from **1602** in having narrowly linear leaves less
than 2mm wide, (leaves 2–3mm wide in **1602**) mostly
3-veined. Leaves rigid, narrowed to a fine point; stipules
tubular below, pointed, strongly veined, papery. Nutlets
brownish-red, 1–2mm. Aug. Lakes. GB, DK, SF, F, D, S.

1604 Lesser Pondweed *Potamogeton pusillus*
Like **1603** but with narrow linear leaves gradually
narrowed to a blunt point, 3-veined. Stipules tubular and
fused nearly to half-way, pale brown (not fibrous and
persistent as in **1603**). Nutlets pale green, 2–2·5mm.
Jun–Sep. Calcareous lakes, ponds, streams. Throughout
area covered.

1604

1605 Blunt-leaved Pondweed
Potamogeton obtusifolius
Distinguished from **1604** by its stipules which are not
fused below, and are separate and curled. Leaves linear
with blunt apex, 2–4mm wide, dark-green, translucent
and with 3–5 veins. Flowering spike 6–13mm, ovoid to
cylindrical. Nutlets 3–4mm, with short dorsal keel.
Jun–Sep. Lakes, ponds, ditches. Throughout area
covered, except IS.

1606 Small Pondweed *Potamogeton berchtoldii*
Differs from **1605** in having smaller nutlets 2–2·5mm, with
rounded dorsal keel. Leaves usually less than 2mm wide,
3-veined. Stipules open, coiled. Jun–Sep. Lakes, ponds,
streams, ditches. Throughout area covered.

1607 Hair-like Pondweed *Potamogeton trichoides*
Distinguished by its very narrow linear pointed leaves,
usually less than 1mm wide, with a prominent mid-vein
thickened towards base and 2 faint lateral veins. Stipules
open coiled, leafy, shining-green. Nutlets 1–3, 2–2·5mm
with keel with rough projections. Jun–Sep. Ponds,
ditches, canals. B, GB, DK, F, D, NL, S.

1608 Grasswrack Pondweed
Potamogeton compressus
Distinguished by its narrow leaves 2–4mm wide, with a
fine point, and with 5 main parallel veins. Stipules coiled,
blunt. Stems strongly compressed, usually winged.
Flowering spikes many-flowered, usually shorter than
flowering stalk. Nutlets usually 2, 3–4·5mm. Jun–Sep.
Lakes, slow streams, ponds, ditches. Throughout area
covered, except IRL, IS.

1609 Sharp-leaved Pondweed
Potamogeton acutifolius
Differs from **1608** in having narrower leaves with 3
parallel veins. Flowering spikes usually few-flowered,
ovoid to globular with 4–8 flowers, shorter than or about
as long as flowering stalk. Leaves 2–4mm wide, fine

455

pointed. Usually only 1 nutlet, with recurved beak.
Jun–Jul. Ponds, streams, ditches. B, GB, DK, F, D, NL, S.

1610 Curled Pondweed *Potamogeton crispus*
Linear–lanceolate blunt leaves 3–15mm wide, toothed
and with conspicuous wavy margins when mature,
translucent and often reddish, shiny. Stems 4-angled,
branched above, up to 1·2m. Stipules open, soon
withering, 1·2cm. Nutlets 4–5mm, with tapering beak the
same length. May–Oct. Lakes, ponds, streams, canals.
Throughout area covered, except IS.

1610

1611 Slender-leaved Pondweed
Potamogeton filiformis
Distinguished by its leaf-sheath which is fused to
leaf-base. Leaves usually less than 1mm wide,
blunt-tipped. Flowering spikes with 2–5 widely spaced
usually 2-flowered whorls. Nutlets fleshy outside,
2–2·75mm. Rhizome slender, creeping. May–Aug.
Brackish water, lakes, streams. GB, DK, SF, F, D, IRL, IS,
N, S.

1612 Fennel Pondweed *Potamogeton pectinatus*
Differs from **1611**, in having leaves with pointed tips, and
sheaths open and coiled, usually white-margined.
Flowering spikes at first cylindrical, later somewhat
interrupted. Nutlets 3–5mm, with short curved beak.
May–Sep. Ponds, rivers, canals, ditches. Throughout
area covered, except IS.

1613 Opposite-leaved Pondweed *Groenlandia densa*
Submerged aquatic with creeping branched rhizome,
with usually opposite, ovate to lanceolate blunt,
translucent leaves, up to 4cm, clasping stem with sheath
fused to leaf-base. Flowering spike borne above water,
usually 4-flowered, short-stalked, recurved in fruit.
Nutlets 3mm, shortly beaked. May–Sep. Swift streams,
ditches, ponds. B, GB, DK, F, D, IRL, NL.

1613

TASSELWEED FAMILY

Ruppiaceae

Submerged, aquatic perennial herbs of salt or brackish water. Leaves linear, sheathing. Flowers in small, pedunculate spikes. Perianth absent, stamens 2. Carpels 4, stalked, indehiscent.

1614 Beaked Tasselweed *Ruppia maritima*
Slender submerged perennial up to 30cm with narrowly linear leaves less than 1mm wide. Flowers without petals or sepals; stamens 2, carpels 4, stalkless in flower, but long-stalked in fruit. Nutlets ovoid curved 2–3mm. Jul–Sep. Salt-marshes, brackish ditches and pools near sea. Throughout area covered.

1615 Spiral Tasselweed *Ruppia cirrhosa* (=*R. spiralis*)
Differs from **1614** in having long fruiting stalks up to 8cm, which are spirally coiled. Leaves usually blunt. Anthers kidney-shaped. (Fruiting stalks less than 6cm, curved not spirally coiled, leaves usually acute, and anthers elliptic in **1614**). Sheaths of involucral leaves usually conspicuously inflated. Jul–Sep. Brackish ditches near sea. Throughout area covered, except IS.

1615

EELGRASS FAMILY

Zosteraceae

Submerged, aquatic perennial herbs of salt-water, with extensive creeping rhizomes. Leaves linear with sheathing bases. Flowers unisexual, in spathe. Perianth absent; stamen and ovule 1. Fruit indehiscent.

1616 Eelgrass *Zostera marina*
Submerged marine perennial, with creeping rhizomes and short non-flowering shoots up to 50cm or more with several dark green linear leaves with sheathing base and rounded fine-pointed apex. Flowering stems up to 80cm or more, much branched. Flowers tiny, with one stalkless stamen and one ovary with 2 long slender styles, borne on one side of the flattened axis and more or less enclosed in the leaf-sheath. Sepals and petals absent. Jun–Sep. Sand, mud or fine gravel in salt-water. Throughout area covered.

1617 Narrow-leaved Eelgrass *Zostera angustifolia*
Like **1616**, but leaves narrower, usually 2mm broad, and stigmas as long as style (leaves 5–10mm broad, stigmas twice as long as style in **1616**). Jun–Nov. Tidal mud-flats in estuaries. GB, DK, IRL, S.

1618 Dwarf Eelgrass *Zostera noltii*
Differing from **1616**, **1617** in having lateral simple or sparsely branched flowering stems, and leaf-sheaths open (flowering stems terminal, branched, and leaf-sheaths closed when young in **1616**, **1617**), also its dwarf habit. Leaves on non-flowering shoots up to 12cm, 0·5–1mm wide; flowering stems up to 10cm. Jun–Oct. Mud on sheltered coasts, in shallow saline waters. Throughout area covered, except SF, IS.

1616

HORNED PONDWEED FAMILY

Zannichelliaceae

Submerged, aquatic perennial herbs of fresh, brackish or salt-water, with creeping rhizomes. Leaves linear with sheathing bases. Flowers inconspicuous, unisexual, axillary in spathe. Perianth absent; stamen 1. Fruit a single achene.

1619 Horned Pondweed *Zannichellia palustris*
Submerged perennial of fresh or brackish waters, with simple or branched, slender leafy stems up to 50cm, and a slender creeping rhizome. Leaves linear, up to 2mm wide, tapering to a point, translucent. Flowers several, in axils of papery cup-shaped bract; petals and sepals absent; male flowers with 1 stamen; female flowers 1 carpel with enlarged wavy-margined stigma. Fruit 3–6mm, beaked. Very variable species. May–Aug. Rivers, streams, ditches, ponds. Throughout area covered.

1619

NAIAD FAMILY

Najadaceae

Submerged, aquatic annual herbs of fresh or brackish water. Leaves opposite, linear with sheathing bases. Flowers unisexual, inconspicuous, axillary. Stamens 1. Fruit a single indehiscent achene.

1620 Holly-leaved Naiad *Najas marina*
Slender brittle annual up to 30cm. Distinguished by its broadly linear leaves 1–6mm wide, having a wavy margin with many spiny teeth, and with entire basal sheaths. Flowers stalkless, in leaf axils, one-sexed on different plants. Male flower enclosed in spathe, with 2-lipped perianth and 1 stamen; female flowers naked, with 1 carpel. Fruit ovoid, to 6mm. Jul–Aug. Fresh and brackish waters. Throughout area covered, except IRL, IS.

1621 Slender Naiad *Najas flexilis*
Distinguished from **1620** by its narrower leaves less than 1mm wide, with 20–36 teeth on each margin; sheaths with sloping shoulders. Fruit c. 3mm. Aug–Sep. Lakes. Native of N. America. Int GB, DK, SF, D, IRL, N, S.

1622 *Najas minor*
Differs from **1621** in having leaf-sheaths with short rounded basal lobes, and leaves with 5–17 teeth on each margin. Leaves up to 3cm long, less than 1mm wide. Male and female flowers on same plant. Fruit 2–3mm. Jun–Sep. Lakes, rivers. B, F, D.

1620

LILY FAMILY

Liliaceae

Perennial herbs often with bulbs, corms or rhizomes. Leaves all basal or alternate. Inflorescence a raceme or umbel. Flowers 3-merous, regular. Perianth-segments 6, petal-like; stamens usually 6. Fruit a capsule or berry with numerous seeds. A large family, chiefly of warmer climates, notably the Mediterranean region.

1623

1623 Scottish Asphodel *Tofieldia pusilla*
Perennial with a basal rosette of sword-shaped and densely tufted leaves, up to 8cm. Flowering-stem leafless up to 20cm, with 5–10 white or greenish flowers in an elongated cluster. Flowers 3–5mm across, with obovate–oblong blunt perianth-segments. Capsule 2·5–3mm. Jun–Aug. Moorlands, bogs, streamsides in mountains. GB, SF, F, D, IS, N, S.

1624 German Asphodel *Tofieldia calyculata*
Differs from **1623** in bract at base of lower-stalk entire, and with 3-lobed bracteole immediately below flowers (basal bract of flower-stalk 3-lobed, and bracteole absent in **1623**). Flower clusters cylindrical, to 6cm, with up to 30 flowers. Flowers yellow, rarely reddish, to 7mm across. Jun–Aug. Wet places, damp meadows. F, D, S. **204**

1625 Bog Asphodel *Narthecium ossifragum*
Moorland or bog perennial, readily distinguished by its spike-like cluster of yellow flowers and sword-shaped leaves in two ranks. Flowering stems up to 45cm, with small clasping leaves at base, and with larger upper leaves bearing 6–20 stalked flowers. Perianth-segments 6–9mm, narrowly lanceolate, greenish outside, spreading in flower and erect in fruit; anthers orange. Capsule narrowly ovoid. Stem and flowers becoming deep orange after flowering. Jul–Sep. Peat-bogs, wet heaths, moorlands. Throughout area covered, except SF, IS. **226**

1626 False Helleborine *Veratrum album*
Erect poisonous perennial 50–150cm, with distinctive broadly ovate leaves which are conspicuously longitudinally folded, the upper narrower. Flowers white and greenish inside, or greenish-white or yellowish on both sides, 1·5–2·5cm across, in a dense terminal branched cluster. Perianth-segments spreading in a star; stamens 6. Fruit a capsule. Jun–Aug. Damp grassland, mainly in mountains. SF, F, D, N. **204**

1627 St Bernard's Lily *Anthericum liliago*
Slender hairless perennial with leaves all basal, and white flowers in a lax elongated cluster on unbranched

stem up to 70cm. Leaves linear, somewhat channelled.
Flowers star-shaped, with 6 oblong–elliptic perianth-
segments 1·6–2·2cm long. Capsule ovoid, up to 1cm.
May–Jul. Open woods, stony slopes, dry grassland. B,
DK, F, D, S. **183**

1628 *Anthericum ramosum*
Differs from **1627** in its branched pyramidal inflorescence and smaller flowers, with perianth-segments
1–1·4cm long, the inner broader than the outer, and style
straight (style curved in **1627**). Stamens as long as
perianth-segments (half as long in **1627**). Jun–Aug. Dry
sunny places, and open scrub. DK, F, D, S. **183**

1629 Kerry Lily *Simethis planifolia*
Perennial with erect flexuous stem up to 40cm, with
white flowers purplish outside, in a lax branched cluster.
Leaves linear, all basal, longer than flowering stem.
Roots tufted, spindle-shaped, fleshy. Flowers with 6
spreading narrowly elliptic, 5- to 7-veined perianth-
segments 9–11mm long. Capsule globular, c. 5mm.
May–Jul. Heaths near the sea, rocky places. F, IRL.

1629

1630 Meadow Saffron *Colchicum autumnale*
Distinguished by its crocus-like flowers which are
pinkish or lilac-purple on long white stalks flowering in
autumn without leaves. Leaves usually 4, appearing in
spring from an ovoid or globular corm with dark brown
scale; leaves broadly lanceolate up to 25cm long, with
central short-stalked capsule up to 6cm. Flowers
bell-shaped with ovate perianth-segments 4–6cm long;
anthers yellow. Aug–Nov. Damp meadows, woods. B,
GB, F, D, IRL, NL; int DK, S. **254**

1631 Snowdon Lily *Lloydia serotina*
Slender hairless perennial 5–15cm or more, with solitary
or paired white flowers with reddish or purplish veins,
and 2–4 basal thread-like leaves longer than the
flowering stem. Perianth-segments oblong, 9–15mm
long, spreading. Stem-leaves broader and shorter than
basal leaves, the upper bract-like. Capsule globular,
3-ribbed. Jun–Aug. Rock ledges, stony slopes, alpine
meadows. GB, F, D.

1632 Yellow Star of Bethlehem *Gagea lutea*
Perennial with hairless flowering stem 10–30cm, bearing
1–7 yellow, bell-shaped flowers 1·5–1·8cm long, in an
umbel-like cluster. Basal leaf solitary, narrowly
lanceolate with hooded apex; stem leaves 2, opposite,
with hairy margins. Capsule globular. Bulb solitary in
tunic. Mar–May. Grassland, stony ground, damp woods.
B, GB, DK, SF, F, D, NL, N, S. **227**

1631

1633 Least Gagea *Gagea minima*
Differs from **1632** in having narrowly lanceolate

1635

long-pointed perianth-segments 1–1·5cm long, and narrow basal leaf 1–2mm wide (basal leaf 7–15mm wide in **1632**). Capsule obovoid. Bulbs 2 in common tunic. Mar–May. Woods, meadows. DK, SF, D, N, S.

1634 Belgian Gagea *Gagea spathacea*
Distinguished from **1633** in having 2 narrowly linear hollow cylindrical basal leaves, and a single oblong–lanceolate, hooded, hairless leaf below the broad bracts. Flowers yellow-green, 2–4, with linear–lanceolate perianth-segments 1–1·3cm. Bulbs 2 in common tunic. Apr–May. Woods, scrub. B, DK, F, D, NL, S.

1635 *Gagea arvensis*
Distinguished by its downy stem and shaggy-haired bracts. Flowers 5–12, with lanceolate perianth-segments, 1·3–1·5cm, with deflexed apices. Basal leaves narrowly linear; stem-leaves 2, lanceolate, hairy. Feb–Apr. Cultivated ground. DK, F, D, NL, S.

1636 Early Star of Bethlehem *Gagea bohemica*
Basal leaves 2, thread-like, stem-leaves lanceolate pointed. Flowers yellow, solitary or 2–3, on stem usually less than 2cm; perianth-segments 1·3–1·7cm, hairy. Capsule obovoid, with notched apex. Feb–Mar. Dry grassland, rocky places. GB, F, D.

1637 Meadow Gagea *Gagea pratensis*
Basal leaf solitary, broadly linear, flat, 2·5mm wide; bulbs usually 3, one with a tunic. Flowers greenish-yellow in umbel-like cluster of 2–6, with a pair of opposite lanceolate bracts with hairy margins; flowering stem hairless. Perianth-segments oblong–linear, 1·5–2cm, spreading in a star. Capsule ovoid. Apr. Fields, grassy places, rocks. DK, F, D, NL, S; int SF.

1638 Wild Tulip *Tulipa sylvestris*
Distinguished by its large solitary erect bell-shaped flower, with yellow perianth, the segments greenish or purplish-tinged outside. Flowering stem 8–45cm, with 2–3 linear–lanceolate grooved leaves at base. Flowers nodding in bud, erect in flowers with elliptic-acute petals 3–5cm. Capsule twice as long as wide. Bulb 1·8–4·5cm long, with a tough outer tunic. Apr–May. Mountain meadows and woodlands, orchards, vineyards. S. and S-E. Europe. F; int B, GB, DK, D, NL, N, S. **227**

1639 Fritillary *Fritillaria meleagris*
Distinguished by its large broadly bell-shaped nodding flower with dull purple perianth-segments mottled with purple-brown, or frequently white. Bulbous perennial, with stem 20–40cm, with 3–6 linear, alternate leaves. Flowers solitary, 3–4·5cm, with linear, green nectaries. Style 3-lobed. Capsule nearly globular, 3-angled.

Apr–May. Water-meadows, stream-sides. GB, F, D, NL; int DK, SF, N, S. **269**

1640 Martagon Lily *Lilium martagon*

Erect bulbous perennial with flowering stem 50–200cm, with whorls of leaves, and 5–10 or more, pink or dark reddish-purple, often spotted nodding flowers. Leaves oblanceolate, in whorls of 5–10, the upper alternate. Perianth-segments to 3·5cm, strongly recurved; anthers reddish-purple or orange-yellow. Capsule ovoid, 6-angled. Jun–Sep. Woods, scrub; often cultivated. F, D; int B, GB, DK, SF, NL, N, S.

1641 *Lilium bulbiferum*

Distinguished by its 1–3 orange or bright red flowers, with erect perianth-segments, spotted within, 5·5–8·5cm long. Flowering stem 30–80cm; leaves lanceolate to ovate–lanceolate, with or without bulbils in the axils. Jun–Jul. Rocks, woods, mountain meadows. F, D; int ?SF, N, S. **235**

1642 Pyrenean Lily *Lilium pyrenaicum*

Flowers usually greenish-yellow with dark purple lines and spots within, usually 1–8, on stem 30–90cm. Leaves alternate, linear–lanceolate. Perianth-segments 5–6·5cm, strongly recurved; anthers reddish-brown. Jun–Jul. Hedge-banks; often cultivated. Native of S. France & N. Spain. Int GB, IRL.

1643 Common Star of Bethlehem

Ornithogalum umbellatum

Distinguished by its flat-topped cluster of white flowers, with flower-stalks unequal, the lower longer than upper, borne on stem 10–30cm. Leaves all basal, linear, grooved, with white stripe on upper surface, longer than flowering stem. Flowers with 6 lanceolate perianth-segments 1·5–2·2cm, with green stripe on outer side. Bulb with numerous bulbils. Capsule obovoid, 6-angled. Apr–Jun. Dry grassy places, waysides. B, GB, F, D, NL; int DK, SF, IRL, N, S. **183**

1644 Spiked Star of Bethlehem

Ornithogalum pyrenaicum

Distinguished from **1643** by its long cylindrical many-flowered inflorescence with small pale yellow flowers within, greenish outside with dark green stripe. Flowers 6–13mm long, with more or less equal flower-stalks. Flowering stem up to 1m; leaves all basal, linear, blue-green, withering at flowering. Capsule ovoid, 3-grooved. May–Jul. Woods, scrub, hedgebanks, vineyards. B, GB, F. **204**

1645 Drooping Star of Bethlehem

Ornithogalum nutans

Distinguished from **1643** by its larger flowers 2–3cm long,

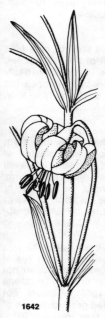

1642

2–12 in a lax spike, borne on stem 25–60cm. Flowers white, greenish outside; stamens with broad filaments with longitudinal crest on mid-vein. Capsule ovoid, 6-grooved, pendulous. Bulb with numerous offsets. Apr–May. Grassy places, vineyards. Native of the Balkan Peninsula. Int B, GB, DK, F, D, NL, N, S.

1646 Spring Squill *Scilla verna*
Small bulbous perennial with small terminal cluster of 2–12 blue-violet flowers appearing in the spring. Leaves all basal, linear, appearing before flowers, about as long as flowering stem. Perianth-segments spreading, ovate–lanceolate pointed, 5–8mm long; anthers violet. Apr–May. Grassy places and cliffs on coasts. GB, F, IRL, N. **288**

1647 Autumn Squill *Scilla autumnalis*
Differs from **1646**, in having purple flowers without bracts and flowering in the autumn. Leaves linear, appearing after flowering. Flowering stem 4–25cm. Perianth-segments oblong, 4–6mm long; anthers purple. Jul–Sep. Dry grassland, often near sea. GB, F. **254**

1648 Alpine Squill *Scilla bifolia*
Distinguished by its few (1–5) bright blue to pale lilac flowers, the lower long-stalked in a one-sided cluster. Flowering stem up to 20cm. Leaves usually 2, broadly linear, sheathing stem to about half-way and appearing with the flowers. Perianth-segments 5–10mm. Mar–May. Meadows, woods, scrub. B, F, D; int NL. **288**

1649 Bluebell *Hyacinthoides non-scripta*
Bulbous perennial with erect leafless flowering stem 20–50cm, bearing a one-sided spike-like cluster of blue-violet drooping bell-shaped flowers. Leaves linear–lanceolate, 3–6, as long as flowering stem. Flowers up to 2cm, richly scented, with tips of perianth-segments outcurved, borne on short stalks in axils of bluish papery bracts. Apr–June. Woods, scrub, heaths, sea-cliffs. B, GB, F, IRL, NL; int D. **288**

1650

1650 Spanish Bluebell *Hyacinthoides hispanica*
Differs from **1649** in having blue flowers without tips of perianth-segments outcurved, and flowering cluster not one-sided. Stamens equal, with blue anthers (stamens unequal with yellow anthers in **1649**). Flowers not scented. May. Shady places, cultivated ground. Native of S. and W. Europe; escaping from gardens. Int GB, F, IRL.

1651 Tassel Hyacinth *Muscari comosum*
Distinguished by its spike of brownish spreading lower fertile flowers and its terminal flat-topped cluster of erect bright violet sterile flowers. Fertile flowers oblong to urn-shaped, 5–9mm; sterile flowers up to 6mm, rounded

or obovoid. Flowering stem 20–60cm; leaves usually 3–5, shorter than flowering stem. Very variable species. Apr–Jul. Fields, vineyards, dry grassland. F, D; int B, GB, DK, NL. **282**

1652 Small Grape Hyacinth *Muscari botryoides*
Flowers bright blue, at first in a dense terminal cluster which later elongates; sterile flowers few, smaller, pale blue, short-stalked. Flowering stem up to 30cm, usually longer than the 2–3 linear–oblanceolate leaves. Fertile flowers globular, 2·5–4mm, with white recurved teeth. Capsule globular. Mar–May. Fields, woods, meadows. F, D; int B, NL. **282**

1653 Grape Hyacinth *Muscari neglectum*
Distinguished by its very dark blue or bluish-black flowers in a dense cluster, smelling of soap. Fertile flowers 3·5–7·5mm, ovoid to urn-shaped, with white curved teeth; sterile flowers smaller, paler. Flowering stem up to 30cm; leaves 3–6 linear–lanceolate, channelled, usually as long or longer than flowering stem. A very variable species. Mar–May. Fields, vineyards, dry banks. F, D; int GB. **286**

ALLIUM
LEAVES LINEAR, HOLLOW AND CYLINDRICAL IN SECTION

1654 Onion *Allium cepa*
Robust bulbous perennial with stout hollow stem up to 1m, inflated below. Leaves up to 10, almost semicircular in section, with sheathing base. Umbel globular, 4–9cm across, dense, many-flowered. Flowers white with green stripe, perianth-segments spreading in a star, each 3–4·5mm; stamens longer. A very variable species. Jul–Sep. Cultivated throughout area covered, sometimes escaping.

1655 Welsh Onion *Allium fistulosum*
Differs from **1654** in having leaves circular in section, and stem widest about the middle (leaves semi-circular in section, stem widest at base in **1654**). Flowers yellowish-white, open bell-shaped with petals 7–9mm and stamens 8–12mm. Jul–Sep. Cultivated, and occasionally escaping.

1656 Chives *Allium schoenoprasum*
Slender perennial with lilac or pale purple flowers, in dense rounded head 1·5–5cm across. Perianth-segments lanceolate, up to 1·5cm, stamens shorter. Flowering-stem 10–50cm, rounded; leaves 1–2, hollow cylindrical, linear, long-sheathed at base. Very variable species. Jun–Jul. Damp meadows, stream-sides, damp mountain rocks, coastal cliffs. Throughout area covered, except IS; int B. **266**

ALLIUM

LEAVES HALF-CYLINDRICAL IN SECTION, FLAT OR GROOVED ABOVE

1657 Field Garlic *Allium oleraceum*

Lax rounded flower cluster of whitish flowers tinged green, pink or brown, on long stalks with few or many bulbils at base of cluster. Flowers bell-shaped, up to 7mm long, outer segments broader than inner; stamens same length; spathes surrounding flower cluster with long slender apex. Flowering-stem up to 1m; leaves 2–4, linear or thread-like, grooved above and ribbed beneath, sheathing at base. Jul–Aug. Rocky ground, scrub, roadsides. Throughout area covered, except IRL; int IS.

1658 Round-headed Leek *Allium sphaerocephalon*

Flowers pinkish to dark reddish-purple in a broad dense globular umbel, usually less than 3cm across, many long-stalked, usually without bulbils. Perianth-segments ovate, c. 5mm, rough on back; stamens longer. Flowering stems up to 80cm; leaves 2–6, linear, grooved, hollow, sheathing below. A variable species. Jun–Aug. Cultivated ground, dry open places. B, GB, F, D. **288**

1659

1659 Wild Onion *Allium vineale*

Flowers pink to dark red, or greenish-white, in a globular umbel 2–5cm across, numerous, stalked, with or without bulbils. Flowers bell-shaped, with perianth-segments 2–4·5mm, the inner usually narrower, stamens longer or shorter. Flowering stems 30–120cm; leaves 2–4, linear, half-cylindrical hollow, sheathing stem below. A variable species. Jun–Aug. Dry grassland, cultivated ground, roadsides. Throughout area covered, except IS.

ALLIUM

LEAVES SOLID, NOT HOLLOW

1660 Keeled Garlic *Allium carinatum*

Has a lax umbel of long-stalked purple flowers with a dense cluster of bulbils at base, and spathes with long apex, longer than the umbel. Flowers cup-shaped with blunt perianth-segments 4–6mm, stamens much longer. Flowering stems to 60cm; leaves 2–4, linear and grooved above, sheath long. Jul–Aug. Meadows, heaths, scrub. DK, F, D, S; int B, GB, IRL, NL. **270**

1661 *Allium suaveolens*

Flowers pink or white with pink keel, in a hemispherical umbel 2–3·5cm across. Flowers cup-shaped, 4–5mm long, with stamens much longer; spathes about as long as umbel. Stem up to 50cm; leaves 2–5, linear, flat-keeled beneath. Jul–Sep. Damp meadows and moors. F, D.

1662 *Allium lineare*

Differs from **1661** in having inner stamens with a small

tooth on each side at base, and dehiscing anthers 0–5mm long (inner stamens without teeth at base, and dehiscing anthers c. 1·5mm long in **1661**). Flowering stem up to 60cm; leaves 2–4, linear, ribbed beneath. Jul–Aug. Rocky slopes, mountain grasslands. F, D.

1663 Three-cornered Leek *Allium triquetrum*
Distinguished by its 3-angled stem, and relatively large drooping bell-shaped flowers, with perianth-segments with green stripe outside. Flowers 3–15, usually in a lax one-sided umbel; each flower 1·5–2cm across. Stem 20–45cm; leaves linear, usually 2–3, all basal, strongly keeled. Mar–Jun. Waste places, hedge-banks, woods, shady places. F; int GB, IRL. **184**

1664 Few-flowered Leek *Allium paradoxum*
Differs from **1663** in having umbel with few white flowers and many bulbils, and only 1 basal leaf (umbel without bulbils and leaves usually 2–3 in **1663**). Usually one flower, up to c. 1cm long, or absent; bulbils numerous, green. Apr–May. Grassy places, roadsides. Locally naturalized. Native of USSR (Caucasus). Int GB, DK, D, IRL, NL.

1664

1665 Rosy Garlic *Allium roseum*
Flowers pink or white, in an umbel of 5–30 long-stalked flowers, the umbel up to 7cm across, with or without bulbils. Flowers bell-shaped to broadly cup-shaped with perianth-segments 7–12mm; stamens shorter. Flowering-stem 10–65cm; leaves 2–4, linear with rough margin, sheathing at base. Bulb with numerous bulbils. Apr–Jun. Cultivated ground, vineyards. F; int GB. **255**

1666 Sand Leek *Allium scorodoprasum*
Flower heads with purplish bulbils and 0–12 flowers which are probably sterile, in a lax umbel up to 5cm across. Flowers reddish-lilac, ovoid; perianth-segments 4–7mm, stamens shorter, the inner stamens having filaments with lateral lobes much longer than the anthers. Flowering stem 25–90cm; leaves 2–5, linear, flat or channelled, sheathing at base. May–Aug. Grassland, scrub. GB, DK, SF, F, D, NL, N, S; int B, IRL. **270**

1667 Babington's Leek *Allium ampeloprasum*
Flowers white, pink or dark red, in a large globular umbel 5–9cm across, with very many flowers (up to 500), without or with a few bulbils. Flowering stem 50–200cm, with 4–10 linear flat grooved leaves with rough margins, sheathing up to half the stem. Flowers bell-shaped or cup-shaped, 4–5·5mm long, with stamens as long or longer. A variable species; the plant found in area covered is a distinct local variety (regarded as a species by some botanists) of a widespread Mediterranean species, the true Wild Leek. Jul–Aug. Waste places, hedges, and banks near the sea. GB, F, IRL. **254**

1668 *Allium angulosum*
Flowers pale purple, many in a hemispherical umbel
2·5–4·5cm across, borne on angled flowering stem up to
45cm. Leaves 4–6, linear, grooved above and sharply
keeled beneath. Flowers cup-shaped, the inner
perianth-segments longer than the outer, and anthers
longer than segments, at first yellow than dark purple.
Jun–Aug. Marshes, damp places. F, D.

1669 German Garlic *Allium senescens*
Very like **1668** but distinguished by its smooth leaves
which are rounded beneath, and stamens usually
distinctly longer than perianth-segments (leaves keeled
beneath and anthers only slightly exserted in **1668**). Stem
up to 45cm; leaves 4–9. Flowers lilac, 3·5–8mm long.
Jun–Aug. Dry, usually rocky places, sands. F, D, S; int N.

1669

ALLIUM
LEAVES LANCEOLATE TO NARROWLY OVATE

1670 Ramsons *Allium ursinum*
Distinguished by its narrowly elliptic to narrowly ovate
stalked leaves, and its lax umbel of white flowers.
Flowering stem 20–50cm, usually 2-angled, sometimes
3-angled; leaves 2–3. Umbel with 6–20 long-stalked
flowers, without bulbils, with perianth-segments
lanceolate, spreading, 7–12mm, stamens a little shorter.
Apr–Jun. Damp woods. Throughout area covered,
except IS. **184**

1671 *Allium victorialis*
Leaves 2–3, broadly elliptic to narrowly lanceolate with
short leaf-stalk. Flowers greenish-white, numerous in a
globular or hemispherical umbel 3–5cm across.
Perianth-segments 4–5mm, the inner broader, stamens
distinctly longer than segments. Stem up to 60cm.
Jun–Aug. Woods, rocks in mountains. F, D.

1672 Lily of the Valley *Convallaria majalis*
Flowers white, bell-shaped, drooping, short-stalked, in a
lax one-sided spike-like cluster, on stem 20–40cm.
Leaves usually 2, arising from the creeping rhizome, with
sheathing base and ovate–lanceolate to elliptic blade.
Flowers c. 8mm, fragrant. Fruit a red berry. May–Jul. Dry
woods, often on limestone. Throughout area covered,
except IRL, IS. **184**

1673 May Lily *Maianthemum bifolium*
Distinguished by its heart-shaped acute, alternate leaves
with prominent parallel veins above. Flowers white,
15–20, in dense terminal cluster on stem up to 20cm.
Perianth-segments 4, spreading, 2–3mm; stamens 4,
shorter than segments. Fruit a red berry. May–Jul.

1673

1674

Woods, shady places. Throughout area covered, except IRL, IS.

1674 *Streptopus amplexifolius*
Distinguished by its oblong–ovate to heart-shaped alternate leaves clasping the stem, and with usually solitary bell-shaped flowers borne on a slender strongly recurved flower-stalk from the axils of the upper leaves. Stem up to 1m, branched above, leaves decreasing in size up stem. Flowers up to 1cm, with 6 perianth segments. Fruit a red berry. Jul–Aug. Woods, damp rocks. F, D.

1675 Solomon's Seal *Polygonatum multiflorum*
Erect perennial with arching upper part of stem, up to 80cm, from a creeping rhizome. Leaves elliptic–ovate, alternate, clasping stem or shortly stalked. Flowers greenish-white, tubular, in stalked cluster of 2–6 from the axils of the middle leaves. Perianth-segments 9–20mm long, with spreading apex. Fruit a bluish-black berry. May–Jun. Woods. Throughout area covered, except IRL, IS. **184**

1676 Angular Solomon's Seal
Polygonatum odoratum
Differs from **1675** in having 1–2 flowers from axils of middle leaves, and flowers scented, with perianth not contracted in the middle (perianth contracted in the middle, and flowers not scented in **1675**). Perennial to 65cm, with angled stem (stem not angled in **1675**). Flowers 1·2–3cm. May–Jul. Woods, shady rocks. B, GB, DK, SF, F, D, NL, N, S. **184**

1677

1677 Whorled Solomon's Seal
Polygonatum verticillatum
Distinguished by its linear to narrowly oblong leaves, the middle and upper in whorls of 3–8. Flowers white tipped green, stalked, 1–2 from axils of leaves; perianth tubular, 5–10mm long. Stem angled, up to 80cm. Fruit red becoming dark purple. May–Jul. Woods, scrub, rocky ground. B, GB, DK, F, D, NL, N, S.

1678 Herb Paris *Paris quadrifolia*
Erect perennial 15–40cm, from a creeping rhizome, with a solitary terminal greenish flower, with a whorl of 4 obovate leaves below flower. Leaves 3–5-veined, with wedge-shaped base, short stalked. Sepals 4–6, lanceolate, green; petals 4–6, linear greyish-yellow, sepals and petals 2–3·5cm. Stamens 6–10. Fruit globular, black. May–Jul. Woods, damp places. Throughout area covered, except IRL.

1679 Wild Asparagus *Asparagus officinalis*
Perennial with creeping rhizome and annual branched stems 150–200cm, with linear leaf-like cladodes in

clusters of 4–15. Flowers greenish-yellow 4·5–6·5mm, narrowly bell-shaped, borne on jointed stalk, usually 2 from each node of the stem. Berry red. Apr–Jun. Sand-dunes and cliffs, fallow land, often as an escape from cultivation. B, GB, DK, F, D, IRL, NL, S; int SF, N. Ssp. *prostratus*, found at some coastal sites, has spreading stems up to 50cm, with shorter, fleshy cladodes up to 1cm.

1680 Butcher's Broom *Ruscus aculeatus*

Distinctive stiff dark green, much branched shrub up to 1m, with numerous stiff sharp-pointed leaf-like cladodes, 1–4cm with tiny flowers borne on their upper surface. Flowers dull green with violet spots, to 7mm across, with spreading segments, male or female; stamens united in a dark violet column. Fruit a red berry, c. 1cm in diameter. Feb–Apr. Woods, scrub, sea-cliffs. GB, F.

1680

DAFFODIL FAMILY

Amaryllidaceae

Glabrous perennial herbs with bulbs. Leaves all basal.
Flowers regular, solitary or in few-flowered umbels,
subtended by papery spathe. Perianth-segments 6,
petal-like; stamens 6. Fruit a capsule with numerous
seeds. A mainly tropical or warm-temperate family.

1681 Summer Snowflake *Leucojum aestivum*
Flowering stem stout, hollow, about equalling the leaves,
35–60cm. Leaves broadly linear, flat, all basal. Flowers
white with green spot just below thickened apex of
perianth-segments, usually 3–5, stalked, in a terminal
cluster. Perianth-segments 10–20mm long; spathe
papery, to 5cm. Seeds black. Apr–May. Marshes, meadows, woods by rivers. B, GB, F, D, IRL, NL; int DK. **184**

1682 Spring Snowflake *Leucojum vernum*
Like **1681** but flowers usually solitary, on flowering stem
15–35cm, usually longer than the leaves. Seeds whitish.
Flowers with perianth-segments 1·5–2·5cm, with white or
yellow spot below apex of segments. Feb–Apr. Damp or
shady places. B, F, D; int GB, DK, NL. **184**

1683 Snowdrop *Galanthus nivalis*
Flower solitary, white, nodding, slightly scented, with
spathe about as long as flower-stalk, distinguished from
1682 by its outer perianth segments which are about
twice as long as inner segments. Flowering stem usually
10–25cm; leaves 2, linear, flat and with membraneous
sheath at base. Outer perianth-segments 12–35mm,
inner segments wedge-shaped, deeply notched and with
green patch near apex. Jan–Apr. Woods, hedges,
streamsides. F, D; int B, GB, NL, N, S. **186**

1684 Wild Daffodil *Narcissus pseudonarcissus*
Flowers large with 6 pale yellow spreading segments,
and a dark yellow tube as long as the segments, borne
solitarily on a leafless stem 10–35cm. Leaves basal, linear
blunt-tipped, usually blue-green, about as long as the
flower-stem. Flowers 5–6cm across, nodding, with
papery spathe. A very variable species. Feb–Apr. Woods,
meadows, rocky ground. GB, F, D, NL.

1685 Poet's Narcissus *Narcissus poeticus*
Readily distinguished by its solitary flower 4–6cm across
with 6 white spreading segments, and a very much
shorter pale yellow tube to 2·5mm with red or papery
toothed margin. Flowering-stems up to 50cm; leaves
linear, more or less blue-green. Apr–Jun. Mountain
meadows, grassy places. Native of C. and S. Europe. F;
int B, GB, D. **186**

1684

YAM FAMILY

Dioscoreaceae

Climbing perennials with large tubers. Flowers small, greenish, unisexual, in axillary inflorescence. Mainly tropical family that includes the yams.

1686 Black Bryony *Tamus communis*
Annual twining stems up to 4m, from a large ovoid tuber. Leaves broadly ovate with heart-shaped base, long-pointed, with 3–6 conspicuous veins, stalked. Flowers greenish-yellow, 3–6mm, in axillary clusters; male flowers with 6 spreading segments; female flowers with 6 narrow segments. Fruit a red berry. May–Jul. Woods, hedgerows. B, GB, F, D; int IRL. **235**

IRIS FAMILY

Iridaceae

Perennial herbs with bulbs, corms or rhizomes. Flowers solitary or many in an inflorescence. Flowers 3-merous. Perianth-segments petal-like. Fruit a capsule with numerous seeds.

1687 Blue-eyed Grass *Sisyrinchium bermudiana*
Distinguished by its 2–4 blue flowers each up to 2cm across, borne from a long lanceolate spathe, on a flattened flowering stem up to 45cm. Leaves linear or sword-shaped, 1–5mm wide. Perianth-segments ovate, wedge-shaped at base with a fine point at base. Capsule rounded, 3-lobed, blackish-purple when ripe. Jul. Damp grassland, lake shores. IRL; int GB, F.

1688 *Sisyrinchium californicum*
Distinguished by its bright yellow flowers to 3cm across, and capsule 9–12mm (capsule c. 5mm in **1687**). Stem broadly winged, to 50cm; leaves 3–6mm wide. Damp grassland, lake-shores. Native of California. Int IRL.

1687

IRIS
OUTER PETALS WITH TUFT OF HAIRS AT BASE

1689 Flag Iris *Iris germanica*
Stout perennial up to 1m, with purple, scented flowers up to 10cm across, and with spathes papery in upper half. Leaves up to 3·5cm wide, spear-shaped, shorter than the branched flowering stem. Outer petals ovate–oblong, dark purple, with yellow tuft of hairs at base, inner petals

incurved, about as long as outer, light purple. May–Jun.
Walls, rocks, waste places; widely cultivated. Native of E.
Mediterranean. Int B, GB, DK, F, D. **282**

1690 *Iris aphylla*
Distinguished from **1689** by its spathe surrounding the
flowers, green except for a narrow papery margin.
Flowering stem up to 30cm, or more, branched below the
middle; leaves usually sickle-shaped. Flowers violet to
purple, 3–5; outer petals narrowly obovate, inner broadly
elliptic and short-stalked. Apr–May. Rocks, screes. F, D.

IRIS
OUTER PETALS WITHOUT A TUFT OF HAIRS AT BASE

1691 Siberian Iris *Iris sibirica*
Flowers violet-blue, rarely white, usually 1–3 borne on
hollow stems up to 120cm, usually with 3 small
stem-leaves. Flowers long-stalked from brown spathes.
Outer petals obovate to rounded, up to 5cm; inner petals
narrowly elliptic, to 4·5cm. May–Jun. Damp grassland,
waste places. F, D; int S.

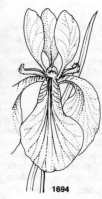

1692 Stinking Iris *Iris foetidissima*
Gives an unpleasant smell when bruised. Flowers c. 8cm
across, violet tinged yellow, rarely all yellow, 1–5 borne
on stem up to 90cm, with 3–4 leaves. Spathes green.
Outer petals 3–5cm, oblong–oblanceolate; inner petals
2·5–4cm, oblanceolate. Seeds scarlet. May–Jul. Woods,
cliffs, sand-dunes, hedgebanks. GB, F; int IRL. **282**

1693 Yellow Iris *Iris pseudacorus*
Distinguished by its 4–12 yellow flowers on flowering
stem to 150cm, with several leaves. Basal leaves spear-
shaped, evergreen, often about equalling the flowering
stem. Flowers 8–10cm across; outer petals short-stalked,
purple-veined, variable; inner petals linear–oblong, shorter and narrower than the style branches. Seeds dark
brown. May–Jul. Marshes, swamps, river- and lake-sides.
Throughout area covered, except IS. **227**

1694

1694 Purple Iris *Iris versicolor*
Flowers lilac-purple, 2–9 on stem up to 1m, with 2–3
stem-leaves. Basal leaves up to 60cm long, often purplish
at base. Outer petals 4–6cm, with rounded blade
contracted into a narrow stalk (claw) about as long; inner
petals shorter, oblanceolate. Jun–Jul. Lake shores,
river-banks. N. America. Int GB.

1695 Butterfly Iris *Iris spuria*
Flowers blue, violet, or whitish, 2–4 on stem 20–90cm,
with several leaves. Outer petals 3–8cm with blade
elliptic to rounded with longer stalk; inner petals 3–6cm,
narrowly obovate; spathe green, up to 8cm. Basal leaves
up to 2cm wide, somewhat strong-smelling. Ovary with

1695

narrow beak. A very variable species. Jun. Ditches, damp fields. GB, DK, F, D, S.

1696 Spring Crocus *Crocus vernus*
Flowers purple or white, usually solitary, flowering in spring with leaves present but shorter than the flower, later elongating. Flowers with a long slender tube 2·5–15cm and 6 oblanceolate to ovate blunt segments 1·5–5·5cm. Leaves 2–4, linear pointed, with white central vein and with colourless sheath at base. Capsule ellipsoid. A very variable species. Feb–Apr. Meadows, pastures. F, D; int GB.

1697 Autumn Crocus *Crocus nudiflorus*
Differs from **1696** in flowering in the autumn without leaves, and with solitary deep blue-purple flower. Corolla-tube white, 10–22cm, segments 3–6cm, elliptic to oblanceolate; corolla-tube sheathed below with scales; style orange with many slender branches. Leaves 3–4, appearing long after flowering, linear 2–4mm wide. Sep–Nov. Meadows, roadsides. F; int GB. **282**

1698 Sand Crocus *Romulea columnae*
Flowers small, pale lilac or violet, yellow towards base, 7–10mm across, 1–3 on short stem. Basal leaves from corm 2, stem-leaves 1–6, short erect or long. Corolla-tube 2·5–5·5mm, segments 1–2cm lanceolate or oblanceolate, acute. Fruit borne above ground. Mar–May. Dry grasslands on sand-dunes and sea-cliffs. GB, F.

1698

1699 Montbretia *Tritonia×crocosmiflora*
Erect perennial with leafy stem up to 90cm, with a one-sided terminal spike of deep orange funnel-shaped flowers with somewhat spreading lobes. Stem unbranched or with 1–2 branches; leaves sword-shaped, up to 2cm wide. Flowers 2·5–5cm, with short corolla-tube and with oblong lobes, the upper a little larger. Jul–Aug. Naturalized by rivers, lake-sides, ditches, cliffs, woods. Garden hybrid origin. Int GB, F, IRL.

1700 *Gladiolus palustris*
Erect perennial up to 50cm, with a terminal one-sided spike or red or reddish-purple curved flowers. Stem with basal green sheaths, basal leaves and one bract-like stem-leaf. Flowers 2·5–4cm; upper petals obovate, the lateral petals rhombic, the lower oblong to wedge-shaped with blade as long as stalk and longer than upper petals. May–Jul. Grasslands. F, D.

1701 Wild Gladiolus *Gladiolus illyricus*
Like **1700**, but flowers 3–10 in more or less 2 rows, and axillary branches often present (spike one-sided, with not more than 6 flowers, and axillary branches absent in **1700**). Flowers red or reddish-purple, 2·5–4cm across. Jun–Aug. Heaths, scrub, open woods. GB, F. **266**

ARUM FAMILY

Araceae

Perennial herbs with rhizomes or tubers. Flowers small, yellowish or greenish, aggregated into a conspicuous, club-shaped inflorescence, enclosed by a spathe. Fruit a berry. A mainly tropical family. Many species have foetid flowers that are pollinated by carrion-flies.

1702 Sweet Flag *Acorus calamus*
Robust rush-like aromatic perennial with creeping under-water rhizome and sword-shaped leaves above water with a dense spike (spadix) of numerous densely packed tiny green flowers. Leaves c. 120cm, acute, with part of margin undulate. Flowering stem 3-angled equalling leaves, with spadix 5–9cm, usually ascending at 45° to the stem. Perianth c. 2mm long. May–Aug. Shallow waters of ponds, rivers. Native of Asia and N. America. Int throughout area covered, except IS. **193**

1703 Bog Arum *Calla palustris*
Perennial with stout green creeping rhizome covered with membraneous leaf bases and with rounded to broadly ovate or heart-shaped stalked leaves. Flowering stem about as long as leaves, with spathe rounded whitish and half as long again as flowering spike. Flowers yellowish-green, numerous and densely clustered. Fruit a red berry. May–Aug. Swamps, ponds, damp woods. B, DK, SF, F, D, NL, N, S; int GB. **192**

1704 Lords and Ladies *Arum maculatum*
Distinguished by its large yellow-green spathe up to 25cm, enclosing at its base the tiny flowers, and with a club-shaped yellow or purple spadix half as long. Spathe often purple-edged or spotted. Female flowers in a zone below and with sterile flowers above, male flowers above, the uppermost sterile. Leaves triangular, arrow-shaped with blunt or acute basal lobes, long-stalked, sometimes spotted. Apr–May. Woods, hedges, shady places. B, GB, F, D, IRL, NL; int DK.

1705 Italian Lords and Ladies *Arum italicum*
Differs from **1704** in having leaves well developed by December, with mid-rib pale yellow-green and spathe 3 times as long as flowering spike (spadix). (Leaves appearing in spring, mid-rib dark green, and spathe twice as long as spadix in **1704**.) Leaves with spreading lateral lobes; flowering stem much shorter than leaf-stalks. Spathe greenish-yellow, 15–40cm; spadix stout, yellow. Apr–May. Woods, hedges, scrub. GB, F; int NL. **192**

DUCKWEED FAMILY

Lemnaceae

Submerged or floating, minute aquatic herbs. Roots simple or absent, shoots reduced to a flattish frond. Flowers tiny, inconspicuous or even absent. Often forming a green mat on the surface of still water.

1706 Rootless Duckweed *Wolffia arrhiza*
The smallest flowering plant, with pale green ellipsoid or nearly globular fronds 0·5–1mm across, floating on surface of water. Roots absent. Flowers not produced in Europe. Still waters. B, GB, F, D, NL.

1707 Common Duckweed *Lemna minor*
Floating plant with light green, elliptic to obovate fronds, flat above and below, 3-veined, 1·5–5mm, each frond with a single root. Flowers with 2 stamens and 1 ovary, enclosed in a sheath. Apr–Jul. Ponds, still waters. Throughout area covered, except IS. **192**

1708 Fat Duckweed *Lemna gibba*
Differs from **1707** in having broadly ovate to nearly rounded thick fronds 2–5mm long, with usually conspicuously swollen under-surface; fronds grey-green or sometimes reddish-brown above, under-surface with 40–50 meshes; each frond with 1 root. Ovules 4–6 (ovule 1 in **1707**). Apr–Jun. Ponds, ditches. Throughout area covered, except IS, N.

1708

1709 Ivy-leaved Duckweed *Lemna trisulca*
Readily distinguished by its translucent oblong fronds narrowed to slender stalks and linking adjacent fronds. Fronds 5–15mm long, submerged, with 1 root to each frond. Flowering fronds floating, pale green and smaller. Ovule 1. Apr–Jun. Ponds, ditches. Throughout area covered, except IS. **186**

1710 Greater Duckweed *Spirodela polyrhiza*
Fronds floating, oval to nearly rounded, 4–10mm, asymmetrical and opaque, with 5–9 veins flat on both sides, dark green above and purplish on underside. Roots 5–15 from each frond. Flowers rarely. Jul. Still waters, ponds, ditches. Throughout area covered, except IS.

1710

BUR-REED FAMILY

Sparganiaceae

Rhizomatous, perennial aquatic herbs. Flowers unisexual, grouped in globose heads. Perianth-segments 1–6, scale-like. Fruit 1-seeded, dry, indehiscent.

1711 Branched Bur-reed *Sparganium erectum*
Distinguished by its usually much-branched inflorescence, with flowers with thick perianth-segments, brown with blackish apex. Robust semi-terrestrial perennial, with erect stem up to 1·5m, or more, with usually erect, linear, non-floating leaves, which are triangular in section. Flowers in spike-like clusters from axils of upper leaves; male clusters, above, globular; female clusters below, globular but much larger. Seed longitudinally ridged. Jun–Aug. Shallow waters, ponds, ditches, marshes, fens. Throughout area covered, except IS. **192**

1712 Unbranched Bur-reed *Sparganium emersum*
Erect or floating perennial up to 60cm, with simple unbranched inflorescence, with 3–10 distant male globular heads, and 3–6 female globular heads below, the lower often stalked. Leaves triangular in section, linear. Perianth-segments thin, light brown. Seed smooth. Jun–Jul. Shallow waters, ponds, lakes. Throughout area covered, except IS. **204**

1713 *Sparganium gramineum*
Stem up to 1m, floating, and with very long linear floating leaves. Inflorescence often branched from base, with 2–3 female heads on branches; main axis with 2–6 male heads and 3–7 female heads. Lower bracts longer than inflorescence, usually floating. Fruit dark grey or brown, with down-curved style. Aug. Lakes, pools. SF, N, S.

1714 Floating Bur-reed *Sparganium angustifolium*
Stem up to 1m, usually floating, with flat leaves with inflated sheath at base. Inflorescence usually unbranched, with 2 male closely clustered heads, and 2–4 remote female heads, the lower stalked with bract twice as long as inflorescence. Fruit brown with straight beak-like style. Aug–Sep. Peaty lakes in hills and mountains. Throughout area covered.

1715 Least Bur-reed *Sparganium minimum*
Distinguished from **1714** by the lower bract scarcely longer than the inflorescence, and leaves only slightly inflated at base. Male flower head usually solitary, globular. Stem floating, up to 30cm; leaves usually translucent. Fruit with short beak-like style. Jun–Jul. Lakes, pools, ditches. Throughout area covered.

1714

1716 *Sparganium hyperboreum*
Distinguished from **1714** and **1715** by the style of the fruit which is minute or absent, and fruit broadly obovoid (fruit ellipsoid or obovoid in **1714** and **1715**). Leaves translucent. Male flower heads usually 1; female heads 2–3, the lower stalked. Jul. Lakes, ditches. SF, IS, N, S.

BULRUSH FAMILY

Typhaceae

Rhizomatous, perennial aquatic herbs. Leaves mostly basal, erect. Flowers unisexual, tiny, grouped into dense, conspicuous cylindrical inflorescence. Fruit dry, splitting.

1717 Bulrush *Typha latifolia*
Robust, with submerged stout creeping rhizome, and erect stem above water up to 2·5m. Leaves linear 8–20mm wide, little longer than flowering stem, sheathing below. Flowers in a terminal cylindrical club-like cluster; male flowers above, scarcely separated from the female flower cluster below which is dark brown and about 8–15cm long. Fruit cylindrical, tapering to slender stalk. Jun–Jul. Reed swamps, lakes, ponds, slow-flowing rivers. Throughout area covered, except IS. **204**

1718 Lesser Bulrush *Typha angustifolia*
Differs from **1717** in having narrower leaves c. 4mm wide, and male and female clusters separated by 3–8cm. Female flowers with scales (without scales in **1717**). Rather less robust perennial, 1–3m, with flowering stem ⅔ as long as leaves. Jun–Jul. Reed swamps, lakes, ponds, slow-flowing rivers. Throughout area covered, except IS.

ORCHID FAMILY

Orchidaceae

Perennial herbs with rhizomes or tubers. Leaves entire, usually spirally arranged. Flowers in spikes or racemes, bilaterally symmetrical, usually conspicuous and brightly coloured. Pollen borne in club-shaped masses. Fruit a capsule, dehiscing by slits. The roots have an intimate association with a fungus (mycorrhiza); some species are saprophytes, living in humus. A large, mostly tropical family; many species occur in the Mediterranean region and reach the northern limit of their range in the area covered.

1719 Lady's Slipper *Cypripedium calceolus*
Very distinctive orchid with reddish-brown, usually solitary, large inflated slipper-shaped lower lip and longer broadly elliptic to broadly lanceolate spreading lobes. Lobes 6–9cm, the upper erect, the lateral down-pointing, the lower narrow lanceolate with two short lobes; lip c. 3cm, pale yellow with reddish spots within. Stem up to 50cm, with brown basal sheath and 3–4 elliptic-pointed leaves. May–Jul. Woods, clearings, grassy places, mountains. GB, DK, SF, F, D, N, S. **270**

EPIPACTIS
LEAVES SPIRALLY ARRANGED

1720

1720 Marsh Helleborine *Epipactis palustris*
Stem up to 50cm or more, purplish below with sheathing scales, from a creeping rhizome. Leaves 4–8, oblong to lanceolate acute, the upper smaller. Flowers in a spike-like cluster in axils of leafy bracts; outer perianth-segments greenish with violet stripes, inner whitish; lip up to 12mm, with ovate blunt terminal lobe, white with red veins and undulate margin and with 2 basal lobes. Jun–Aug. Marshes, fens, damp places in sand-dunes. Throughout area covered, except IS.

1721 Broad-leaved Helleborine *Epipactis helleborine*
Stem up to 80cm or more, from a short erect rhizome. Leaves 4–10, broadly elliptic to nearly rounded. Flower spike with 15–50 drooping flowers; outer segments greenish, inner purplish-violet. Lip up to 11mm, with heart-shaped to broadly ovate terminal lobe with recurved apex, greenish-white, pink or purple, with 2 basal swellings. Jul–Oct. Woods, hedge-banks, grassy places. Throughout area covered, except IS.

1722 Violet Helleborine *Epipactis purpurata*
Differs from **1721** in having greyish or purplish leaves and flowers with terminal lobe of lip at least as long as wide

1721

479

(terminal lobe not longer than wide, and leaves green in **1721**). Outer perianth-segments up to 12mm, green outside, whitish within, inner segments whitish, sometimes pink-tinged. Lip triangular to heart-shaped acute, with incurved apex. Stem up to 70cm, with many flowers and 5–10 leaves. Jul–Sep. Beechwoods on calcareous soils. B, GB, DK, F, D.

1723 Epipactis microphylla
Perennial with densely hairy stem up to 40cm, with 3–6 short linear to lanceolate leaves 1–2·5cm. Flowering spike with 4–15 spreading flowers. Outer perianth-segments greenish with reddish tinge outside, whitish-green within, like inner ovate segments. Lip up to 7mm, with white or pale pink rounded blunt lobe with shallowly lobed margin. Ovary densely hairy. Jun–Aug. Woods on calcareous soils. B, F, D.

EPIPACTIS
LEAVES ARRANGED IN TWO RANKS

1724 Narrow-lipped Helleborine Epipactis leptochila
Slender perennial with leafy stem and short terminal spike of pale green flowers subtended by green bracts, the lower longer than flowers. Stem purplish below, hairy, up to 70cm; leaves in two ranks, 4–10, ovate to lanceolate. Flowers with lanceolate perianth-segments 7–15mm; lip 4–9mm, with terminal lobe heart-shaped, pointed, yellowish-green with white margin, and basal lobe cup-shaped, reddish-mottled within. Jun–Aug. Shady woods, scrub. B, GB, DK, F, D, NL.

1725 Epipactis muelleri
Differs from **1724** in having terminal lobe of lip blunt, with recurved apex and outer perianth-segments blunt (terminal lobe with pointed flat apex and outer perianth-segments long-pointed in **1724**). Jul. Open woods, clearings. B, F, D, NL.

1724

1726 Dune Helleborine Epipactis dunensis
Differs from **1725** in having terminal lobe of lip as long as wide and anther stalked (terminal lobe wider than long, anther stalkless in **1725**). Jun–Jul. Sand-dunes. GB.

1727 Green-flowered Helleborine
Epipactis phyllanthes
Differs from **1724** in having drooping flowers, and basal lobe of lip greenish-white inside (flowers spreading or slightly drooping and inner lobe of lip mottled in **1724**). Stem up to 45cm, green, sparsely hairy; leaves 3–6. Flowers with perianth-segments 8–10mm, greenish-yellow; lip 6–8mm, with terminal lobe greenish-white to pinkish, longer than wide. Jul–Aug. Open woods, scrub, sand-dunes. GB, DK, F, IRL, S.

1727

1728 Dark Red Helleborine *Epipactis atrorubens*
Distinguished by its deep purple flowers and densely
hairy upper part of stem. Stem up to 60cm or more, violet
below. Leaves in two ranks, 5–10, ovate to broadly
lanceolate. Flowers spreading; perianth-segments
6–7mm; lip up to 6·5mm, the terminal lobe heart-shaped
to kidney-shaped with acute curved apex,
reddish-purple, the inner lobe cup-shaped with red
margin and red spots within. Jun–Jul. Woods, rocky
slopes, screes. Throughout area covered, except IS. **271**

1729 White Helleborine *Cephalanthera damasonium*
Erect perennial with angled hairless stem 20–60cm, with
leaves ovate–lanceolate at base and narrowed above.
Flowers white or cream, 3–12, in a spike up to 12cm long,
with bracts longer than ovary. Perianth-segments
1·5–2cm, blunt, the inner shorter than the outer; lip white,
yellowish within at base, terminal lobe with 3–5
orange-yellow ridges, blunt. Jun–Jul. Woods, shady
places. B, GB, DK, F, D, NL, S.

1729

1730 Narrow-leaved Helleborine
Cephalanthera longifolia
Differs from **1729** in its narrower lanceolate leaves, the
uppermost linear, and stem ridged above. Bracts of
flowers shorter than ovary, and perianth-segments
1–1·6cm, acute, white. Stem up to 60cm. May–Jul.
Woods, shady places. Throughout area covered, except
IS, NL.

1731 Red Helleborine *Cephalanthera rubra*
Distinguished by its pink or purplish flowers, and lower
lip with acute terminal lobe. Stem up to 60cm,
glandular-hairy above; leaves few, oblong–lanceolate
acute, the upper narrower. Outer perianth-segments
17–22mm, lanceolate, spreading; inner shorter incurved;
lip white, the terminal lobe with purple margin and 7–9
yellowish ridges. Ovary glandular-hairy. Jun–Jul. Woods.
B, GB, DK, SF, F, D, N, S.

1731

1732 Limodore *Limodorum abortivum*
Violet saprophyte with robust stem 40–80cm, with
numerous scales below, arising from a rhizome densely
covered with thickish roots. Flowering spike up to
30cm long, with many conspicuous violet flowers.
Perianth-segments to 2cm spreading; lip triangular with
undulate margin, yellow or violet; spur slender,
cylindrical, up to 1·5cm. May–Jul. Woods in mountains,
scrub, shady grasslands. B, F, D.

1733 Ghost Orchid *Epipogium aphyllum*
Inconspicuous pinkish saprophyte with erect stem
5–20cm, swollen at base, and with few short brownish
sheathing scales. Flowers 1–5, with short up-curved

1733

spurs and slender down-curved perianth-segments. Lip erect, ovate to triangular, with 2 short lateral lobes and large middle lobe, white or pinkish, tinged with yellow or reddish outside. Rhizome with lobed fleshy branches. Jul–Sep. Shady woods, usually beech. B, GB, DK, SF, F, D, N, S.

1734 Birdsnest Orchid *Neottia nidus-avis*
Yellowish-brown saprophyte, with erect stem up to 45cm, with numerous brown scales. Flowers numerous in a spike-like cluster 5–21cm long, with short bracts. Perianth-segments usually brownish, 4–6mm, blunt, somewhat incurved; lip 8–12mm with spreading blunt lobes and with sac-like base. Rhizome covered with thick fleshy roots. May–Jul. Shady woods, especially beech. Throughout area covered, except IS. **204**

1735 Common Twayblade *Listera ovata*
Distinguished by its 2 opposite ovate–elliptic leaves, 5–20cm, borne just below the middle of the slender flowering stem, Flowers greenish-yellow, numerous in a spike-like cluster; bracts minute. Perianth-segments 4–5mm, the outer ovate, inner narrower; lip 7–15mm, divided almost to middle into 2 narrowly oblong lobes. Jun–Jul. Damp woods, pastures, scrub. Throughout area covered. **193**

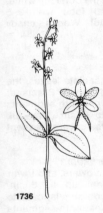

1736 Lesser Twayblade *Listera cordata*
Differs from **1735** in having smaller paired leaves to 2·5cm, and flowering spike 1·5–6cm, few-flowered (leaves 5–20cm and flowering spike many-flowered, 7–25cm in **1735**). Perianth-segments 2–2·5mm, the outer green outside and reddish inside; lip 3·5–4·5mm, divided to middle into 2 spreading linear purplish lobes, and with broader basal lobes. Jun–Sep. Mountain woods, moors. Throughout area covered, except B.

1736

1737 Autumn Lady's Tresses *Spiranthes spiralis*
Flowers tiny, scented, white in axils of green bracts, in spirally twisted spike. Leaves in a basal rosette, ovate–elliptic. Flowering stem 6–20cm, glandular hairy, with lanceolate scale leaves, and terminal flower spike 3–10cm. Perianth-segments 6–7mm, oblong, the upper three in a hood; lip forming a tube at base round column and with up-curved margin with undulate, toothed apex. Aug–Sep. Hill pastures, calcareous grassland, sand-dunes. F, B, GB, NL, DK, IRL, D. **186**

1738 Summer Lady's Tresses *Spiranthes aestivalis*
Differs from **1737** in having leaves linear–lanceolate blunt, erect, not all basal with some on stem. Flowers white, in one spiral row, with bracts 6–7mm. Perianth-segments 6–7mm, lip similar in length with up-curved margin and down-curved apex. Jul–Aug. Marshy ground with sedges and rushes. B, †GB, F, D, NL.

1738

1739 Irish Lady's Tresses *Spiranthes romanzoffiana*
Differs from **1738** in having flowers in 3 spiral rows,
with larger bracts 10–17mm and leaves acute.
Perianth-segments c. 12mm, white tinged green or
cream, fused together below. Jul–Aug. Damp meadows,
bogs. GB, IRL.

1740 Creeping Lady's Tresses *Goodyera repens*
Perennial with erect stem up to 25cm, with slender
branched stolons, and with a terminal spike of tiny white
fragrant flowers. Leaves ovate, conspicuously
net-veined, short-stalked, upper leaves sheath-like.
Flowers 3–4mm, in a slender one-sided spike 3–7cm;
perianth-segments ovate to lanceolate, the uper in
a hood, having a short lip with terminal triangular
lobe. Jul–Aug. Pine and mixed woods, sand-dunes
Throughout area covered, except IRL, IS. **204**

1741 Musk Orchid *Herminium monorchis*
Small perennial 5–25cm, with lower leaves elliptic to
narrowly lanceolate, the upper bract-like, and with a
slender spike 1·5–9cm of tiny yellowish-green flowers.
Perianth-segments to 3·5mm, oblong–lanceolate, often
lobed; lip to 4mm, 3-lobed with oblong lobes, the two
outer spreading shorter than the mid-lobe. Tuber
globular. Jun–Jul. Calcareous grasslands. Throughout
area covered, except IRL, IS. **193**

1742 Lesser Butterfly Orchid *Platanthera bifolia*
Perennial 20–50cm, with 2 basal obovate to broadly
elliptic leaves and smaller stem-leaves, and with a spike
of white flowers tinged green with long slender spurs.
Flowering spike rather dense, up to 20cm;
perianth-segments 5–10mm, the upper in a hood; lip
linear–oblong, to 12mm, pendent; spur 2·5–3cm, nearly
horizontal, longer than ovary. May–Jul. Open woods,
meadows, damp heaths. Throughout area covered,
except IS. **186**

1743 Greater Butterfly Orchid *Platanthera chlorantha*
Differs from **1742** in having flowers greener, spur
strongly downcurved with slightly inflated apex, and
anther lobes converging above and widely separated
below (anther lobes parallel in **1742**). Flowering spike
pyramidal, flowers 18–23mm across; lip 10–16mm
(flowering spike cylindrical; flowers 11–18mm across; lip
6–10mm in **1742**). May–Jul. Woods, meadows, damp
heaths. Throughout area covered, except IS. **186**

1744 *Platanthera hyperborea*
Distinguished by its short spur only 3·5–4·5mm, curved,
and shorter than ovary. Perennial 6–35cm, with leaves all
similar in shape but diminishing in size up stem. Flowers
greenish, fragrant, with perianth-segments 3–4mm. Jul.
Meadows, moorlands. IS.

1746

1745 *Platanthera obtusata*
Like **1744** but stem with 1 well-developed leaf; flowering
spike with 3–6 flowers (stem with at least 2
well-developed leaves, spike with numerous flowers in
1744). Perennial 6–20cm. Perianth-segments 2–3mm;
spur 2·5–3mm, half as long as ovary. Jul. Calcareous
mountain heaths. N, S.

1746 *Chamorchis alpina*
Hairless perennial with linear pointed leaves, all basal,
and a lax spike of 3–10 yellowish-green flowers tinged
purplish-brown, with bracts longer than flowers.
Perianth-segments 3·5mm, the upper in a hood; lip
slightly longer, 3-lobed; spur absent. Tubers 2, ellipsoid.
Jul–Aug. Mountain pastures. SF, F, D, N, S.

1747 Fragrant Orchid *Gymnadenia conopsea*
Flowering stem to 65cm, leafy, with pink or reddish-lilac,
rarely purple or white, fragrant flowers, in a cylindrical
spike 6–16cm. Flowers with upper perianth-segments in
a hood, the lateral segments spreading, 4–5mm; lip
rhombic with nearly equal rounded lobes; spur curved,
longer than ovary. Leaves linear–oblong, in a lax rosette,
the upper bract-like clasping stem. Tubers lobed.
May–Jul. Grasslands, marshes, woods. Throughout area
covered, except IS. **255**

1748 *Gymnadenia odoratissima*
Differs from **1747** in having flowers with a short blunt
spur not longer than the ovary. Flowering stem up to
30cm, with linear pointed leaves. Perianth-segments
2·5–3mm; lip with lateral lobes much shorter than the
mid-lobe. May–Jul. Meadows, fallow land. B, F, D, S.

1749 Small White Orchid *Pseudorchis albida*
Flowers tiny, yellowish or greenish-white, 2–3mm, in a
dense cylindrical spike 3–7cm, on leafy stem up to 30cm.
Leaves oblong, the lower blunt, the upper narrower
acute. Outer perianth-segments ovate blunt, inner
shorter; lip 3-lobed, with mid-lobe larger; spur short,
down-curved, c. 2mm. Jul–Aug. Damp meadows,
pastures, grassy heaths. Throughout area covered,
except NL.

1749

1750 Black Vanilla Orchid *Nigritella nigra*
Flowers dark purple, rarely red, white or yellowish,
vanilla-scented, numerous in long conical spike up to
2·5cm long. Leaves linear to linear–lanceolate, grooved,
with finely toothed margin; stem up to 30cm. Flowers
5–10mm, with narrow lanceolate pointed perianth-
segments; lip more or less triangular–pointed; spur
sac-like, blunt. Jun–Aug. Damp meadows, usually in the
mountains. F, D, N, S. **270**

1751 Frog Orchid *Coeloglossum viride*
Flowers greenish, often many in a cylindrical spike, borne on stem 5–35cm. Leaves 2–5, basal leaves rounded to lanceolate, the upper lanceolate pointed. Perianth-segments 4·5–6mm, the outer ovate, inner linear; lip wedge-shaped with mid-lobe shorter than lateral lobes; spur blunt, sac-like, c. 2mm. Jun–Aug. Pastures, grassy hillsides, sand-dunes, wood verges. Throughout area covered. **271**

1752 Elder-flowered Orchid *Dactylorhiza sambucina*
Flowers pale yellow or purple with yellow spots, in a short oval spike, on stem up to 30cm, with 4–5 leaves on lower half. Leaves obovate to narrowly oblanceolate, the uppermost lanceolate, all without dark spots. Perianth-segments 7–10mm, the upper in a hood, the lateral spreading; lip nearly rounded, 3-lobed, the lobes ovate–triangular; spur curved, up to 15mm. Apr–Jul. Mountain meadows, clearings. DK, SF, F, D, N, S. **227**

1753 Early Marsh Orchid *Dactylorhiza incarnata*
Flowers red, purple, pinkish or lilac, with purple spots on lip, in a dense many-flowered cluster, on leafy stem up to 70cm. Leaves lanceolate, the uppermost as long or longer than inflorescence. Perianth-segments 5–6mm, narrowly ovate, blunt; lip ovate to rounded, entire or 3-lobed, shallowly toothed; spur up to half as long as ovary. A variable species. May–Jul. Marshes, fens, bogs, damp areas in sand-dunes. Throughout area covered, except IS. **255**

1754 Northern Marsh Orchid *Dactylorhiza majalis*
Distinguished from **1753** by the lower leaves which are more or less elliptic, not more than 4 times as long as wide (leaves more than 4 times as long as wide, usually lanceolate in **1753, 1755**). Flowers reddish-purple to lilac; outer perianth-segments 6–12mm; lip 5–14mm, rounded entire or 3-lobed; spur down-curved, half to almost as long as ovary. May–Aug. Damp meadows, fens. B, GB, DK, F, D, IRL, NL, S.

1755 Narrow-leaved Marsh Orchid
Dactylorhiza traunsteineri
Like **1753** with lower leaves more than 4 times as long as wide, but perianth-segments larger, 7–8mm (usually 5–6mm in **1753**). Flowers purple, in a many-flowered, more or less lax cylindrical cluster. Stem leafy, up to 50cm. May–Jul. Fens, marshes, damp hollows. GB, DK, SF, D, IRL, N, S.

1756 Heath Spotted Orchid *Dactylorhiza maculata*
Flowers pink, lilac, reddish or purple, in a conical inflorescence later elongating, on stem up to 60cm. Upper leaves bract-like, lower linear–lanceolate to ovate or oblong, with or without dark spots. Perianth-segments

1755

485

7–11mm; lip with mid-lobe narrower and shorter or as long as broader lateral lobes; spur 3–11mm, up to ¾ as long as ovary. Jun–Aug. Moorland, grassland, damp woods. Throughout area covered. **255**

1758

1757 Common Spotted Orchid *Dactylorhiza fuchsii*
Differs from **1756** in having lip of flowers deeply 3-lobed, the mid-lobe as long and as wide as lateral lobes. Bracts shorter than flowers. Flowers pink, lilac or reddish-purple, rarely white; perianth-segments 6–9mm; spur cylindrical, 6–9mm. Jun–Aug. Grasslands, open woods. Throughout area covered. **255**

1758 Dense-flowered Orchid *Neotinea maculata*
Flowers dull pink or greenish-white, never opening fully, in a dense spike 2–6mm, on stem up to 25cm, or more. Leaves 3–6, basal oblong, fine-pointed, spreading, upper smaller erect, with purplish-brown spots in lines. Perianth-segments 3–4mm; lip 3-lobed, the lateral linear, the mid-lobe oblong, larger and longer and often lobed at apex; spur conical blunt, up to 2mm. Apr–May. Woods, scrub, stony grassland. GB, F, IRL.

ORCHIS
AT LEAST OUTER PERIANTH-SEGMENTS SPREADING OR DEFLEXED

1759 Early Purple Orchid *Orchis mascula*
Distinguished by its pink or purple flowers, with lateral perianth-segments ascending, and spur cylindrical, more or less horizontal and as long as ovary. Stem up to 60cm, with 3–5 leaves below and often purple-spotted, and with bract-like leaves above. Flowering spike dense, cylindrical or ovoid; perianth-segments 6–8mm, upper broader; lip broadly ovate, 3-lobed with mid-lobe longer, almost square and often 2-lobed. Apr–Jun. Woods, copses, hedge banks, open pastures. Throughout area covered, except IS. **282**

1760 Pale-flowered Orchid *Orchis pallens*
Differs from **1759** in having a dense spike of pale yellow flowers, smelling of elder, and with spur slightly shorter than ovary. Perianth-segments 7–9mm, blunt, the lateral downcurved; lip 3-lobed. Stem up to 35cm, with leaves in lower half and sheaths above. Apr–Jun. Woods, sub-alpine meadows. F, D.

1761 Loose-flowered Orchid *Orchis laxiflora*
Flowers purple, in a lax ovoid or cylindrical spike, on a stem up to 80cm, with 3–8 spreading leaves. Perianth-segments 7–10mm, oblong, the two lateral down-curved; lip rounded to triangular–obovate with wedge-shaped base, 3-lobed, with mid-lobe entire or shallowly 2-lobed; spur cylindrical, shorter than ovary. May–Jun. Damp meadows, marshes. B, F, D, S. **266**

1762

1762 Green-winged Orchid *Orchis morio*
Flowers purple, red, pink, greenish or white with green veins, with perianth-segments converging into a hood, lip broader than long with dark purple spots, and spur stout, horizontal or up-curved. Stem up to 50cm, with basal rosette of lanceolate to narrowly ovate leaves and stem with crowded sheaths above. Lip of flowers up to 10mm, shallowly 3-lobed, the mid-lobe usually longer. Apr–Jun. Meadows, pastures, rocky places. Throughout area covered, except SF, IS.

1763 Bug Orchid *Orchis coriophora*
Flower with violet-brown hood and purplish-green 3-lobed lip longer than wide, and spur down-curved, half as long as lip. Stem up to 40cm, with 4–7 linear to narrow lanceolate leaves below, and sheaths above. Flowering spike dense, cylindrical; perianth-segments 5–10mm; lip with blunt lobes. Apr–Jun. Damp meadows. B, F, D. **255**

1764 Toothed Orchid *Orchis tridentata*
Flowers pale violet-lilac, with hood and lip with purple spots, lip 3-lobed with mid-lobe twice as long as lateral lobes; spur down-curved. Stem up to 45cm, with 3–4 leaves below and sheaths above. Perianth-segments 6–8mm, acute; lip 6–9mm with lateral lobes oblong and toothed at apex; mid-lobe notched with 2 squarish lobes and often with a central point. Mar–May. Woods, meadows. F, D.

1765 Burnt Orchid *Orchis ustulata*
Flowers with outer segments brownish-purple, the inner pink, all in a hood; lip white or pale pink with purple spots, 3-lobed; spur down-curved. Stem 5–35cm, with 2–3 oblong basal leaves, 1–3 oblong stem-leaves and sheaths above. Perianth-segments up to 3·5mm, outer ovate, inner narrower; lip up to 8mm, mid-lobe swollen at apex and 2-lobed, lateral lobes blunt. May–Jun. Dry limestone meadows in mountains. B, GB, DK, F, D, S. **270**

1766 Monkey Orchid *Orchis simia*
Pinkish-purple monkey-like lip with 2 curved linear basal lobes, a narrow central lobe with two narrow terminal lobes with a central tooth between. Stem 15–45cm, with 3–5 leaves in the lower half and sheaths above. Flowering spike cylindrical; perianth-segments c. 1cm, in a hood, greyish-pink; lip 16mm, pinkish-purple with purple spots; spur down-curved, ½ length of ovary. May–Jun. Grassy hills, bushy places. B, GB, F, D, NL. **255**

1767 Military Orchid *Orchis militaris*
Distinguished from **1766** by its larger flowers with lip 12–15mm, purple and white at base, with linear lateral

487

lobes and central oblong lobe, with ovate to oblong terminal lobes and a small tooth between. Stem up to 50cm, with 3–5 leaves near base and with sheaths above. Flowering spike at first conical, later cylindrical. Perianth-segments whitish or greyish-pink, in a hood, the outer narrow ovate pointed, up to 1·5cm, inner linear; lip to 1·5cm; spur down-curved half as long as ovary. May–Jun. Meadows, bushy places, wood verges, grassy hills. B, GB, F, D, NL, S. **282**

1768 Lady Orchid *Orchis purpurea*

Flowers with a broad, brownish-purple or pink, purple-spotted hood, and lip 3-lobed, white or pink with purple spots. Stem up to 80cm, with 3–6 leaves in lower half, with sheaths above; leaves oblong to oblong–ovate. Flowering spike cylindrical; perianth-segments up to 14mm, outer ovate pointed, inner linear–lanceolate; lip up to 1·5cm, with linear lateral lobes and mid-lobe heart-shaped or rounded, 2-lobed with large tooth between; spur down-curved, half as long as ovary. May–Jun. Clearings in woods, copses, banks. B, GB, DK, F, D, NL.

1769 Man Orchid *Aceras anthropophorum*

Flowers greenish-yellow, often with reddish margins and streaks, in a narrow cylindrical dense spike with papery bracts. Stems up to 40cm, or more, brownish, with oblong to oblong–lanceolate blunt leaves, the upper smaller, bract-like. Perianth-segments in a globular hood, 6–7mm, blunt; lip up to 1·5cm, yellowish or often reddish-brown, man-like with linear lateral lobes and long middle lobe with two slender terminal lobes; spur absent. May–Jul. Meadows, grassy slopes, scrub, open woods. B, GB, F, D, NL. **227**

1770 Lizard Orchid *Himantoglossum hircinum*

Readily distinguished by its very long lip with strap-shaped spirally twisted mid-lobe 3–5cm, and shorter curled lateral lobes. Stem stout, up to 90cm, purple-blotched; lower leaves elliptic–oblong, upper smaller pointed and clasping stem. Flowers in a long spike, smelling of goats; perianth-segments c. 1cm, pale green with purplish spots and streaks, in a globular hood, outer ovate, inner linear. Lip whitish with purple spots, dark green outside, lateral lobes often purplish; spur conical, short. Jun–Jul. Grassland, scrub, open woods, sand-dunes. B, GB, F, D, NL. **255**

1771 Pyramidal Orchid *Anacamptis pyramidalis*

Distinguished by its dense pyramidal cluster of purplish-red, rarely white, flowers with very long slender spurs twice as long as the ovary. Stem up to 40cm, with linear to oblong–lanceolate pointed leaves, the upper smaller bract-like. Perianth-segments 4–6mm, outer spreading, upper 3 in a hood; lip 6–8mm, broadly wedge-shaped with 3 oblong nearly equal lobes; spur up to 14mm. Jun–Jul. Grassland, scrub, sand-dunes. Throughout area covered, except SF, IS, N. **266**

1772 Fly Orchid *Ophrys insectifera*
Distinguished by its green, ovate–oblong outer perianth-segments; its linear blackish-violet inner segments, and blackish-violet or purple lip. Stem 10–60cm, with linear–lanceolate pointed leaves. Flowers 3–14, in a lax spike; perianth-segments 6–8mm, the outer spreading; lip 9–10mm, 3-lobed, lateral lobes blunt, mid-lobe ovate, notched or 2-lobed and with squarish pale blue-violet central area. May–Jul. Bushy places, woods, grassy hillsides, fens. Throughout area covered, except IS. **271**

1773 Early Spider Orchid *Ophrys sphegodes*
Distinguished by its rounded to ovate, convex, velvety-haired lip with H-shaped bluish-violet or blackish-purple hairless centre. Stem up to 45cm, with basal leaves ovate–lanceolate blunt, with scales above. Flowering spike lax, 2–10-flowered; perianth-segments 6–10mm, green, rarely purplish or white, the inner segments ½ as long and green to brownish-red with undulate margin; lip 10–12mm. Apr–Jun. Grassy slopes, banks. B, GB, F, D. **271**

1774 Late Spider Orchid *Ophrys fuciflora*
Distinguished by its broad dark brown or brownish-purple velvety lip, with two small basal swellings, and blue or violet central patch with yellowish or greenish margin. Stem up to 55cm, with basal leaves ovate–oblong blunt, upper narrower pointed. Flowering spike usually with 2–6 flowers; perianth-segments pink, whitish or green, outer 9–13mm, blunt, inner much shorter, hairy; lip 9–13mm, with upcurved apical lobe. May–Jul. Grassy chalk slopes, field borders, open woods. B, GB, F, D.

1775 Bee Orchid *Ophrys apifera*
Flower with broadly ovate brownish or blackish-purple lip with small 3-lobed apical lobe, and perianth-segments spreading or down-curved, purplish or purple-violet, the inner triangular to linear, half as long as outer. Stem up to 50cm; basal leaves ovate to lanceolate blunt, stem-leaves similar pointed. Flowering spike lax, with 2–7 flowers; perianth-segments 1–1.5cm; lip shorter with shield-like violet or reddish-brown centre and yellow margin. May–Jul. Pastures, copses, field verges, woods. B, GB, F, D, IRL, NL. **271**

1776 Coralroot Orchid *Corallorhiza trifida*
Yellowish-green saprophyte, with stem 7–30cm with 2–4 scales, and flowers in a lax spike of 2–12. Outer

1776

489

perianth-segments greenish c. 5mm, the lateral with incurved margin, inner segments narrower, greenish or yellowish with reddish margin and spots; lip oblong, whitish with red lines or blotches and with 2 wide ridges at base. Jun–Aug. Damp woods, damp places in sand-dunes. Throughout area covered, except IRL, NL.

1777 Calypso *Calypso bulbosa*
Flower solitary, pinkish-purple, in axil of linear bract, on slender stem up to 20cm with few leaf sheaths towards base. Leaf solitary, elliptic to oblong, short-stalked, arising direct from ovoid pseudobulb. Perianth-segments 1–2cm, narrowly lanceolate; lip large inflated, slipper-shaped, whitish with pinkish or yellowish spots or blotches, 1–2cm; spur absent. May–Jun. Marshes, wet coniferous woods. SF, S.

1777

1778 Fen Orchid *Liparis loeselii*
Flowers yellowish-green, 3–8 in a lax spike, with lip pointing upwards oblong–ovate and somewhat toothed, on stem 6–20cm which is 3-angled above. Perianth-segments linear–lanceolate spreading, c. 5mm long, the inner narrower and shorter; lip longer, ovate with recurved apex; spur absent. Jun–Aug. Bogs, fens, damp places in sand-dunes. Throughout area covered, except IRL, IS.

1779 *Microstylis monophyllos*
Like **1778** but pseudobulbs borne one above the other, and leaf usually solitary (pseudobulbs joined by a short stolon, leaves 2 in **1778**). Flowers numerous, greenish, in a lax spike 3–15cm, on stem up to 30cm; leaves ovate to elliptic. Perianth-segments 2–2·7mm, the lateral erect, the mid-lobe pointing downwards; inner lobes linear, pointing downwards. Lip pointing upwards ovate–lanceolate, thickened beneath. Jun–Jul. Bogs, wet meadows, scrub. SF, D, N, S.

1778

1780 Bog Orchid *Hammarbya paludosa*
Like **1778** but pseudobulbs borne one above the other, basal leaves 2–5 and lip of flower pointing upwards. Flowers greenish-yellow, numerous, in a dense spike later becoming lax, on stem 3–12cm. Perianth-segments 2·5–3mm, the lateral erect, with mid-lobe down-pointing and somewhat larger; inner segments narrower, spreading; lip lanceolate, shorter than outer segments; spur absent. Jun–Sep. Peat-bogs. Throughout area covered, except IS.

1780

GLOSSARY OF TERMS

ACHENE Simple, 1-seeded dry fruit that does not split to release seeds.

ADVENTITIOUS ROOTS Roots that arise secondarily from the stem.

ALTERNATE LEAVES Leaves borne singly along the stem.

ANNUAL Life-cycle completed within one year.

ANTHER Head of **Stamen**, containing pollen.

ASCENDING Orientated upwards but not erect.

AWN Hair-like appendage, usually terminal.

AXIL Angle formed by leaf and stem.

AXILLARY Borne in an **Axil**.

BERRY Many-seeded fleshy fruit, derived from one ovary.

BIENNIAL Life-cycle completed over two years, the plant overwintering as a rosette of leaves and flowering in the second year of growth.

BRACT Leaf-like structure associated with the **Inflorescence**.

BRACTEOLE Small accessory **Bract**.

BULB Underground storage structure derived from a condensed shoot of fleshy **Scale-leaves**.

BULBIL Small, detachable bulb-like structure that is able to grow into a new plant.

CALYX Whorl of **Sepals**.

CAPSULE Dry fruit that splits to release seeds.

CARPEL One unit of a fruit.

CATKIN Cluster of small wind-pollinated flowers.

CILIA Fine marginal hairs, forming a fringe; hence **Ciliate**.

CLADODE Leaf-like branch with terminal spine.

CORM Underground storage structure derived from swollen base of stem.

COROLLA Whorl of **Petals**.

DRUPE 1-seeded fleshy fruit.

DRUPELET One of a group of small **Drupes**.

ELLIPSOID Solid oval shape.

ELLIPTICAL Regularly oval.

ENTIRE LEAF Leaf without lobes or teeth.

EPICALYX Whorl of leaf-like structures associated with **Calyx** (Rose and Mallow Families).

FILAMENT Stalk of **Stamen**, bearing the **Anthers**.

FOLLICLE 2- to many-seeded dry fruit, splitting longitudinally to release seeds.

GLAND Secretory structure, sticky to the touch.

GLANDULAR-HAIRY At least some hairs tipped by **Glands**.

INFLORESCENCE Cluster of flowers.

INVOLUCRE Whorl of **Bracts** around flower or **Inflorescence**; hence **Involucral**.

LANCEOLATE Spear-shaped, broadest at the middle.

LATEX White gummy exudate, often drying brown.

LINEAR Very narrow, with more or less parallel sides.

LINEAR-LANCEOLATE Very narrowly spear-shaped.

LINEAR-OBLONG Very narrowly rectangular.

LIP Prominent pendent, usually lower, petal.

NECTARY Gland at base of flower that secretes nectar (mainly sugars) which attracts insects to the flower.

NUT 1-seeded, dry, hard or stony fruit.

NUTLET One of a group of small **Nuts**.

OBCONICAL Shape of inverted cone.

OBLANCEOLATE Spear-shaped, broadest above the middle.

OBLONG More or less rectangular.

OBLONG-ELLIPTICAL More or less rectangular, but with curved margins.

OBOVATE Oval, broadest above the middle.

OPPOSITE LEAVES Leaves borne in pairs on the stem.

ORBICULAR Round.

OVARY Unfertilised fruit.

OVATE Oval, broadest below the middle (i.e. like a longitudinal section of an egg).

OVATE-LANCEOLATE Broadly spear-shaped, broadest below the middle.

OVATE-TRIANGULAR Shape of a rounded triangle.

OVOID Egg-shaped.

PARASITE Plant that obtains food and water from another plant; hence **Parasitic**.

PERENNIAL Life-cycle continuing over more than two years.

PERIANTH Whorl of **Petals**, **Sepals** or intermediate structures.

PETALS Usually brightly-coloured floral structures, in whorls, often enclosed by **Calyx**.

PINNATE LEAF Compound leaf with paired leaflets and normally a terminal leaflet.

PSEUDOBULB Swelling at base of a stem (Orchid Family).

RACEME **Inflorescence** with stalked flowers arising singly from the stem.

RAY Flower-stalk in an **Umbel**.

RECEPTACLE Swollen base of flower from which other floral parts arise.

RHIZOME Underground storage structure derived from a swollen stem, usually orientated horizontally.

RHOMBOID More or less rhombus-shaped.

SAPROPHYTE Plant that obtains food from decayed plant matter.

SCALE-LEAF Simplified scale-like leaf associated with underground structures and buds.

SEPALS Usually green floral structures, in whorls, enclosing other floral parts.

SESSILE Stalkless.

SHRUB Woody **Perennial** plant with branched habit of growth.

SPATHE Large **Bract** enclosing whole **Inflorescence** (notably in Arum Family).

SPIKE Condensed **Raceme** of stalkless flowers.

SPUR Tubular petal often containing nectar.

STAMEN Male floral structure, consisting of a **Filament** and **Anther**.

STAMINODE Fleshy, sterile, stamen-like structure.

STIGMA Region of the female floral structure that receives pollen.

STIPULE Small leaf-like structure on stem, associated with the leaves.

STOLON Above-ground creeping stem that provides a means of vegetative reproduction.

Parts of a flower

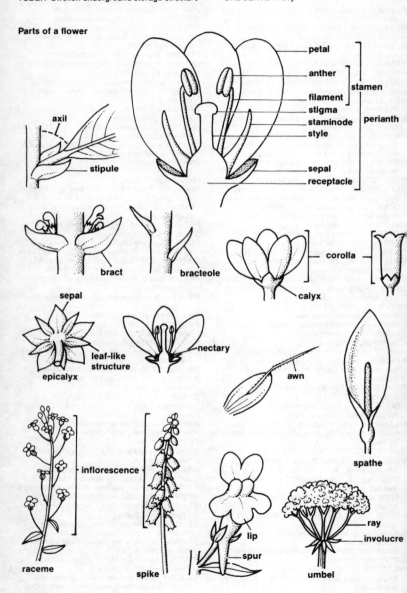

492

BOTANICAL INDEX

The numbers refer to the running numbers in the text; **pl.** is the plate number for colour photographs; dr indicates line drawings.

ENGLISH INDEX

The numbers refer to the running numbers in the text. Pl. is the plate number for colour photographs. dr. indicates drawings by the descriptions.

502

503

505

508